A HISTORY OF
INDUSTRIAL CHEMISTRY

The Windscale Plutonium-producing factory at Sellafield, Cumberland. Filters at the top of the 400-foot high chimneys prevent the escape of the last traces of radioactive matter.

A
HISTORY OF
INDUSTRIAL CHEMISTRY

by

F. SHERWOOD TAYLOR
Ph.D., M.A., B.Sc.

HEINEMANN

MELBOURNE   LONDON   TORONTO

FIRST PUBLISHED 1957

PUBLISHED BY
WILLIAM HEINEMANN LTD
99 GREAT RUSSELL STREET, LONDON, W.C.I
PRINTED IN GREAT BRITAIN BY THE WHITEFRIARS PRESS LTD,
LONDON AND TONBRIDGE

CONTENTS

▼

PART II

THE SCIENTIFIC CHEMICAL INDUSTRIES

ACKNOWLEDGEMENTS

THANKS are due to the following for their kind permission to reproduce the illustrations contained in this book:

Crown Copyright, Central Office of Information: Frontispiece, Plates XVIIIB, XIX. The Rio Tinto Company Ltd.: Plate IA. The National Museum, New Delhi: Plate IC. The Victoria and Albert Museum: Plates IB, XA. Crown Copyright, the Science Museum: Plates IIA, IIIA, IVA, IVB, VIA, VIB, VIIIA (and Mrs. C. C. Titchmarsh), XIA, XIB, XIIIB, XVA, XVI, XVIIA, XVIIB, XVIIIA, XXB, XXIA, XXIB, XXIIB; Figs. 8, 9, 17, 21, 30, 34, 35, 36, 43. Crown Copyright, the Master of the Armouries, Tower of London: Plates VIIA, VIIB. The Rijksmuseum, Amsterdam : Plate VIIIB. The British Museum: Plates V, IXA. The Burndy Library, Norwalk, Connecticut: Plate IXB. The Oxford Museum of the History of Science: Plates XB, XVB. Messrs. Morland Braithwaite: Plate XII. Glaxo Laboratories Ltd.: Plate XIIIA. Shell Ltd.: Plate XIVA. I.C.I. Ltd.: Plate XIVB. *The Mineralogical Magazine:* Plate XXA. The British Oxygen Company: Plate XXIIA. The Bodleian Library, Oxford: Fig. 4. The Folio Society and C. Singer, Esq.: Figs. 25, 26, 27. Messrs. Griffin & Co. Ltd. and T. Turner, Esq.: Figs. 54, 55.

LIST OF PLATES

LIST OF FIGURES

PREFACE

MY intention is to present a short history of industrial chemistry from the earliest times down to the present day. It has not been easy to delimit the scope of such a book, but in the event ' industrial chemistry ' has here been interpreted in a very wide sense, so as to include all modifications of the composition of matter that have been undertaken for profit or use, even though they may not in earlier times have been recognized as belonging to chemistry nor yet have been carried out on what we to-day regard as an industrial scale. So much, then, for the matter to be treated, but how to treat it? In writing on any industry attention may be focused upon the principles that inform it or the men and organizations that do the work. Of the latter aspect little is known for the period preceding the rise of modern chemistry, and even in modern times it can be truly traced only by those who have spent their lives in the industry and followed the changes and chances of its components. I have therefore chosen to concentrate upon the principles rather than the men and have tried, as far as possible, to relate the developments of the chemical industry to those of chemistry itself.

In the prescientific period the chemical crafts or industries were little influenced by the chemical theories of the day, and it is therefore impossible to relate the industries to these theories and unnecessary to describe them. From the beginning of the eighteenth century, however, the chemical philosophers, as they would have termed themselves, began to record and generalize the facts well enough to act as a guide to the maker of chemicals; since that time the main theme of the history of the chemical industry has been the following-up of new practical possibilities revealed by the advance of chemical theory. Thus chemical theory, since the early eighteenth century, has been an essential and causal part of industrial chemistry, the history of which cannot be understood except in terms of that theory. It is therefore impossible to write the history of nineteenth- and twentieth-century chemical industries without the history of the chemical theories from which they sprang, and I make no apology for the introduction of much that is ordinarily regarded as belonging to the history of chemical theory rather than to that of the industrial or applied aspects of the subject.

I am glad to acknowledge with sincere thanks the help of Dr. D. B. Harden of the Ashmolean Museum, Oxford,[1] who kindly read and commented on the part of the book concerned with the prescientific chemical industries. I have an equal debt of gratitude to Mr. A. H. Willbourn, who has done the like office for the part dealing with the scientific period. I have also received the same kindness from Mr. E. A. Lane of the Victoria and Albert Museum, who read the chapters on ceramics and glass, and from my colleagues in the Science Museum, namely Mr. A. Barclay, Dr. F. A. B. Ward, Mr. F. St.A. Hartley, Mr. W. T. O'Dea, Mr. F. Lebeter, Mr. F. Greenaway and Mr. W. Winton, all of whom have read the portions relating to their special subjects and have given me very real assistance.

I also wish to record with sincere appreciation the kindness of the publicity department of Unilever Ltd., which gave me access to notes concerning the history of soap. My thanks are also due to the several experts who acted as readers for the publisher.

Acknowledgement of the many who have provided material for illustrations is made in the individual captions.

1956   F. S. T.

---

[1] Now Director of the London Museum.

PUBLISHER'S NOTE

THIS work was completed shortly before Dr. Sherwood Taylor's death, and thanks are due to Mr. F. Greenaway, for seeing the book through the press.

INTRODUCTION

THE chemical achievements of man—that is to say, his power to transform one kind of matter into another—fall into two great periods, the prescientific and the scientific. The former extends from man's first appearance at a date distant by scores of millennia, and as yet unknown, till the time, some two hundred years ago, when chemical science was usefully applied to chemical technology; the latter, a mere two hundred years, vastly outweighs all that was done in the former.

Prescientific Chemical Industry

The prescientific period of chemical industry again falls into two clearly marked parts. Up to the fourth millennium before Christ, man's highest technical level was that which we characterize as neolithic, in which he practised very few of the chemical crafts—perhaps only the use of fire, alcoholic fermentation and the baking of pottery. The neolithic culture has persisted here and there till modern times, but towards the end of the fourth or early in the third millennium before Christ it was succeeded in several parts of the world by a new way of life which we term civilization, notably in Egypt, Mesopotamia, Crete, Persia, the Indus Valley and, perhaps somewhat later, in China. In these parts of the world men began to live in cities; they invented the art of writing and developed many new techniques. Some of these, such as medicine, surveying and the observation of the heavens, graduated to the status of sciences: that is to say, they were systematized, recorded in writing and treated as a branch of learning. Others, among which were the chemical techniques, retained the lower status of empirical and traditional crafts throughout the 5,000 years that elapsed between the beginning of the old Kingdom of Egypt and the eighteenth century after Christ.

The second or scientific period, in which the scientific method was successfully applied to the chemical crafts and industries, began only after the middle of the eighteenth century, yet, such is the power that science gives to man, it has transformed our way of life and led to what has been, not unreasonably, termed a chemical age.

The first part of this book (Chapters II–XII) deals with the prescientific chemical industries of the first period, the second and longer part with the scientific chemical industries typical of the second.

The Succession of Technical Cultures

The reader who is unfamiliar with archæology and early history may welcome a few notes on the succession of the principal cultures which have contributed to chemical technique.

(1) *The Near East before the Roman Empire.* The greatest and best-known early civilizations were those of Egypt and Mesopotamia. Their history is more or less parallel, for both show three roughly contemporary periods of high technical achievement separated by periods of relative obscurity when these river-valley civilizations were overrun by less civilized peoples from nearby.

Thus the Old Kingdom of Egypt and the Sumerian culture of Mesopotamia cover several centuries during the third millennium B.C. In both cases a decline ensued for a few hundred years, to be followed by another period of high technical achievement about 2000 B.C. or a little later; this period is characterized as the Middle Kingdom of Egypt and the Babylonian period of Mesopotamia. After another period of obscurity both cultures again attained a high level of prosperity and technique in the years between *c.* 1600 B.C. and 500 B.C.: these periods are described as the New Kingdom or Empire in Egypt, beginning in 1580 B.C., and the Assyrian period in Mesopotamia, beginning about 1300 B.C. Both succumbed to the Persian invasion, about 530 B.C., and finally to that of Alexander the Great, about 330 B.C. Thereafter the Near East—Egypt, Mesopotamia, Syria and for a time Persia —shared a common *Hellenistic* culture, in which their native techniques were shared with those of Greece and, later, of Rome.

(2) *Aegean and Prehistoric Greek Civilization.* On the islands and coasts of the Aegean Sea and in Asia Minor there existed from the early third millennium B.C. several centres of culture with many common elements; these included the Minoan

civilization in Crete and its counterparts in neighbouring Aegean islands, the Hittite civilization with its forerunner in Asia Minor and the several successive culture stages at Troy, ending in the Homeric city. There were also important settlements from *c.* 3000 B.C. or earlier in Cyprus, an island which was not only an important source of early copper, but was also, because of its position, a frequent place of contact for influences from the Syrian and Asia Minor coasts and seafarers from farther west. Cultures on the Greek mainland were developed much later and it was not until the mid-second millennium B.C., when Crete declined, that the Mycenæan civilization of Tiryns and Mycenæ obtained sway over most of the eastern Mediterranean, excluding Egypt. All these cultures were a source of fine metalwork, but their known technical achievement in the chemical field did not attain to those of the great centres of Mesopotamia and Egypt.

(3) *Classical Greece.* The Aegean and Asiatic cultures of the second millennium B.C. were to some extent preliminary to that of classical Greece. From about 600 B.C. or a little earlier the Greek-speaking peoples, both on the mainland of Greece and in Ionia, underwent a hitherto unparalleled mental development and may be thought to have founded not only philosophy but also theoretical science. Their achievements in the fine arts, also, were unsurpassed, but it is not known that their chemical techniques came up to, let alone exceeded, those of the older cultures from which they were probably derived. Greek philosophy, science and technique were inherited both by the Hellenistic Near East and by the growing power of Rome.

(4) *The Roman Empire* (27 B.C.–A.D. 476). The small city of Rome gradually extended her conquests in the years from 500 B.C. onward, until towards the beginning of the Christian era, when Augustus founded the Empire, she controlled most of southern and western Europe, North Africa, Egypt and Syria; Mesopotamia she held for a short time only, while Persia remained on her frontier. The early years of the Empire were a period of great wealth and prosperity in which all the known techniques of the peoples included in it were exercised to the full and some new inventions made. Invasions by northern peoples enfeebled the Western Roman Empire in the fourth century A.D., and in the fifth destroyed it as an organiza-

tion. The technical heritage of the Romans was, in part at least, retained in those regions of the Western Empire, such as Gaul, which continued to enjoy some degree of prosperity, while at Byzantium, which was not overrun by the barbarians, the Eastern Roman Empire remained as a fertilizing source of craft-knowledge until that city was sacked by the Turks in 1453.

(5) *Islam.* In the years round A.D. 650 the Arabs, united by Mohammed, conquered the Near East, Persia, North Africa and most of Spain. Within a century or so these regions became the site of a relatively homogeneous Islamic culture, in which almost all techniques were carried to a far higher point than anywhere in Europe. These techniques derived not only from the Hellenistic world that Islam had conquered, but also from India and the Far East, with which it had close relationships of commerce. The Islamic culture retained its supremacy until the thirteenth century, when the sack of Baghdad by the Mongols began its decline. The conquest of Persia by Timur at the end of the fifteenth century was followed by that of most of the Islamic world by the Turks in the sixteenth; this was the end of Islam as a source of technical tradition.

(6) *India and China.* The prescientific chemical arts that were practised in these populous countries have been less well studied than those of Europe and the Near East; the dating of their progress is still very difficult, for which reason they have received less attention in this book than they perhaps deserve.

Both in India and China there existed early cultures with good pottery and metal-work. These may date from c. 2500 B.C., but our knowledge of the periods intervening between these and c. 300 B.C. remains shadowy. The Indian technical culture thereafter, though always reaching a high level of craftsmanship, especially in steel-work, did not in most respects exceed that of the Western world, nor is it known to have contributed much thereto.

China, on the other hand, excelled in every manner of craft, but in the present state of technological history it is impossible to date the periods at which, for instance, her various metallurgical techniques came into use or to discover whether these were indigenous or derived from Western sources. Her greatest achievement, and the best chronicled, is her pottery and

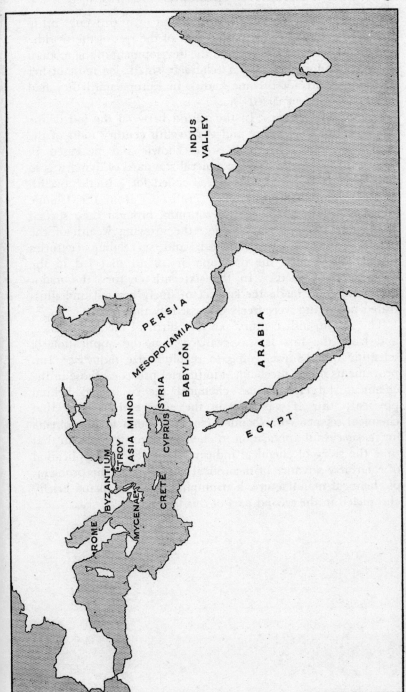

FIG. I. Sites of early technical cultures.

porcelain, which from the T'ang period (A.D. 618–907) up to modern times greatly surpassed that of the rest of the world.

The influence of China upon the development of the modern chemical industry has been relatively small, for most of her techniques did not become known in Europe until they had been generally surpassed.

(7) *Western Europe.* In the period between the fall of the Western Roman Empire and the twelfth century most of the traditional chemical crafts were known and practised in Western Europe, though the general standard of living was so low that no great perfection was called for. In the twelfth and thirteenth centuries many craftsmen from the Islamic world, Moorish Spain, and Byzantium, brought their special knowledge to Western Europe; the growing wealth of the Western world in the fifteenth and succeeding centuries rapidly accelerated the development of all that led to the production of goods. In the sixteenth century the major industries were made the subject of finely printed and illustrated books and were freely discussed by the learned.

The seventeenth century saw the birth of modern science, and from the first it was realized that the application of scientific method was going to revolutionize industry. Improvements in the mechanical industries preceded those in the chemical, largely because chemical theory lagged behind physical; thus it was only in the eighteenth century that chemical science corresponded closely enough to phenomena for its successful application to chemical industry. From that time the story of chemical industry has been the application of each new advance of theoretical chemistry to the problems of chemical manufacture, a triumphal progress all too briefly chronicled in the second part of this book.

CHAPTER ONE

An Introductory Survey of
Chemical Industry

The Impact of Science on the Chemical Crafts

TO-DAY we distinguish as chemical a large group of industries concerned with the making of new kinds of matter. Many of these industries, such as the smelting of metals, have a history as long as that of civilization and far antedate the idea which we express by the term ' chemistry ' and which itself dates only from the sixteenth century. Chemistry, as a science, is but a recent development and it was not until the close of the eighteenth century that the theories of chemistry so far corresponded to reality as to be of practical use to those who were engaged in the industries concerned with the transformation of matter. Indeed it is only in the period following the chemical revolution initiated by Lavoisier that we find chemical manufactures beginning to be transformed from empirical crafts to industries informed by scientific principles.

Here, then, is to be found the prime division of our subject. Every chemical industry which has a history of more than a couple of centuries falls into two periods, the prescientific and the scientific, joined by a comparatively short period of transition. In the prescientific period the efficiency of the industry increases, often but slowly, through discoveries and inventions which result from chance or mother-wit or, in some cases, from mistaken chains of reasoning: in the scientific period the advances result chiefly from the study of the chemical reactions involved, a study either deliberately undertaken for the improvement of the industry or following upon the general advance of chemical science. It is obvious that man's understanding of the nature of the changes which he wishes to bring about enormously accelerates his power to achieve his desires, and accordingly the last 150 years have seen chemical industry

7

progressing to an extent beside which the advances of the 3,000 preceding years must seem but trifling.

Yet we should be making a mistake if the attention which we give to the prescientific and the scientific periods were to be proportioned according to their respective results. The past gave birth to the present, and we can understand ourselves and our age only in the light of the past whose ideas we inherit and whose air we still breathe. It is of much interest, not only for the scientist but even more for the student of social history, to know the powers and limitations of the industry of the past, to trace the sources of its materials, to understand the techniques that lay behind its activities. For this reason more than a third of this book is devoted to the industries concerned with the transformation of matter in the years before science came to their aid.

Prescientific Chemical Industries

What then were the characteristics that distinguish these early chemical industries from the scientific industries of to-day?

First of all, we must note that these prescientific industries did not arise from a learned or even, generally, a literate class. Throughout most of their history they were carried on by skilled artisans who learnt their trade by apprenticeship. There were rarely any books which they could have consulted with profit, even if they had had access to them and had been able to read them. There is some evidence, it is true, that in ancient Egypt some of these chemical crafts were temple industries, concerning which there may have been written records, but in view of the scantiness of the evidence we must not presume the former existence of a chemical literature of which nothing has, in fact, survived. The general picture of a prescientific industry is that of a traditional craft—an attitude which was very well expressed by the men of the Middle Ages when they spoke of a trade or handicraft as a ' mystery '. Many of the earlier records of these industries were made by people who were not engaged in them. Thus encyclopædic writers on natural science, such as Pliny, made notes on the chemical trades of their time, but we cannot be sure how often they got their information right, though we are quite sure they often got it wrong. Other information comes from compilers of recipe books, of which many have survived—the earliest being the numerous chemical tablets of seventh-century Assyria—but these are commonly no more than notes giving materials and quantities, and taking for granted (like the modern cookery book) just those manipulative processes which we would like to hear described in detail. In this respect there was a change for the better in the Renaissance, when the merchant and practical man came to form an important section of the reading public. From the beginning of the sixteenth century we begin to find adequate accounts of trades written down by those who had some experience of them; among them, indeed, are a few magnificent productions, such as the distillation books of Braunschweig and the metallurgical works of Ercker, Agricola and Biringuccio.

Another consequence of the lack of learning of the artisan is the absence of scientific theory from his craft-knowledge. There was a chemical theory, prevalent from the fourth century B.C. to the eighteenth century, based upon the four elements of Aristotle and the ' spiritus ' of the Stoic and Hermetic philosophers. The alchemists interpreted some of their work in these terms, as likewise did the physicians, but the technician, who made his living by an accurate knowledge of the observable changes that took place during the making of metals or glass or soap, did not try to relate these phenomena to the Aristotelian or any other theory. He did not think in philosophical terms, because he was not educated in the schools; but, even if he had been the most learned Doctor of the Peripatetic School, his learning would not have enabled him to make more or better metal or glass.

It is probable—nay, certain—that magical and superstitious practices were important in the earliest technology, as they are in that of primitive peoples to-day; but, in fact, the recorded processes and recipes show very little trace of this. The technical literature of prescientific times, such as it is, is severely practical and makes little or no allusion either to the science or to the superstition of the day.

The lack of any adequate chemical science put the technician in many serious difficulties, chief of which was the characterizing, recognition and valuation of materials. He had to discover among the infinite variety of natural products those which could be successfully used to make the subject of his trade. Thus if he were a glass-maker he had, in fact, to

B*

be able to find materials which would furnish silica, potassium or sodium carbonate, and lime; but he did not know that these were what he needed. He knew that some sands, or flint, or the mineral that we call quartz, but which he often thought of as a hard kind of marble, would yield glass when melted with ashes, and experience had to teach him what sands or rocks would do this. In this instance he evolved the rough test that rock which would strike a spark from steel would serve for glass-making, and he knew that the whiter was the rock or sand the more nearly colourless the glass would be. The glass-maker also requires an alkali. He had no notions about soda or potash or lime, but he knew that the sort of stuff that would make lye for washing or soap-making would also serve to make glass. He commonly used ashes of plants, trees, herbs or even seaweeds, and these happened to contain both potassium carbonate and lime; but he did not generally add any calcium compound as a separate ingredient. Wood-ashes or fern-ashes (generally preferred) gave a potash-glass; but the best glass was made from the ashes of certain maritime plants (pp. 71, 75), and these contained soda, potash and lime. We do not know who discovered glass or how it was discovered, but clearly some ancient glass-makers found out what sort of materials succeeded. The would-be glass-maker had to look for these materials locally (unless he were prepared to import them), try out his process and then set up his workshops and furnaces—if he could find the skilled workmen with the specialist knowledge that was not to be found in books. He would have to tempt these men away from some already existent glass-working centre, which would make strenuous efforts to retain them. This dependence on the men with the traditional knowledge could make the diffusion of techniques very slow. Thus certain cities kept special secrets: some kinds of dyeing could only be done in Constantinople, others in Florence, while some arts, such as that of porcelain, long remained in the oriental parts of the world and quite inaccessible to Europeans.

In the recognition of materials or other native products the chief need was for the trained senses. Thus miners knew the look and feel of the kind of mineral that would yield metal, through the teaching of their elders and long experience of such materials. Once a possible source of metal was detected, it was tried out by a small-scale smelting; this trial smelting developed into assaying, which finally became chemical analysis. It will be seen, then, that trial and error was the chief test of materials.

The difficulty of identifying materials led to some curious results. Often two or more substances were distinguished by different names and price, while in fact they consisted of the same chemical individual. Oil of sulphur *per campanam* and oil of vitriol both consisted of sulphuric acid, but the former was much more expensive than the latter. Vitriolated tartar, vitriolated nitre, sal polychrestum and sal enixum were four different names which in the eighteenth century represented more or less impure potassium sulphate. On the other hand a single name might be applied to quite different substances; thus at some periods ' nitrum ' meant both sodium carbonate and potassium nitrate.

In the process itself the same lack of understanding often stood in the way of success. Given for example a new copper ore, how was the copper to be won? The natural procedure was to treat it in the traditional manner by roasting and smelting (p. 37); but how was the operator to know whether he was getting all the copper out of it? It was not possible to discover the percentages of copper in the ore and in the slag, and so the smelter could not know what proportion he had recovered; in fact, the greater part of the metal often remained in the old slags, which indeed are sometimes profitably re-worked to-day.

The absence of any scheme of chemical analysis meant that the products of industry could not be adequately tested. In many cases, such as those of glass or soap or pigments, the quality of the product was assessed by use, and gold and silver were the only products which could be subjected to quantitative tests (p. 31). The buyer had to use his wits and assess the value of the product, nor was it possible, as to-day, to agree upon a specification.

Another difficulty in devising or using a process was to know what materials and processes were essential. Somebody might add a few pounds of some new ingredient or might let a solution stand for a few hours instead of using it at once, and then find that a specially good result followed. The new process might not be the cause of the good result, but it would be adopted and might persist for many years until someone happened to discard it without detriment. To-day we should want to know why the new addition was effective and we should probably conduct controlled quantitative tests, but before the advent of scientific chemistry none of this was possible. This explains some of the curiously complex recipes occasionally used; yet, on the whole, it is remarkable to what extent the long practice of a craft led to the selection of the essentials and the discarding of non-essentials.

Many processes were uncertain in action and often unaccountably failed, especially those that depended upon fermentation—witness the account of the making of white lead (pp. 83–84). It was not possible to define the optimum conditions in the scientific terms of temperatures, percentage compositions, etc., and even the highest skill was an insufficient substitute for our modern precision.

Other practical difficulties of prescientific chemical industries are obvious, and it is surprising how well they were overcome.

In the first place we may set the lack of mechanical power. The vessels had in general to be of no greater size than could be readily handled by man-power. Pounding and grinding were usually hand operations (though water-mills were sometimes used) and therefore very slow. The regulation of temperature was a difficult art only to be learnt by long experience, and the highest temperature obtainable before the seventeenth century was insufficient to melt soft iron. The notion of oxidizing and reducing conditions in the furnace could not of course be arrived at before the discovery of oxygen in 1774, yet in fact the potters had long used this factor, without understanding it, so as to obtain colour effects which elude us even to-day.

This fact may indeed point to the most important difference between the old chemical industries and the new. The old industries were arts, conducted by skills of eye and hand, acquired by long practice of the craft; for this skill there was no substitute. The new industry has steadily discarded judgment and skill in favour of analytical control, calculation of the optimum conditions and the check of experiment. The old industry owed its success to the skill of the worker; the new industry steadily discards the skilled worker in favour of the machine—culminating in the chemical separation of artificial radio-elements by remote control, unseen by any human eye.

Transition to Scientific Chemical Industry

This revolution in chemical industry did not come about at once. The notion that man should look to science for the improvement of his industries was first clearly and strongly expressed by Sir Francis Bacon shortly after 1600: the Royal Society in its early years (1661–c. 1690) tried to give effect to it and instituted a number of enquiries into the practice of various trades, chemical and otherwise. The information preserved in these ' Histories ' is valuable to us to-day, but we do not learn that the Fellows of the Royal Society were able to make effective suggestions for new chemical processes or the improvement of old ones. There were not, in fact, yet sufficient generalizations concerning chemical facts to allow of an explanation even of the simplest industrial processes in terms of chemistry. With the eighteenth century, however, a certain number of fruitful classifications and generalizations began to be made—the acid, base and salt relationship was elucidated, combustion was explained and a beginning was made with chemical analysis. Even these simple ideas were a means to great improvements, such as the manufacture of cheap sulphuric acid, and of sodium compounds from salt. After the turn of the century came the atomic theory, adequate quantitative analysis and, in fact, a simple but generally true outline of inorganic chemistry. In these years came the first consciousness of the existence of two great departments of chemistry, pure and applied.

Pure and Applied Chemistry

Pure Chemistry and Industrial or Applied Chemistry can be distinguished by their respective motives. The workers in the former intend to increase knowledge, whereas the workers in the latter have as their primary object the satisfaction of the material needs or desires of mankind. Pure chemists, it is true, commonly discover things of great industrial use, and industrial chemists things of the highest theoretical interest; but there has always been a clear distinction between their functions—a distinction maintained not only by their purpose, but also by the circumstances of their employment. Until the last few decades at least the pure chemist worked in a university laboratory, almost always on research and along the lines chosen by himself. The industrial chemist, on the other hand, worked under the direction of a commercial firm and in a works laboratory. Much of his work was the routine analysis needed for control of manufacturing processes, although a good deal of research also came his way. Thus the ' pure chemist ' of the nineteenth century knew too little about industrial needs and possibilities, while the industrial chemist was too often precluded from any research not obviously directed to earning a profit. The growth of the great chemical firms in the last fifty years has gone far to break down this barrier between workers in pure and applied chemistry. They support university research and are in touch with the pure chemist: at the same time they maintain their research laboratories, the work of which often seems remote from the purposes of the corporation that maintains it. Furthermore, chemical research is to-day carried on by public bodies, notably government departments, and much of this is industrial, inasmuch as the intention is the public use, yet is not narrowly tied down to problems of which the solution could yield an immediate return. In the latest period, and especially in time of war and its imminence, state and university research have joined forces to meet a common need. Especially notable was the project of the atomic bomb, in which the states, the universities and industries of four countries combined to meet the common need.

During the greater part of the last hundred years, however, the production of goods and the provision of services has been almost entirely in the hands of private individuals and corporations. Thus chemistry has been divided into one department that sought knowledge and another that sought to earn money for a private firm. Yet, in fact, this money had to be made by selling goods or services to the public; so that, even if the first intention of the industrial chemist was to enable his firm to earn a profit, the result, whether by intention or accident, was to give mankind what it wanted. The particular means of doing this, namely, private enterprise, put certain limitations on the intention to fulfil man's needs. First of all, the objective aimed at had to be capable of showing a profit within a reasonable period and with a reasonable capital expenditure:

consequently the short-term objective was sought and large-scale projects of doubtful outcome generally eschewed. Secondly, research was not directed to man's most pressing needs, but to those most easily and profitably to be satisfied. Thus it was much more urgent that the 400,000,000 sufferers from malaria should be supplied with drugs capable of curing or relieving that disease than that women should have pretty new textiles, yet the expenditure of money and labour on the latter problem enormously exceeded the outlay on the former.

In 1800 the chemical industry was important but very limited in scope, extending only to the manufacture of metals, acids, alkalis, pigments, tan-stuffs, medicines and a few other products made on a comparatively small scale. It is true that a variety of chemicals could be purchased, but these were mostly made by what may be termed enlarged laboratory processes, using barrels and carboys instead of beakers and flasks. There was as yet little in the way of specifically chemical plant. The control of industrial processes by the chemist, almost universal to-day, was then unknown. To-day the most concise dictionary account of modern industrial chemistry runs to tens of thousands of pages, for there is scarcely a manufactured or even a natural product to which the chemist has not in some way contributed.

Research and Industry

A survey of the scientific period of the development of chemistry gives us some idea of its causes. There are two chief roads by which industrial chemistry advanced: first, by research deliberately directed to discover a way of filling a want; secondly, by the utilization of discoveries not made with a view to their usefulness. Contrary to expectation, the latter has in the past been by far the most fruitful.

Thus a man or a team may deliberately seek to achieve some end, as when Alfred Nobel set out to find a way of making nitro-glycerine a safe explosive and invented dynamite and blasting gelatine; or when Herman Frasch worked out his method of mining sulphur from the surface by forcing super-heated water into the deposit and pumping up the melted sulphur.

But such deliberately planned researches are never the means of making the most novel discoveries; the undertaking of such a research implies a knowledge of its end, and so its intention cannot be to lead to something not yet imagined as possible. Much the most fertile method of industrial chemistry has, in fact, been the exploitation of discoveries never intended by the worker, or intended for some other purpose. Thus Perkin, trying to synthesize quinine, made something that no one had thought of, the first aniline dye, mauve; and by investigating this he initiated a new industry. Baekeland, seeking to make a synthetic varnish, discovered Bakelite, the first self-hardening synthetic plastic. Such examples could be many times multiplied.

So we may, perhaps, classify the researches of modern chemistry as follows:

(1) *Researches designed to fulfil a known need.* This need may be the discovery of a material not yet known; thus the textile chemist may seek for something as good as silk but much cheaper. Or the need may be to find a better means of making something already known, and so of making it more abundant: thus the manufacturers of new synthetic dyes and explosives called for more and better concentrated sulphuric acid, and the contact process was developed to meet that need. The need may even be to find a use for some natural product or by-product: *e.g.* to discover some way by which something useful could be made from natural gas or alkali-waste.

(2) *Researches arising out of an accidental discovery.* The example of Perkin's discovery of mauve and the consequent establishment of the dye industry may be instanced. The condition for such discoveries is that much research should be done by men alive to the possibility of the industrial exploitation of their results.

(3) *Researches designed to apply the results of the researches of the pure chemist.* A good example is the catalytic hydrogenation of an unsaturated substance in presence of a metallic catalyst. This was developed by Sabatier and his colleagues as a useful means of synthesis about 1900; it has since been exploited in numerous industries, of which the hydrogenation of oils to make fats suitable for margarine and the hydrogenation of coal to make gasolene are examples.

(4) *Researches arising out of a new industrial technique.* The greatest example is the flood of new chemical processes which arose from the work of Wilde, Gramme, Siemens, Edison and

others, who developed the dynamo and made the use of electricity available at a low cost from about 1875: the theoretical possibility of the processes had long been recognized, but their cost had been prohibitive.

So the story of industrial chemistry is not simply that of a continuous research directed towards the fulfilling of human needs. Its minor aims are often achieved in that fashion, but commonly a great new advance takes its rise from an unexpected observation whose significance has been grasped, from a new advance in the theory or practice of pure chemistry, or from the availability of a new material or technique. This variety of possible sources of progress makes the subject at once difficult to survey and intensely interesting when examined in detail.

In the succeeding chapters which constitute Part I of this book I shall give a brief survey of the prescientific chemical industries. Almost all of these are so ancient that it is scarcely possible to place the chapters in chronological order. I have therefore adopted the usual order of chemical treatises, namely, the elements, inorganic chemistry and organic chemistry; and I begin with a consideration of ancient metallurgy.

PART I

THE
PRE-SCIENTIFIC
CHEMICAL INDUSTRIES

CHAPTER TWO

Metallurgy

Mining

METALLURGY began, perhaps as early as 4000 B.C., with the finding of native metals and metalliferous minerals; their extraction from the earth by mining came later, but shaft-mining was carried on as early as 2500 B.C. in Egypt. Gold and silver were the first metals to be found, because they commonly occur in the form of metal and are easily recognized, but the important step, from the point of view of the chemist, was taken when certain stony or earthy minerals were recognized as containing metals. Whilst native copper, which could be beaten into shape or cast into weapons or ornaments, had long been known, the first smelting of ore for metal was that of the ores of copper. The chief ores of that metal were the bright green and blue malachite and azurite and the metallic-looking sulphide ores. We do not know how men first discovered that certain types of rock could yield metal; it has been supposed that malachite, used in Egypt as a green eye-pigment, accidently found its way into a wood or charcoal fire and was reduced to metallic copper, which would be recognized as the same sort of thing as the known and valued gold, but it is by no means certain that the sulphide ores were not the first to be used. We may tentatively suppose that other rocks or stones which, like malachite, were heavy or strongly coloured, were treated in the same way by the miners in order to find out whether they would yield metal. Prospecting, indeed, remained an art rather than a science until modern times. Miners came to know the sort of formations that were associated with metalliferous minerals and learnt to recognize their general appearance. Such knowledge was traditional and not committed to paper. As late as the sixteenth century the finding of metallic deposits depended on the chance discovery of or deliberate search for likely-looking stones or outcrops, followed by the sinking of trial trenches: the earth over mineral veins was observed to affect the vegetation that grew over them and, so it was said, remained free from frost while the surrounding country was covered by it. Divining by the hazel-twig was much in use in the sixteenth century and, then as now, its efficacy was hotly disputed.

Mining long preceded metallurgy, and so it was natural that most of the minerals, once identified, were sought by sinking vertical shafts, often drained and ventilated by horizontal passages, known as adits. In ancient times the miners were slaves or criminals and no account was taken of their lives. Little was done to avoid accidents, though many of the tunnels were timbered in the modern style. No attempts were made to increase ventilation, despite the fact that some of the Roman shafts went down to a depth of 650 feet. The miners' characteristic tools were some form of the mallet and wedge; very hard rocks were broken by lighting fires against them (sometimes followed by quenching the hot rock with cold water [1]), a practice which persisted almost into modern times. The method was effective in cracking most of the hardest rocks, but the lighting of large fires in the galleries of mines must have caused grave danger of asphyxiation. The ore was carried in bags or baskets up long ladders to the surface. Water was often troublesome in ancient mining, and where it could not be drained off by an adit it could be baled out into skins which were passed from hand to hand, sometimes for nearly a mile. Slave labour was hardly worth saving; nevertheless in the Roman copper workings at the Rio Tinto mine were found several water-wheel pumps constructed of wood, which has been perfectly preserved by the copper-impregnated water. There are records also of Archimedean screw-pumps being used in classical times to raise water from the Egyptian mines.

We lose sight of mining technique after the decline of the ancient world and have our next clear view of it in the wonderful books on metallurgy that appeared in the sixteenth century, especially in the *De Re Metallica* (1556) of Georg Bauer, usually known as Agricola.

The world's great mining centre throughout the Middle Ages was Southern Germany, and it is probable that some of

[1] Vinegar is said by ancient authors to have been used but it cannot have been more effective than water.

FIG. 2.   Ball-and-chain mine-pump as illustrated by Agricola.

the methods which Agricola records are older by many centuries than his writings.   Nevertheless the late fifteenth and early sixteenth centuries saw a great expansion in the German

mining industry. Enormous wealth was made by its practice
and the educated classes were for the first time becoming
sufficiently interested in mining to wish to read about it.
From the thirteenth to the sixteenth century the miner had
been advancing from the status of a serf to that of a paid
worker, and sometimes owner of a small mine or partner in
its proceeds. Naturally such men took care to save their lives
and spare themselves labour as far as they could. The ore
was still extracted by the ancient methods, but it was commonly
raised by a windlass or capstan, which in large mines was
driven by the power of several horses. As the German mines
were in the mountains, it was usually possible to drain off
water by means of a tunnel, or adit, sloping gently downward
from the bottom of the shaft to a lower part of the hillside:
under favourable conditions of wind these adits provided a
good deal of ventilation. If water could not be cleared in this
way mechanical methods were used. Mine pumps of several
types were employed. Some were ordinary suction pumps;
others consisted of an endless chain of buckets; the ball-and-
chain pump was also popular. These latter types could raise
water to any height, whereas the common suction pump could
raise it only 33 feet—and often much less: thus suction pumps
were normally arranged in series, each delivering water to a
sump from which the next drew it. Pumps were operated by
human labour, by horse-mills, or very often by water-wheels
driven by the mountain streams. None of these could, however,
cope with any large influx of water nor raise it from a very
great depth, and the scope of mining was correspondingly
limited.

Natural ventilation, as described above, was often ineffective or impossible to arrange. Circulation of air could be
promoted by means of a second shaft, beneath which a fire
was maintained. Alternatively air could be forced down the
shaft by means of ducts with openings adjustable so as to face
the wind, and sometimes rotary fans or gigantic bellows,
driven by water power, were used to this end. Even so
mining remained an even more dangerous trade than it is
to-day. Long standing in cold water caused foot trouble,
while the corrosive waters of metallic mines could cause ulcers.
Dust was also recognized as very dangerous. We may suppose
that silicosis, tuberculosis and other lung diseases took a heavy

toll. The use of fires to break up rock probably liberated arsenical fumes and gave rise to arsenical poisoning. The

Fig. 3. Ventilation of mines.

mining of mercury was peculiarly fatal owing to the presence of its poisonous vapour. The accident rate must also have been high: thus the lack of ventilation gave rise to ' damps ', accumulations of carbon dioxide or other irrespirable gases, which were sometimes fatal. Although shafts and drifts were usually timbered, falls of rock often took their toll, and the carrying of heavy loads of ore up long ladders was the source of many accidents.

A contemporary description of a small Derbyshire lead-mine, visited by Sir John Pettus in 1630, will give us an idea of the smaller mines and the cheerful prosperity of the free miners:

> I ask't, whether I might be safely let down in the basket to see their works? They assured me I might, and so . . . I was let down (not in the basket) but by a strong stick, laid cross the hook of the rope. I sat on it between my legs, one hand holding the rope, the other guiding me from grating on the sides; so as soon as I was down (being about 24 fathom or 48 yards) the labourer that waited for the basket, was quickly informed of my intents, who presently, at my request (promising reward) fetch't two candles lighted, by which I saw, that there was no other passage than what I came down in, and by what I was to go into the mine, but by the time that I had gone halfway I told my conductor that I could not keep my candle alight and at the same instant both candles went out. Sir, said he, I pray stay here, and I will go fetch more candles, for it is nothing but a damp; at which words my spirits were much discomposed, yet I had so much left as to crawl back to the shaft, and sucked in as much air as relieved me. My conductor soon returned with more attendants to light me but I was very unwilling to return again but gave them liberally something to drink, which the more obliged them to persuade me to see their works, assuring me that those damps were not killing, but they had taken care (by keeping open the passage of their waters) that no such accidents should occur while I was there, and that they had good aqua vitae, rosa solis[1], and good ale to cheer me. With that I went to the mine where their constant lamps and candles which they lighted for my sake did make the glitterings of the ore very pleasant to me, by which I also saw their method of digging, and was well treated with their promised drinks, besides good beef and bread, so as their liberality increased mine, and then I was attended to the shaft and so drawn up as I went down. . . .

Such a mine was, of course, much less well organized than the great German mines described by Agricola eighty years

---

[1] A cordial made from the plant sundew.

before, but it is probably representative of the industry as a whole.

The reader of the sixteenth-century books on metallurgy cannot fail to be impressed by the high technique of the mining and smelting industry. It was a highly profitable business, and where big money is concerned men have always been careful and accurate. In an age when arithmetic was by no means a universal accomplishment the mine-owner or manager worked out careful cost estimates. The infant art of surveying was practised, as for example in calculating the place to drive an adit to meet a shaft, while the compass was used to make sure of the direction. The design and size of the machinery (mostly of wood) much excelled any other mechanical contrivances that existed at this time.

Thus these miners and metallurgists used the sciences of mathematics and surveying, which were just becoming common property in the sixteenth century, and so began the fruitful association of science with industry; but unfortunately the sciences they needed most, geology and chemistry, had no theory that was of any use to guide them. The place of geology and mineralogy was taken by the keen experienced eye of the miner, trained to recognize minerals and the lie of the land that promised success: the place of theoretical chemistry was supplied by an empirical technique for the testing of ores.

Assaying

The sixteenth-century miners very well knew how to estimate the value to them of an ore or a sample of metal, and they developed a quite adequate system of chemical analysis.

We do not know how ancient these analytical methods are. They were well developed in 1500, and we may suppose that they had been evolving throughout the Middle Ages.

How were the men of those days, when chemistry was rudimentary, to tell the proportion of silver contained in a lead ore, or of silver and copper in gold? The obvious way to test the former was to smelt a weighed trial charge of the material in their furnaces and see how much of the desired metal they could obtain from it. That was not very satisfactory, because a large-scale test would be wasteful of time and fuel if the material turned out to be poor. Thus arose the idea of small-scale tests, using perhaps a hundred pounds of

ore; and later very small-scale tests, using only a few ounces.
The test was designed to reproduce fairly nearly the conditions
of large-scale smelting, so that its results should be borne out
in practice. Small muffle-furnaces (Fig. 4) were used for firing
the charges. The ore was finely ground, first in the mortar,
then on a slab with a muller, and delicate balances (Fig. 5)
had to be used in order to weigh the ore and the few grains of
metal that were obtained. These balances were made commercially in Cologne and Nuremberg: balance-cases were

FIG. 4. Assayer's laboratory in the sixteenth century (Ercker).

used to protect them. They may be regarded on the one
hand as a development of the goldsmiths' scales, which go back
to ancient Egypt, and on the other as the first precursors of the
modern chemical balance.

The assaying of ores in the sixteenth century was an important profession: the assayer often devoted his whole time
to this work and may be compared to the analytical chemist
of to-day. The type of assaying room illustrated by Lazarus
Ercker (Fig. 4) was the first industrial laboratory. We see in
it various small-scale furnaces, arrangements for making nitric
acid for the separation of gold from silver, and flasks in which

this process was carried out. These processes are further referred to on p. 92.

Smelting

The smelting of ores was, generally speaking, carried out by heating them with charcoal, often after a preliminary roasting. None-the-less a great variety of furnaces and tech-

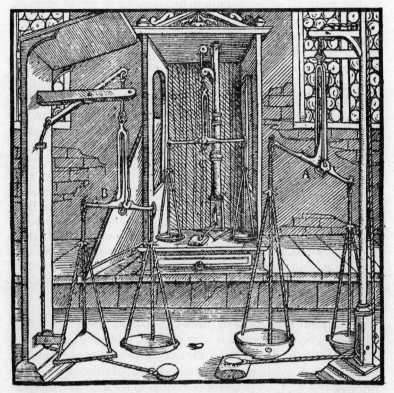

FIG. 5. Assayer's balances of the sixteenth century as figured by Agricola.

niques was used. To give accounts of all the methods used for all the metals would expand this chapter to a volume, but it will at any rate be possible to give an outline of the more usual methods of smelting and refining the individual metals.

Gold

Gold seems to have been the first metal to be used by man, and it was known in Egypt well before 3000 B.C. We have no written records of methods but Egyptian pictures show the washing of sand in a large round vessel, the fusion and weighing of the metal, and various metallurgical operations, including the beating of gold-leaf. Very large quantities of gold, to be reckoned in millions of pounds sterling per annum, are said by Diodorus Siculus (*c.* 60 B.C.) to have been obtained from the Nubian mines.

The methods of gold-mining in the ancient world seem to have included small-scale washing—' panning '—and a process more like placer-mining. Pliny tells us how in Spain galleries were dug in gold-bearing strata and then made to collapse. Streams of water, brought to the spot from a distance, were run first through the debris and then through trenches filled with foliage, which retained the heavy gold while the mud passed on with the water. Another account, given us by Agatharchides (*c.* 100 B.C.), shows us that auriferous quartz was mined in Egypt by slave labour and pulverized to obtain the gold.

> The soil, naturally black, is traversed by veins of brilliant white rock.[1] Out of this the overseers cause the gold to be dug by a vast multitude of people. For the kings of Egypt condemn to these mines notorious criminals; prisoners of war, sometimes with their whole families, are bound in fetters and compelled to work day and night without intermission or hope of escape, for the guards set over them speak a foreign language. The earth [rock] which is hard, they soften by the application of fire.

The splitting of rocks by fires has already been mentioned (p. 22). Pliny tells us that vinegar was also used (*hos igne et aceto rumpunt*), while Livy and Plutarch give a story of Hannibal using vinegar to destroy the rocks which obstructed his way through the Alps. Vinegar was known to corrode and dissolve certain rocks; it was also regarded as especially cold: for these reasons it may have been thought to be the liquid most suitable to be thrown on the rocks which had already been heated by large fires. However, it can scarcely have been plentiful enough for economic use in practical mining.

---

[1] Agatharchides calls this ' marble ', but quartz is obviously intended. There are in Egypt formations of quartz which contain gold in pockets with oxides of iron and titanium.

Let us return to Agatharchides. When the ore
has been reduced to such a state that it yields to moderate labour,
several thousands of wretches break it up with iron picks. An
engineer presides and directs the labourers, the strongest of whom
hew the rock with iron chisels by brute force and without skill.
In excavating below ground they follow the ore without keeping
to a straight line. They have lamps fastened to the foreheads and
their bodies are soiled with the colour of the rock: they work
without intermission and are lashed by the overseers. Little boys
follow them and carry the fragments to the open air. Men about
thirty years old pound the rock in stone mortars with iron pestles
till it is as fine as flour. At length the masters take the ground
stone and carry it away for the final process. They spread it on a
board, somewhat hollow and inclined, and, pouring water upon
it, rub and cleanse it till all the earthy part, separated from the
rest by the water, runs off the board and the gold by reason of its
weight remains. This operation is repeated frequently, the stone
being rubbed lightly with the hand. Afterwards they take up
the earthy part with fine sponges, gently applied, leaving clean,
pure gold.

It is not certain whether mercury was used to extract the
gold, but other passages, especially in the Greek alchemical
texts, seem to hint at this process, which was usual in the
Middle Ages and later.

These mining methods were certainly effective, for large
quantities of gold were used in Egypt, and enormous quantities
in Imperial Rome. We must envisage a vast population of
slaves captured in war and forced to expend their lives upon
this labour.

Gold was refined in antiquity by fire: the gold was melted
and maintained at a high temperature, whereupon all other
metals present, except silver, were gradually oxidized, a slow
process and one of only moderate efficacy. The cementation
process, to be mentioned later (p. 34), seems to have been
practised for improving the surface colour of base gold, but
not for refining it in bulk. It follows that the ancient gold
varied in quality and that all of it contained varying proportions of copper and silver. Tests for gold were very necessary
for this reason, and also because fairly colourable imitations of
it were made from various brassy alloys. It was known that
the best gold kept its colour when heated, had a high melting-
point and was not affected by brine or vinegar; but none of

these tests would indicate the presence of a little silver or copper in the metal, and indeed there was no standard pure gold. The usual test, which remained in use till modern times, was that of the touch-stone. A series of twenty-four touch-needles (Fig. 6) were made from the purest gold obtainable alloyed with different but known amounts of copper, silver or both. The gold to be tested was drawn over a hard black stone, making a streak of yellow; the needle, the streak of which was found to match it in size and colour, was supposed

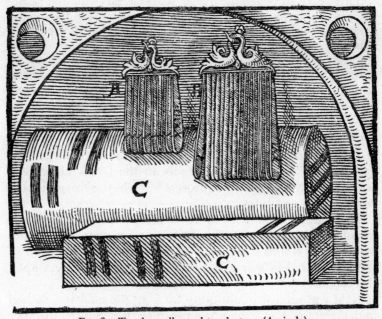

FIG. 6. Touch-needles and touch-stone (Agricola).

to be of the same copper or silver content as the gold tested, and the metal was valued accordingly.

Gold-mining much declined in the later years of the Roman Empire, and still further after its fall. Nevertheless a small but steady supply could always be obtained by washing certain river-sands. From the eleventh to the sixteenth century gold-mining greatly increased. By the thirteenth century the Rhine sands were being systematically washed for gold; the amalgamation process (*v. infra*) was being used to recover the metal from the concentrates.

PLATE I

A.—Roman Water Wheel used for pumping water from a copper mine, probably dating from 240 B.C. to A.D. 411.

B.—Sacrificial Colander for steaming herbs and grain. Bronze, Chinese, attributed to Shang Dynasty (Eighteenth to Eleventh Centuries B.C.) (see p. 51).

C.—Early Indian Copper Casting, Indus valley c. 2,000 B.C. (see p. 51).

PLATE II

A.—Primitive Roman Blast Furnace—*Model*.

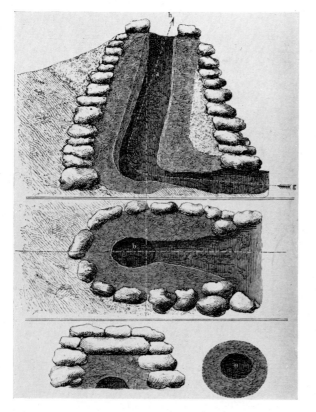

B.—Early Iron Furnace at Cernetat, South East France (see p. 46).

By the sixteenth century the mining of gold was thoroughly
systematized. The gold-bearing alluvium was washed through

Fig. 7. Sixteenth-century goldwashing as figured by Agricola.

sieves and along wooden channels furnished with cross-battens
or riffles, which arrested the gold and heavy minerals as they

settled out. The crude residues were mixed with mercury, which dissolved the gold and left the other heavy minerals. The mercury was squeezed through leather or canvas, leaving a solid amalgam of gold and mercury, from which the mercury was driven off by heat.

Auriferous rocks were pounded in stamp-mills driven by water-power at least as early as 1519; the gold was recovered by washing and amalgamation as described above.

Not only was gold obtained from alluvium or ore, but it was also recovered from silver and copper (p. 39). The first problem was to know if the silver contained any gold. One method was to dissolve a known weight of silver in nitric acid (p. 92), whereupon any gold remained undissolved in the form of a dark precipitate. This was recovered and melted to a gold bead, which was weighed on a delicate balance. Specific gravity determinations were also used. The supposedly auriferous silver was balanced against pure silver. If on immersing the balance in water the scale containing the silver under test tipped the beam, it was known to be denser than normal silver and therefore to be auriferous. Alternatively the silver under test and pure silver were drawn into wire through the same die; equal lengths were cut and weighed against each other, the auriferous silver being heavier. These tests were no more than qualitative and the assayer does not seem generally to have calculated the proportion of gold from the difference of density. On the large scale the gold was recovered from the silver in the same way, by dissolving it in nitric acid and melting up the residue. The silver was recovered from the acid by diluting it and adding copper, which precipitated the silver as a powder; this was melted up into ingots.

In the sixteenth century gold was usually refined by *cementation*. Thin plates of gold were interleaved with mixtures containing brickdust, ' vitriol ' (*i.e.* ferrous or copper sulphates) and salt; the whole was then strongly heated. The mixture evolved the vapours of sulphuric and hydrochloric acids. These did not attack gold but converted the surface silver and copper into chlorides, which could be scraped off. The process might have to be several times repeated if the gold was to be made really pure.

The most effective way of refining gold was supposed to

be the use of antimony, *i.e.* native antimony sulphide, stibnite. The gold was fused with antimony sulphide, whereupon all the other metals which might be alloyed with the gold were converted into sulphides, while gold, containing some metallic antimony, settled out as a greyish-yellow metallic ' regulus '. This was strongly fired on a shallow bed of bone-ash, whereupon the antimony was slowly oxidized by the air, leaving pure gold. Purification by antimony, unlike the simple refining by fire, was capable of removing silver from gold.

Gold, both in ancient and mediæval times, was beaten out into gold-leaf, but this was not of the extreme thinness that is usual to-day.

Silver

Silver in ancient Egypt (*c.* 3000 B.C.) began by being rarer than gold, but it soon became a far commoner metal. We know very little about the methods of smelting silver in antiquity, but we may guess that the ores were smelted with lead, as in later times; for the cupellation of lead to obtain silver (p. 194) is clearly described. Silver, unlike gold (p. 31), was very easily debased and imitated, and the Alexandrian technical treatises dating from *c.* A.D. 250 give a variety of methods of making white alloys that might pass for silver. In the early sixteenth century many silver ores were known, but most of the world's silver seems to have been recovered from copper and lead.

Silver ore was treated by smelting it with lead or lead ore, and the result was a lead-silver alloy containing other base metals. This alloy was placed on a shallow dish-shaped bed of bone-ash and strongly heated in a dome-shaped furnace. The lead and other metals were oxidized. The lead oxide melted; some of it ran off, some was raked off, some soaked into the bone-ash; finally only the silver remained unoxidized. The lead oxide was generally smelted again to recover the lead.

Small-scale cupellations were performed in assay-furnaces in order to ascertain the proportion of silver in specimens of lead.

Much silver was also recovered in the sixteenth century, and probably much earlier, in the course of the smelting of copper ores by the process described on pp. 37–39. The lead-silver alloy so obtained was cupelled as described above.

In the sixteenth century enormous quantities of rich silver

FIG. 8.   Cupellation and its materials as figured by Agricola (1556).

ore and mercury ore were discovered in the New World.   The
silver was mostly extracted by means of mercury.   We do not
know the date of the discovery of the amalgamation process

for the extraction of silver, which persisted till modern times; the affinity of mercury for silver was, however, known to all those who, like the alchemists, made a study of metals, and it would have been natural to try its effect upon silver ores. Biringuccio in his *Pirotechnia* (1540) narrates the process as a secret for which he exchanged a ring with a diamond worth twenty-five ducats! A similar process seems to have been introduced into Mexico in 1566. In the Mexican version of this process the ore, with mercury and salt and water, was trampled on a stone pavement by mules: the silver compounds reacted with and dissolved in the mercury, which was then collected and distilled, leaving behind the silver.

Silver was anciently refined by maintaining it in fusion at a red heat, but the mediæval and later method was repeated cupellation at a high temperature and under a strong blast.

Copper

The first of the metals to be smelted was copper. We may date the beginnings of copper-smelting in Egypt and Mesopotamia as *c.* 3500 B.C. Copper was smelted and converted into bronze (p. 39) at an early period in the Indus Valley and in China, perhaps *c.* 2500–2000 B.C. The earliest sources of copper ore were the Sinai peninsula and Anatolia. Cyprus had a well-developed copper industry by 2500 B.C. and was the chief source of copper in the millennium before the Roman period, but later very large amounts were obtained from Spain. There were two main classes of copper ores, the carbonates (malachite and azurite) and the sulphides. These sulphides normally contain a proportion of iron, and often some precious metals.

The carbonate ores were quite easy to smelt merely by burning them in a charcoal fire, but they are comparatively rare, and from *c.* 2000 B.C., as to-day, the sulphide ores were the main source. These ores vary from nearly pure copper sulphide to various mixtures of copper sulphide and iron sulphide. The smelting of them is far. from easy and the ancients succeeded in extracting only about a fifth of the copper in the ore, the rest being left in the slags.

The sulphide ores were first roasted to remove most of the sulphur; the roasted ore was mixed with charcoal and fed into a high cupola furnace. The resulting metal still contained

FIG. 9.   Liquation of lead containing precious metal from the cakes or ' bottoms '
of mixed lead and copper (Agricola, 1556).

much sulphur and was smelted again to purify it further.
Indeed the process of making copper from its sulphide ores
was regarded as repeated smelting.

In the early Middle Ages the carbonate ores appear to
have been the chief source, for Theophilus (end of the tenth
century) tells us that the ore is a green stone and that it was
first roasted, then heated with charcoal.

By the sixteenth century the process had been much elabor-
ated, probably because of the necessity of using the sulphide
ores and the desirability of recovering the gold and silver that
they contained. The ores were smelted with lead or lead-ore
in a small blast-furnace. The lead dissolved the gold and
silver present in the ore, and this enriched lead mixed with the
copper but did not actually alloy with it. The result of the
smelt was a large flat ' cake ' containing copper, unchanged
copper sulphide, enriched lead, etc. These cakes or ' bottoms '
were stood on end in a furnace and carefully heated; the lead
liquefied and gradually drained out of them. This lead was
then cupelled to recover the gold and silver, which were then
separated as described on p. 92.

The cake of impure copper was then melted on an open
hearth with a strong blast which gradually oxidized its sulphur
content. A certain amount of copper was converted in the
process into cuprous oxide which, if allowed to remain in the
copper, would have rendered it brittle. The molten copper
was therefore ' poled ' by stirring it with green wooden poles,
which, in contact with the molten copper, evolved hydrocarbon
gases which reduced the cuprous oxide to metal. The whole
process differed remarkably little from that in use in the
nineteenth century. The chemically-trained reader will be
impressed by the power of the craftsmen to discover and perfect
all these processes without the aid of chemical theory, or
indeed any idea of the principles involved, and will acquire a
deep respect for the men who controlled these operations by
sheer skill born of experience.

Much copper was used for cooking-pots (which had to be
tinned), but the greater part of it seems to have been turned
into alloys—bronze and brass.

Bronze

The most important use of tin in ancient times was in the
making of bronze, an alloy containing about 7 parts of copper
to 1 part of tin (p. 43). We do not know how the effect of tin
in toughening and hardening copper came to be discovered,

and it is remarkable that not only in Egypt and Mesopotamia, but also in the Indus Valley and China, bronze became known and was in general use soon after copper itself. The use of this alloy was so widespread as to cause modern archæologists to give the name Bronze Age to the two thousand or so years during which metals were known and before iron came into common use. It may be said to have been the metal of choice from the beginnings of civilization in most parts of the world, and to have been slowly displaced by iron from about 1000 B.C., though still preferred for many purposes for which we should now use the latter metal. In the Middle Ages it was further displaced not only by iron and steel, but also by brass or ' latten ', which became the commonest of the non-ferrous metals.

Brass

Brass is essentially an alloy of copper and zinc, though many early brasses also contain lead or tin or both. Metallic zinc was unknown in Europe before the sixteenth century; but the Chinese were making it at least as early as the fifteenth century and exported it to Europe in the seventeenth. In the eighteenth century zinc was produced in Europe in increasing quantities, which were not, however, considerable until near the end of that period. Thus until comparatively modern times brass was not thought of as a mixture of metals, but as the material made by treating copper with ' calamine ' or ' cadmia '. Calamine, before the period of chemical analysis, was thought of as ' the mineral that makes copper into brass ', and consequently the name was applied both to native zinc carbonate and to its hydrated silicate.

True brass was apparently unknown in the Egyptian and Babylonian civilizations, but there is some evidence of its use in Palestine at an early date. The Greeks and Romans do not seem to have had the metal before the first century B.C. From about 20 B.C. at least the Romans made brass (*aurichalcum*) by treating copper with calamine or something that they called *cadmia*. This was not, of course, a compound of cadmium, but some sort of deposit from copper-smelters' furnaces or flues, presumably containing the oxides of the more volatile metals, especially of zinc and arsenic, etc. Brass was not, however, particularly important in Græco-Roman times, when bronze was the metal of choice, but it was greatly in use in the Middle Ages. The Chinese made brass in the seventh to tenth centuries, and from about this period it came into wide use in Europe. Thus the monk Theophilus (tenth century) tells us that it was made by heating copper in crucibles with calamine, and in the sixteenth century Ercker describes it as being made in the same way. The best early description of the process is given by Albertus Magnus, patron saint of scientists (*c.* 1250):

> For those who work much in copper in our parts, that is at Paris and Cologne and in other places where I have been and seen it done, turn copper into brass (*aurichalcum*) by means of the powder of a stone called *calamine*; and when the stone evaporates there still remains a darkish lustre inclining somewhat to the appearance of gold. To make it whiter and more like yellow (citrinated) gold, they mix in a little tin; also because the brass loses much of the ductility of the copper. And those who wish to deceive and produce a lustre like gold bind the stone so that it remains longer in the brass in the fire, not evaporating swiftly from the brass. And it is bound by the ' oil of glass ': fragments of the glass are taken and converted into powder and sprinkled on the brass after the calamine is put in: and then the glass thrown on it floats on the brass and prevents the stone and the virtue of the stone from evaporating, but reflects the stony vapour on to the brass and so long and powerfully purges the brass, and the feculent material in it is hardened.

It will be seen that although Albertus observed the technique in a manner somewhat unusual in a mediæval scholar, he had no idea that an alloy was being formed, supposing rather that a ' virtue ' was imparted to the copper by the calamine.

In the sixteenth century it was known that copper greatly increased in weight when converted into brass: recorded figures show that the brass then used contained some 35 % of zinc—which is about the optimum. We note once more that the craftsman was able by experience to obtain the best material, even though he was quite ignorant of the nature of the process he was operating.

The making of brass by smelting copper with some compound of zinc rather than metallic zinc itself continued into the nineteenth century. The usual agent was calamine, mined in Derbyshire and also in Limburg; but calcined zinc-blende was used and even in some places ' cadmia ', the deposit from copper-smelters' flues.

Lead

Lead was known in Egypt and we may suppose that it was known as early as silver, with which it is normally associated. Rods and lumps of lead were used for currency purposes in Assyria and Anatolia about 1500–1000 B.C., and leaden coins were used in Numidia, India and Persia at various times between 200 B.C. and A.D. 300. It also served a variety of purposes in Greece and Rome, amongst which may be mentioned the making of water-pipes, solder and white lead. We are told by Pliny that it was found in Spain and Gaul, but most abundantly in Britain. Roman pigs of lead are often found in England, the earliest belonging to the reign of Claudius (c. A.D. 44–48) and the latest to about A.D. 160–170. It is probable, however, that lead-mining and smelting increased rather than diminished in succeeding centuries.

The ore of lead is galena, lead sulphide, a bright metallic-looking mineral. Lead can be obtained from it by heating it with charcoal, with some access of air. A Roman lead-furnace has been found and consisted of a cylindrical pit 11 feet deep and $8\frac{1}{2}$ feet wide. In England, until the middle of the seventeenth century, the lead was smelted by the simple method of burning the ore with wood or charcoal in low stone hearths built high on the hills with a west aspect, so that the prevailing wind should provide a strong draught. In Germany in the sixteenth century, however, a small blast-furnace was employed, the molten metal running out at the bottom. More elaborate furnaces, especially of the reverberatory type, came into use in England in the seventeenth and eighteenth centuries. These enabled the lead to be smelted by means of coal instead of, as formerly, by wood, which was then becoming scarce.

There was a very large demand for lead throughout the later Middle Ages for cisterns, pipes, and roofs. A great deal of lead was used in the extraction of silver and gold from copper (p. 34), though most of this was recovered from the lead oxide produced in the process.

Mediæval lead was not ordinarily desilverized, for the only known process involved oxidizing the whole of the lead on the cupel and once more smelting the resulting litharge in order to recover the lead. This process did not pay unless the lead was rich in silver; accordingly mediæval lead roofs always contained silver and were commonly removed from old churches in the nineteenth century for extraction of the silver by the process of Parkes or Pattinson (pp. 194–5).

Tin

Tin has been known since about 3000 B.C. and throughout antiquity was alloyed with copper in order to make the much harder and more useful bronze. The source of the early Egyptian tin is a puzzle. It may have come from Anatolia, Persia or India; at a later period it seems that Phœnician traders acquired it at first or second hand, from Cornwall and Spain.

Tin occurs as the heavy black mineral, cassiterite, and this was obtained in just the same fashion as gold by washing river-sands or finely-crushed ores.

It was very easy to smelt and required only to be gently heated with charcoal without too much air-blast, which was known to convert it into ' ashes ', i.e. the white stannic oxide.

There was a good deal of confusion between tin and lead in ancient times, nor was any means known of separating one from the other. However, since cassiterite occurs in a fairly pure state, the tin obtained from it was naturally fairly free from impurities. A rough test was to melt the metal and pour it on papyrus. Melted tin would not scorch papyrus whereas melted lead would do so. But tin containing a small proportion of lead melts at a lower temperature than pure tin, so the test would do little more than indicate which metal was present in the greater proportion.

From early Egyptian and Sumerian times tin was used for making bronze and, from the Roman period, for tinning copper or bronze cooking pots and also for mirrors, brooches and the like.

Mirrors

Mirrors are of high antiquity, being found in Egypt from the Old Kingdom and in all subsequent civilizations. The oldest type was of polished metal, gold, silver, copper, bronze or brass: the use of polished black obsidian and of dark blue glass is also recorded. The white alloys of copper and tin with a little arsenic, which constituted the speculum metal of the seventeenth and eighteenth centuries, were made in Egypt during the Græco-Roman period as imitations of silver, and there is evidence that they were also used to make mirrors. The Romans used silver-plated bronze or silver. Glass mirrors coated with lead or tin were certainly known in the third or fourth century A.D. These were usually convex, having been cut from a blown glass flask. Alexander of Aphrodisias (A.D. 220) also mentions the coating of glass with tin, but tin foil was probably the substance used rather than the tin amalgam used in recent times, as described below.

Mediæval mirrors were commonly made of steel or silver and were of no great dimensions, but glass mirrors were known. Vincent of Beauvais in the thirteenth century speaks of mirrors of glass coated with lead: tin, which was much confounded with lead, may be meant. In the early sixteenth century metal mirrors were cast from a brittle alloy of copper and tin, containing much more tin than does bronze. From about 1507 the glass-makers of Murano began to make much larger glass mirrors and to coat them with tin amalgam: the invention of plate glass by Perrot was first utilized for the production of mirrors in 1688. The application of the tin amalgam was a specialized process. Tin foil was laid on a flat slab, bedded in a wooden frame, and rubbed lightly with mercury to amalgamate it. Mercury was now poured on the tin foil about a quarter of an inch deep, the glass was floated on the mercury and pressed down by weights. After twenty-four hours it could be removed with the adherent tin amalgam and left to dry and harden for up to a month. The effect of the mercurial vapours on the workers was serious. The present method of silvering glass was introduced, as a result of the work of Liebig, about 1840, and tin mirrors soon disappeared.

Tin-plate

The tinning of brass and bronze cooking vessels to prevent their corrosion and the imparting of an unpleasant taste to foodstuffs dates at least from Roman times. Tinning of brass cooking-vessels was practised throughout the Middle Ages and indeed up to the present day. The process is a simple one. The vessel is scraped bright or pickled with acid. Some tin and a flux, such as resin or sal-ammoniac, is placed in it; the tin is melted and rubbed on the vessel with linen rags. So thin is the coating that Pliny supposed that the vessels were not increased in weight.

The tinning of iron is alluded to by Chaucer about 1384. The process is mentioned by Agricola in the middle of the sixteenth century, and it throve during the seventeenth century in Germany, where iron articles were tinned by dipping them into a bath of molten tin covered by a layer of melted fat. Agricola also mentioned the use of vinegar and sal-ammoniac for cleaning metal before tinning.

The English tin-plate industry began in the sixteen-eighties when the Company of Tin-Plate Workers was formed. The South Wales tin-plate industry began about 1720. In 1728 the iron sheets began to be rolled instead of being forged by hand. In 1806 dilute sulphuric acid replaced sour barley-water as a means of cleansing them from oxide. Tin-plate slowly grew in importance until the 1860's, when the canning of food rapidly increased the scale of its manufacture. Steel plates replaced iron from about 1875. The pejorative sense of the word ' tin ' dates from this time: formerly the word denoted a metal esteemed only less than gold and silver. Pure tin and also pewter, four-fifths of which consists of tin and one-fifth of lead, were much valued in the Middle Ages as being relatively uncorroded by air, water or foodstuffs. Thus a chalice, normally made of gold or silver, was permitted to be made of tin, and tin bottles were sometimes used for carrying wine.

Iron

Meteoric iron was known and used in Egypt at a very early period, but the smelting of iron seems to have been introduced by peoples from the north. It seems that the earliest iron industries were in Armenia. The Hittites are known to have been working iron about 1300–1200 B.C., but were probably producing the metal a good deal earlier than this: the Assyrians seem to have been the first of the great nations of antiquity to adopt it as a material of warfare. Iron seems to have emerged from the status of a precious metal between 1400 and 1000 B.C., and thereafter to have become a usual but still valuable material. Steel picks, dating from 700 B.C., have been found in Assyria, but we do not know whether the steel was made deliberately or whether it was the 'steely iron' which sometimes resulted where the smelting was prolonged and much charcoal was employed.

Our knowledge of the ancient methods of making iron is drawn from various rather slender accounts that have come down to us (*e.g.* those of Pliny and Dioscorides), and from the remains of furnaces which have survived. The first step was to find the mineral, which was probably identified by its colour and weight. Sometimes the mineral was washed to free it from earthy matter. Among the minerals used were magnetite, hæmatite and various carbonate ores. The mineral was sometimes first roasted in a kiln, a process which, by removing moisture and carbon dioxide, makes it easier to smelt. Sometimes silica or silicate rocks (such as lava) were added before the ore was reduced to metal. Charcoal was both the reducing agent and the fuel employed.

The attainment of the necessary temperature depended mainly on the supply of air. The most primitive type of furnace was a simple hole dug in the side of a hill in such a way as to catch the wind, but its operation must have been very uncertain. A further advance is shown in the furnace (Plate II, B) found at Cernetat in the south-east of France. No artificial draught seems to have been used, but the height of the shaft and the force of the wind blowing into the draught-hole must have given quite a rapid combustion: this furnace was lined with refractory clay which showed signs of having been subjected to a high temperature. A similar Roman furnace found at Dreimühlenborn in the Taunus (Plate II, A) had apertures at the bottom intended for the clay nozzles of bellows, some of which were found on the site. Presumably the bellows were bags made from the skins of beasts, such as appear in Greek and Roman representations of smiths' forges.

The result of the process was the reduction of the oxide of iron to metallic iron and the conversion of the earthy impurities into a slag. The heat of the furnace was, save in rare instances, insufficient to melt the iron, which, however, became sticky and plastic, so as to form a spongy mass containing in its pores a good deal of liquid slag. This mass, later called a *bloom*, was repeatedly forged until the slag was squeezed out and the particles of iron cohered to become a tough fibrous mass of metal. This metal could not be cast, for it would not melt at any temperature obtainable, and so it had to be forged into the shape required.

This type of process, which survives among primitive peoples in many parts of the world, was inherited by the iron-workers of the Middle Ages. Their first contribution was the more effective use of blast, as in the Catalan Furnace, and the second was the casting of iron.

The Catalan furnace was probably introduced in the thirteenth century and survived into the twentieth. It consisted, as shown in Plate III, A, of a small square cavity or hearth with an inclined copper tuyère designed to direct the blast on

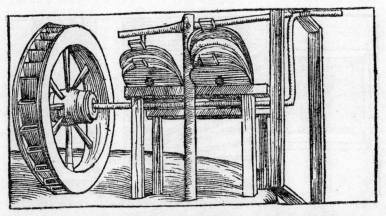

FIG. 10. Sixteenth-century bellows operated by a water-wheel (Biringuccio, 1540).

to the mixture of charcoal and ore. Into this tuyère opened the nozzle of the device that provided the blast, thus drawing in much more air, on the principle of the injector. The earliest Catalan furnaces were presumably operated by bellows, but in 1640 a very ingenious blowing device, the *trompe*, was introduced. It may be described as a gigantic edition of the chemist's filter-pump. Water ran through a nozzle enclosed in a pipe, perforated at the top with holes. Air was drawn in and the froth of air and water fell into a large wooden tank. The water flowed away and the entrapped air was forced out to the tuyères of the furnace. The combustion and reduction took place in the lowest part of the hearth. The management of the furnace was somewhat complicated: it

resulted in a bloom of iron or steely iron, as in the earlier types
of furnace.

Forging did very well for the making of smaller objects, but
as heavier cannon came into use in the late Middle Ages, the
forging of them became more and more difficult, and at some
period, not certainly known but prior to 1500, the casting of
iron cannon became a regular practice. The blooms of low-
carbon iron obtained from various types of bloom-furnace
could not be melted in any furnace then available, but iron
containing a high proportion of carbon melts at a lower
temperature, and it became possible to produce this by means
of rudimentary blast-furnaces, which were really developments

Fig. 11.   Bellows and small blast furnace (Biringuccio, 1540).

of the old bloomeries. The first stage was the Osmund furnace
(Swedenborg, 1734) shown in Plate III, B. The next stage was
the high bloomery, like the Osmund but 10 to 16 feet in height,
the shaft either widening towards the top or having the characteristic form of the modern blast-furnace, i.e. two truncated cones.
This furnace, like the Osmund, was originally used to make
solid blooms, but by increasing the proportion of charcoal and
keeping the temperature as high as possible, fused high-carbon
iron, i.e. cast-iron, could be obtained. This stage is well illustrated by an account given by Henry Powle of the smelting of
cast-iron in the Forest of Dean in 1676. Coal was then in use
for calcining the ore, but not for smelting it:

. . . In former times, when their Works were few, and their
Vent small, they made use of no other Bellows but such as were

TAB: XVII. de Ferro.

I.W.Stir fec Dresd.

FIG. 12.   High bloomery (Swedenborg, 1734).

moved by the strength of men: by reason whereof their fires were much less intense, than in the Furnaces they now employ. . . .

After they have provided the Ore their first work is to Calcine it : which is done in Kilns, much after the fashion of our ordinary Lime-Kilns. These they fill up to the top with Coal and Ore, *stratum super stratum*, until it be full; and so putting fire to the bottom, they let it burn till the coal be wasted and then renew the Kilns with fresh Ore and Coal. . . .

From hence they carry it to their Furnaces, which are built of Brick or Stone, about 24 foot square on the outside, and near 30 feet in height. . . .

Behind the Furnace are placed two huge pairs of Bellows, whose Noses meet at a little hole near the bottom. These are compressed together by certain Buttons placed on the axis of a very large wheel, which is turned about by water. . . .

At first they fill these Furnaces with Ore and Cynder [1] intermix'd with Fuel, which in these Works is always of Charcoal; laying them hollow at the bottom so that they may more easily take fire: But after they are once kindled, the Materials run together into a hard cake or lump which is sustained by the fashion of the Furnace, and through this the Metal as it melts, trickles down into the Receivers which are placed at the bottom where there is passage open, by which they take away the Scum and Dross, and let out the Metal as they see occasion. Before the mouth of the Furnace lies a great Bed of Sand, wherein they make Furrows of the fashion into which they desire to cast their Iron. . . .

The development of these high bloomeries into the modern blast-furnace is discussed on pp. 196–199.

Steel is a mixture of iron and carbides of iron, containing *c.* 0·5–1·5 % of carbon. Its great hardness and strength made it everywhere the material of choice for tools and weapons. Steel was sometimes produced in the bloomeries when the temperature was high and charcoal was present in excess, and the earliest steel objects are probably of this character. It seems first to have been systematically made in the Græco-Roman period by repeatedly heating iron in glowing charcoal and forging it. The cementation processes (p. 34), namely the heating of iron coated with various carbonaceous mixtures, *e.g.* horn-dust, were known to Theophilus (tenth century A.D.),

---

[1] Cinder —the residues from the old iron workings, still containing much iron.

and, like most of the process described in his recipes, probably originated many centuries earlier.

The characteristic property of steel is that it can be hardened by heating it to redness and plunging it into water: many recipes for quenching-liquids to give special hardness are recorded in late Roman times and after, but probably none of them were more effective than water.

The technique of forging together iron and steel so as to give a metal with the toughness of the former and the hardness of the latter seems to have been an Indian art, and to date back to a period before the Christian era. Indian metallurgy was of a high order at this period: the famous iron pillar of Asoka (third century B.C.) stands as witness thereof. Of the making of steel in the Middle Ages not much is known. Some was imported from the East, but a good deal was certainly made in Europe. We know that in the sixteenth century steel was made by heating lumps of iron in a bed of charcoal. These were taken out, quenched and tested: the process was repeated as often as might be necessary. The surface of the lumps was thus converted into high-carbon steel and they were finally forged till homogeneous. Steel was valuable; thus in Scotland, in 1549, 20 pence a pound was paid for it. Its uses were therefore limited. Knives, weapons, armour, and mirrors were commonly made of it. On account of the expense of steel, tools were often made of iron ' steeled ': thus a hammer head might be of iron with a plate of steel welded to its face.

Mercury

It is improbable, but not impossible, that mercury was known in ancient Egypt or in the West before the Græco-Roman period, though its compound cinnabar (p. 85) was a native mineral and well-known pigment. The Chinese, however, appear to have been familiar with mercury at a much earlier era. Cinnabar may well have been suspected of containing a metal but ordinary smelting methods would, of course, volatilize the mercury. We do not know how the mercury was discovered, but we first hear of it in the works of Dioscorides (c. A.D. 50), who describes the making of mercury from cinnabar by heating it on an iron saucer contained in a pot covered by another pot. The mercury condensed on the upper pot in droplets, which could be scraped out. Some of the cinnabar would react with the iron (HgS+Fe→FeS+Hg) and some would be oxidized by air diffusing through the porous earthenware (HgS + O$_2$ → Hg + SO$_2$). Pliny makes a false distinction between *argentum vivum* (living or *quick* silver), made in this way or found native, and *hydrargyrum*, 'water-silver' made by grinding cinnabar with vinegar in a copper pestle-and-mortar (HgS + Cu → CuS + Hg). The latter probably contained some dissolved copper.

Mercury was much in request in the Middle Ages as a remedy, *e.g.* for destroying lice, as a means of extracting gold, for gilding, and for making the pigment, mercury sulphide, vermilion. The metal was prepared, we may suppose, in the same fashion as in the sixteenth century. At this period flask-shaped pots were filled with cinnabar ore and loosely plugged with moss. They were then inverted in a second series of pots, buried in the earth. A fire was then lighted on top of the upper pots: the cinnabar was oxidized and the mercury liberated condensed in the lower pots, kept cool by the earth. Alternatively the ore could be distilled. The mercury was

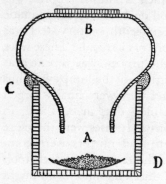

FIG. 13. Mercury still of Dioscorides (reconstruction).

purified by treatment with vinegar and salt, and then squeezed through canvas or soft leather into pots.

The famous source of mercury ore for some 2,000 years was Almaden, in Spain—the very word is Arabic for ' The Mine '. The mines of Idria, in Italy, were discovered in 1470. In the sixteenth century the production of mercury was undertaken on a very large scale in the New World. In the seventeenth century the Spanish were said to have produced a million pounds of mercury every year at the mines of Pulcas.

The poisonous character of the metal was well known, but few precautions seem to have been taken against its deadly vapour. From the late seventeenth century mercury came to be used in many scientific instruments; its use for silvering mirrors was also greatly augmented during the eighteenth and early nineteenth centuries.

Conclusion

We have seen that from the earliest periods of civilization metals have been produced on a considerable scale. Few records of technique have survived from the early periods, but the quantity and quality of the metals that have survived witness the adequacy of the results of ancient practice, wasteful

FIG. 14. The preparation of mercury by downward distillation (Agricola, 1556).

though it may have been in ore, fuel and labour. There is reason to suppose a rapid increase in the extent and systematization of mining from the thirteenth to the fifteenth century (A.D.), and the extensive records of the sixteenth century show a highly organized and skilfully conducted industry of mining and metallurgy. Mining, however, remained limited to moderate depths and to favourable conditions as long as the supply of air, removal of water and raising of ore depended on the muscles of men and animals or comparatively small water-wheels. The need for another source of power for mining was urgent and soon to be supplied. What metallurgy, on the other hand, chiefly lacked was some chemical theory that might guide it in the recognition and treatment of ores, processes which remained entirely empirical until the latter part of the eighteenth century.

CHAPTER THREE

Cements and Mortars

Types of Cement and Mortar

CEMENTS and mortars are materials which can be applied in the form of a soft paste and later set into a hard mass. Five chief types of these have been used throughout history. First are the natural plastic materials such as *clay* and some types of mud which harden by drying and soften again when moistened. The second is a mixture of *lime* and water, alone or mixed with sand; this sets first by drying, then by absorbing carbon dioxide from the air and forming an insoluble mass of calcium carbonate. The third is *anhydrous calcium sulphate*, made by heating the mineral gypsum: this, when moistened, sets to a solid mass of hydrated calcium sulphate. If lightly fired this sets quickly, like plaster of paris, but if strongly fired it sets slowly. The fourth is *pozzolanic cement*, made by mixing certain siliceous volcanic earths with a lime-mortar: these will set even under water. A fifth type, *Portland cement*, brought into use only in the eighteenth century, is made by firing various mixtures of chalk and clay. Almost all the cements and mortars in use to-day are of this last type.

Ancient Mortars and Cements

The use of mortar to join the stones or bricks of a building into a solid mass is very ancient, though not so old as building itself. Much ancient building consists of stones and earth rammed together, and some ancient masonry is laid dry; but the use of mortar or cement dates back to ancient Egypt and Mesopotamia. The Egyptians used Nile mud to join their unburnt bricks; the Sumerians normally employed clay, sometimes with a small proportion of bitumen, while the early Babylonians employed bitumen, applied hot, which formed a very efficient cementing material. The Egyptian stone buildings were mortared with burnt gypsum; this is less strong than lime-mortar, but was probably chosen because the makers were short of fuel and gypsum is much easier to burn than limestone, which requires a prolonged high temperature to convert it into lime.

The Greeks used lime with very little sand as their mortar. The Romans also used lime-mortar, and the reason for the great strength and hardness of Roman mortar has been a problem to later ages. Their mortar, like ours, was simply sand and lime (3 : 1 as a rule), and its strength and hardness were due only to very thorough mixing and ramming.

Vitruvius (Book I, Chapter IV) gives careful directions for selecting the sand: a sharp, clean pit-sand was to be preferred to any earthy sand or sea-sand. He also gives his theory of the setting of mortar. He knows that the lime is lighter by a third than the limestone from which it was made, and he supposes this loss of weight to be due to the escape of air and moisture. This process opens the pores of the stone, and when the lime is slaked the water rushes in and expels the heat which has been left in the lime. The porous character of the wet lime makes it stick to the sand: its setting, he thinks, is simply due to drying.

Roman lime-mortar was used not only for setting stones but also for water-resisting layers, e.g. the linings of cisterns. The Romans also used a cement of the silicate type. They knew that certain volcanic earths, when finely ground and mixed with lime and sand, gave a mortar which was very strong and would set under water. The most famous source of these earths was the volcanic tuff of Pozzuoli, near Naples; from this place-name comes the name, *pozzolana*, which is given to this sort of cement. The Romans recognized deposits of tuff in other localities and used it in the same way. They used their cement not only as a mortar but as a building material, casting it between boards.

Mediæval Mortar and Plaster

The mediæval builders of the twelfth century and later used lime-mortars. The lime was burned in kilns, usually no more than holes in the hill-side; the fuel was charcoal, it appears, rather than wood. Sand was, if possible, dug near the building, for mediæval transport was laborious: it was sometimes washed to remove clay. It was also usual for builders to set up their lime-kilns and burn their lime close to the work they were doing rather than to bring lime from a distance. Both sand and lime were well sifted, water was added and the mortar very well mixed by treading. This mortar was used not only to join dressed stone and brick but also to make a sort of concrete, known as *attractum*, which consisted of a mixture of lime-sand mortar with stones of fairly small sizes. This was a favourite building material. Thus the huge piers of the twelfth-century cathedrals are faced with dressed stone, but within they consist of ' attractum ', which, when well made and thoroughly rammed, has proved to be very durable. Aggregates of lime with sand, stones, crushed bricks, potsherds, etc., were also used as flooring plasters. When worn, the floor could be taken up, burned again and relaid.

Gypsum cements were used throughout the Middle Ages: thus in the fourteenth century plaster of paris was brought to Windsor Castle for use as a wall-plaster and for chimney-pieces. The pozzolanic cements were not employed in northern Europe, but in Italy and some of the Mediterranean islands they have continued to be made and used in the same way from ancient times until the present day. Up till the nineteenth century they were also the material of choice for work exposed to water.

We may say, then, that the typical cement and mortar of the period before the eighteenth century was the familiar mixture of lime, sand and water.

The Discovery of Portland Cement

The greatest discovery in this field was that of Portland cement, the history of which is not altogether clear. It begins in 1756 with the experiments of Joseph Smeaton, designed to discover the best materials for the projected Eddystone lighthouse. He discovered that in making a pozzolanic cement a lime made from a clayey limestone gave the best results, and thus he discovered hydraulic lime. In 1796 James Parker discovered that he could make a hydraulic cement by calcining the ' septaria ', nodules of clayey limestone dredged up from the Thames estuary. In the years between this discovery and 1824 several other cements of this kind were discovered, the most important being that made in France by L. J. Vicat by calcining a mixture of chalk and clay ground together in a wet mill. Joseph Aspdin patented the process of grinding limestone and clay, calcining the product and grinding it finely, but he did not appreciate the fact that a very high temperature was needed to make a first-class cement; his son, William Aspdin, in 1848 set up the first kiln (Plate IV, A) for this purpose and was the first to produce the modern Portland cement.

The names applied to these products are confusing. Thus the name 'Roman cement', which should mean the pozzolanic type, was often applied to other cements that set under water: Portland cement never came from Portland, but was named from a supposed resemblance to Portland stone.

CHAPTER FOUR

Ceramics

Egyptian and Assyrian Practice

THE baking of plastic clay so as to form a hard body unaffected
by water dates back at least to 5000 B.C. No civilized peoples,
and very few primitives, are known to have been without the
knowledge of this process. The mere baking of clay is hardly
to be admitted even as a primitive kind of industrial chemistry,
but quite early in history it led to the discovery of coloured
slips and glazing, which entailed the recognition and manipulation of numerous chemical substances.

In the civilizations of Egypt, Mesopotamia and the Indus,
brick was used for building. Egyptian bricks were of Nile
mud, which was not a good plastic material and had to be
held together by chopped straw or reeds; such bricks were
sun-dried and but rarely baked, presumably because fuel was
scarce. Mesopotamia consists largely of alluvial clay, which
makes good bricks. These were sometimes burned, the
abundant reeds being used as fuel, but sun-dried bricks were
the more usual. The Assyrians (*c.* 1200 B.C.) commonly glazed
their bricks. The peoples of the Indus civilizations used
burned brick of high quality at least as early as 2500 B.C. All
later civilized peoples seem to have used burned brick.

The Egyptian pottery made from clay was not glazed, but
much of it, especially in early times, was highly burnished or
ornamented with white slip (liquid clay) or red ochre; some
of it was blackened in a manner which does not seem to be
very certainly known, but possibly by baking in a very smoky
atmosphere. The famous Egyptian glazes were not applied
to baked clay, for they would not adhere to this material and
could only be fired on a body consisting mainly of silica. Thus
the Egyptian glazed ware or faience is of ground quartz held
together with a minimum of clay or perhaps natron.

The early Egyptian glazes were coloured with copper
compounds, which gave shades of blue, green and violet, but

in later times a red was achieved with iron oxide or with copper compounds fired under reducing conditions; a black was obtained with magnetite, purples with manganese, and a yellow, in one case at least, with lead and antimony.

The Egyptians' greatest ceramic discovery was their famous blue glaze, the secret of which was lost in classical times and not rediscovered until the nineteenth century.   It was made

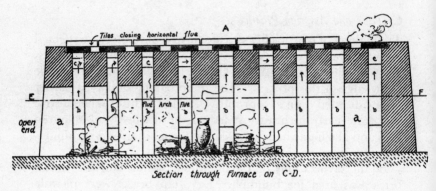

Section through furnace on C-D.

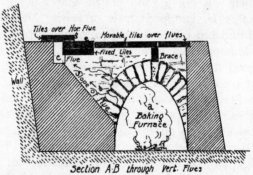

Section A.B through Vert. Flues

FIG. 15.   Pottery kiln from Nippur perhaps *c.* 2000 B.C.

from pure white sand, natron, limestone and a copper compound, perhaps malachite.   It had to be maintained at 830°–900° C. for a period of some forty-eight hours, and the regulation of temperature must have required no little skill. The blue thus made could either be powdered and used as a pigment, or could be applied as a glaze to a siliceous body such as is described above.

The peoples of the Indus civilization (*c.* 2500 B.C.) made excellent pottery, shaped on the wheel.   Some was decorated by painting with coloured slips and some was glazed, and it seems likely that the glazing of pottery was first practised in India and Egypt at about the same period.

The Chinese, who later attained world-primacy in ceramics, appear to have used the art of glazing about 400–300 B.C., but not to have used lead glazes until the first century B.C. Chinese ceramics did not attain remarkable excellence until the T'ang period (A.D. 618–907). Towards the end of that period they began to exert a strong influence on the ceramics of the Near East, but their influence on Western Europe was, however, small or negligible until the seventeenth century, and we may therefore consider the Chinese contribution separately at the end of this chapter.

A very important discovery was made by the Assyrians about 700 B.C., when they began to use lead oxide as a base, and so made the first glazes which would adhere readily to baked clay. They obtained a good yellow from lead antimonate, presumably made by roasting native antimony sulphide with litharge (lead oxide). Their blues and reds were derived from copper and their white probably from antimony oxide and not from tin oxide, which was the essential constituent of the opaque glazes which attained great perfection in later times.

Greek and Roman Ware

Another and quite different perfection of ceramics was attained by the Greeks. The invention of pottery decorated in black and red belonged to the Mycenæan period (c. 1500 B.C.), but the Greeks of Attica during the sixth century B.C. developed this technique so as to produce ceramics of much greater beauty than any before them. The red colour is that of the burned clay, though it was probably augmented by mixing in ruddle (red ochre). The thin lustrous black coating has been the subject of much controversy. The vases were apparently painted with a mixture of ordinary clay and water ' peptized ,' i.e. liquefied to a ' sol ', with a little alkali (e.g wood-ash) and milk or egg white. The design was made in this medium, the piece was then fired and subjected to a reducing atmosphere. The red ferric oxide of the clay was thus reduced to black ferrous oxide and the piece appeared uniformly black. It was then reheated with some access of air. The ferrous oxide in the more porous and open body reoxidized more quickly than that locked in by the compact peptized clay of the glaze. The figures thus remained black on the red ground of the body.

A similar mystery has surrounded the *terra sigillata*, the lustrous red ware of the Romans, but it is at least probable that its fine surface resulted from a coating of the peptized clay described above. Glazing in colours, though practised, seems to have made little progress in the period of the Greeks and Romans.

The Burning of Pottery in Ancient Times

The earliest pots were burned in the open fire. In the remains of the cities of the Indus (*c.* 2500 B.C.) and later in Babylonia we find ceramic furnaces with a combustion chamber separate from the kiln which contained the pots, so as to heat them by the flame and gases alone. This arrangement allows reducing or oxidizing conditions to be realized at the will of the potter by increasing or reducing the access of air. The early Babylonian furnaces much resembled the ' furnace with eyes ' described on p. 70. Roman pottery kilns had a fire-chamber at the side or beneath, communicating with the kiln by a flue. High temperatures were undesirable, as pottery (as distinguished from porcelain) readily fuses.

Lustre-ware and Maiolica

The history of pottery in the first millennium of the Christian era is obscure, but soon after A.D. 1300 we find a new development in Europe, namely, the production of lustre-ware, which owes its beauty to a thin film of metal. It is, however, certain that this ware was made in Mesopotamia in the ninth century A.D. and that the technique found its way throughout Egypt, Persia and the Islamic world. We hear of the manufacture of lustre in Egypt in the tenth century, and in Persia about 1180; the manufacture was established in Moorish Spain by the fourteenth century. This lovely and valuable ware was exported all over Europe. One Henrique Cock visited the village of Muel, near Saragossa, in 1585 and described the process. His account is a little confused, but shows that the process then used was approximately the same as that which was used in the eighteenth century, and of this we have elsewhere a clear account.

The pottery was baked and then glazed with a white or blue glaze containing lead and a variable but much smaller quantity of tin. To this end lead and tin were melted together and kept hot until they were entirely converted into oxide, which was then mixed with sand. This mixture was very finely ground and mixed with water. The ware was coated with it and again baked. The next process was to apply the lustre, which was made by heating copper and silver with sulphur. The resulting sulphides were pounded very fine and mixed with red ochre and vinegar to form a paste. This was painted on the ware and when fired left a very thin lustrous layer of copper and silver. The pottery must have been heated in a reducing atmosphere obtained by restricting the supply of air: the conditions for this would be traditionally reproduced by the workers, but could hardly have been described in the period before chemistry was established.

Maiolica ware has a history similar to that of lustre. The use of a tin-lead glaze in Assyria has been asserted, but it is probable that the white colour is due to antimony oxide; in any case there is a gap of a thousand years between the Assyrians and the earliest known Persian ware that is glazed in this way. The early history of maiolica in Italy is likewise obscure, but glazed ware was being made in Italy in the twelfth century and probably earlier, the technique being borrowed from the East, perhaps *via* Byzantium, where it was very popular. The art of maiolica developed very rapidly in Italy in the fifteenth century, probably under the influence of the Spanish lustre-ware described above. Luca della Robbia initiated a new and delightful ceramic art by applying polychrome tin-glazes to sculpture.

There exists a manuscript, written by one Picolpasso in 1548, which tells us just how the maiolica makers of the period worked.

The ware itself was of white clay and was normally coated with two layers of glaze. The first ingredient of the glaze was what we now call potassium carbonate; this was made by burning wine-lees or tartar, both of which contained much potassium hydrogen tartrate. Alternatively soda-ash from the Levant (p. 75) could be used. The pure white ash was mixed with 3 parts of pure white sand, and this was the material for the *marzacotto* or basic frit.

To make the white glaze on which the painting was to be done, tin was calcined with lead in the proportion of one of the former to three to seven of the latter in furnaces holding 1 or 2 cwt., the oxides being continually skimmed off. The best lead was from Germany, the best tin from Flanders. Presumably the Flanders tin was that imported from Cornwall.

While the ware was being baked, the various materials already mentioned were heated in crucibles in the same furnace. The potash and sand fused to a mass of potassium silicate glass which was finely pulverized, sifted and washed. This with the lead-tin mixture (*c.* 3 : 1) gave the frit for the white glaze; this was extremely finely ground and stirred up with water to form a sort of milk in which the pottery was dipped. On the resulting powdery coat of white frit, before firing, the design was executed in the colours described below.

He then describes the pigments to be used. For the white, tin was heated till it was converted to ' ashes ' (white stannic oxide). For green, copper was burnt with sulphur and salt (*cf.* p. 88) and was then mixed with antimony and lead: since these are stated to be pounded together, presumably the calcined metals or oxides were intended. Dark yellow was produced from iron rust (the best was from old anchors) with lead and antimony, and the paler yellow (the modern Naples yellow) was given by lead and antimony with a little potash and salt. For blue, the cobalt mineral zaffre (p. 78) was used; and for violet, manganese.[1] A black was made with copper, manganese and zaffre. With these colours finely ground and mixed with water, the design was painted on the powdery surface of white frit.

When dry, the pieces were dipped in a bath consisting of a suspension of finely-ground transparent lead-glaze. The pieces were then fired. This delicate operation was not to be commenced without prayer to God, nor yet at the waning of the moon, nor when the sun was in a watery sign of the zodiac.

Picolpasso does not call the material made in this way by the name of maiolica, as do we, but reserves this term for the lustre-ware already described.

[1] *i.e.* pyrolusite.

PLATE III

A.—Catalan Furnace, *Drawing by Leonardo da Vinci* (see p. 47).

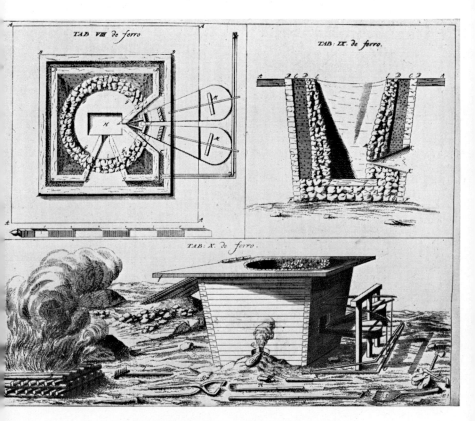

B.—Swedenborg's Osmund Furnace (see p. 48).

PLATE IV

A.—Bottle Kiln for Portland Cement Manufacture, erected by William Aspdin in 1848.—*Model* (see p. 58).

B.—Glass Furnace, *c.* Tenth Century. *Model after Theophilus* (see p. 72).

Chinese Ceramics

The great Chinese art of porcelain was soon to influence Europe. The Moslems greatly esteemed the Chinese ware; thus in the latter part of the twelfth century Saladin sent a present of china to the Sultan of Damascus. A few pieces had reached Europe by the early sixteenth century, and even at this date attempts were made to imitate them (pp. 67–8).

Chinese ceramics are of very great antiquity, for pottery, painted though not glazed, has been found in sites dating from the third millennium B.C. After 100 B.C. some of this pottery was made on the wheel, and after the third century B.C. some of it was rather crudely glazed, probably with felspar. The first use of lead glaze belongs to the Han period (206 B.C.–A.D. 220), probably a little before the Christian era. The early Chinese ceramics are not of porcelain but of clay, or clay and quartz; of this material were made the bodies of the fine sepulchral figures of the T'ang period (A.D. 618–906). At a later period stone-ware, a strongly fired siliceous clay, was often used.

The greatest discovery of the Chinese ceramics was, however, true porcelain, the raw material of which is a mixture of two minerals: first, the infusible *kaolin*, or china-clay; secondly, *petuntse*, a fusible mixture of felspar, clay and quartz. The earliest porcelain bodies date from the eighth or ninth century, but come to their full development only in the Sung period (A.D. 960–1127). These bodies had to be fired at a much higher temperature than was required for ordinary pottery.

The glazes used by the Chinese potters were of unparalleled beauty. Their effects, however, did not depend upon any special chemical knowledge but on the greatest skill in the mixing and firing of simple materials.

The principal colouring matters of Chinese pottery are compounds of iron, copper and, later, cobalt. The beauty of the ware did not depend only upon colour but on the lustre, texture and crazing of the glaze. The texture of the glaze was affected by the presence of bubbles or crystals, which gave an effect of softness; and remarkable effects were produced by using glazes which had coefficients of expansion slightly different from those of the bodies and so became covered with a pattern of minute cracks.

Glazes containing iron, if fired in a reducing atmosphere, so that the iron assumed the ferrous condition, gave the delicate jade-green known as celadon; if fired in an oxidizing atmosphere the iron gave the yellow and browns characteristic of the ferric state. If there was much iron in the glaze, ferric oxide or ferrosoferric oxide separated from it as minute crystals and gave many beautiful texture effects; while coral reds were produced by undissolved particles of ferric oxide. The amount of iron dissolved or crystallized depended on the acidity or alkalinity of the glaze, which depended, of course, on its composition.

All these effects, of course, were produced deliberately, but without any knowledge of the chemical and physical principles that determined them. The effect was first obtained by chance or by trial and error, the conditions were noted and the potter learned to reproduce them and taught his pupils to do the like.

The second great colouring agent was copper. In oxidizing atmospheres compounds of copper give blue-green effects: in reducing atmospheres they are converted into colloidal metallic copper, usually deep red, but sometimes assuming other hues. The wonderful effects known as flambé, sang-du-bœuf, peach-bloom, etc., are all derived from copper in the reduced state. Pots could be fired in reducing atmospheres which gave shades of red and then partly reoxidized to the blue-green state by admitting air, so producing all manner of intermediate colours and shadings.

By using an alkaline glaze mixed with copper compounds very beautiful turquoise blues, well seen on Persian pottery, were attained, but these glazes were unstable and were not much used by the Chinese.

The Chinese blues were derived from cobalt compounds, the use of which was of course well known in the West. Cobalt minerals, however, always contain a proportion of other metals, e.g. copper, iron, manganese and nickel, all of which dull the colour, and the Chinese potters did not know how to purify the mineral. Moreover, the blues that are most admired are not from the pure cobalt, as used on modern porcelain, but from a material which the Chinese called ' Mohammedan Blue ', which was evidently a cobalt mineral which happened to have just the right admixture of other metals to produce the loveliest Chinese blues. This material was imported into China, probably from Persia, in the fifteenth and sixteenth centuries, and was paid for at the rate of twice its weight in gold. The supply later became exhausted and the Chinese had then to use their own cobalt minerals, which gave an inferior and duller blue.

Manganese minerals were used to a small extent. In combination with cobalt or iron they gave a fine black, and by themselves, a purple in alkaline glazes and a brown in acid ones. At a later period gold was used to give the pinks of the *famille rose* type.

Porcelain in Europe

Chinese porcelain occasionally found its way to Europe during the Middle Ages, and from the sixteenth century onward many attempts were made to imitate it. The European potter had a good knowledge of glazes, but he had no clue to the material from which the hard semi-transparent body of porcelain was made.

Porcelain seemed to be half-way between pottery and glass, so the earlier attempts to imitate it employed glassy materials. It appears that the first successful attempts at a glassy ware resembling porcelain were made in Venice in 1519. Venice was a great technological centre, especially for the making of glass, and the Italians were, with the Spaniards, the chief makers of maiolica and fine pottery. There were in Italy many alchemists and experimentalists in various technical arts, and the conditions were therefore very favourable for experiment. It seems that very little of this first Venetian ware was made, for none survives, and the first European imitation of porcelain known to us is that made at Florence in the years round 1570. The body was composed of china clay, fine white sand and powdered glass.

All the so-called porcelains made in Europe in the sixteenth and seventeenth centuries are glassy and relatively fusible materials; and the true porcelain made from china clay and felspar was first made by the German alchemist Johann Friedrich Böttger, who began to work on the problem soon after 1701 in the royal laboratory of Friedrich August II, Elector of Saxony. In 1711 Böttger came across kaolin, which was being sold as a wig powder, and presumably also felspar, which is found with it; from these he made a true porcelain. So much was the discovery valued by his royal patron that to ensure secrecy he was compelled to live and work in semi-captivity under an armed guard. By 1716 Böttger had so far perfected the making of porcelain that specimens were placed on the market. The secret could not long be kept. All over Europe experiments were made both on hard porcelains of the Oriental type and on soft porcelains, mixtures of china clay with glassy materials. The addition of bone-ash to the latter was an important discovery. Porcelain remained a rare and costly material till the beginning of the nineteenth century, when with the industrial revolution ' china-ware ' began to be turned out in large quantities for general domestic use.

CHAPTER FIVE

Glass

Glass in Antiquity

CONTRARY to common belief, glass is among the most ancient of artificial materials. Objects of true glass have been found on sites dating from *c.* 2500 B.C. in Egypt and in Mesopotamia. The glass made between these ancient times and up to about 900 B.C. was usually coloured green, blue or yellow and was almost opaque: it was, in fact, a decorative material somewhat resembling enamel. Vessels of this material became reasonably common in Egypt, and perhaps also in Mesopotamia, from about 1500 B.C. Translucent greenish, horny-looking glass was made between 900 and 600 B.C. in Assyria and elsewhere, and after that date transparent glass is first met with. All this glass was modelled or moulded or cut from a solid block. The blowing of glass is first heard of at Sidon at the beginning of the Christian era.

Glass is made by heating silica (sand, quartz, flint, etc.) with an alkali and lime; if lead oxide is added the brilliance of the product is enhanced. It is coloured in much the same way as ceramic glazes, namely, by the addition of compounds of certain metals, *e.g.* iron, copper, cobalt, etc. Oddly enough, almost all the early recipes, even up to the seventeenth century, fail to mention lime as a constituent, though analyses of glasses of these periods show it to be present. In some cases there may have been lime in the sand or the alkali used, but this does not always account for its presence, and we can only suppose that the glassmaker added it as a routine which the readers of the recipes tacitly recognized. Colourless glass can only be made from materials containing no iron, and since these are difficult to obtain most glass is faintly green. This colour could be removed by adding a little native manganese dioxide ('glassmakers' soap'), which oxidizes the iron to the ferric state in which it gives much less colour to glass. Transparency was attained by raising the glass to a high temperature at which it was thinly fluid. Bubbles and alkaline salts (sandiver or glass-gall) were thus enabled to rise to the surface, where they could be scummed off, while stony particles sank, leaving homogeneous transparent glass.

The making of good glass therefore demanded great care and cleanliness and the use of pure materials; so it is not surprising that the industry took a long time to attain perfection.

An Egyptian glass-factory of the fourteenth century B.C. was discovered at el-Amarna, but although there were great quantities of materials for the working of glass, no trace of the furnaces for glass-making has been found. Broken white quartz pebbles were used as the source of silica, and native manganese dioxide for removing the greenness from the glass. We know rather more about the Assyrian technique for glass-making. The materials were fused in a ' furnace with a floor of eyes '—that is to say, a furnace with a separate combustion chamber in which was burnt dry wood, the flames from which passed through its perforated roof into an upper chamber where the glass-pots stood. The Assyrian glassmakers employed a second furnace, the ' arched furnace ', which was probably an annealing oven. It is interesting to note that the glass furnaces figured by Agricola some twenty-two centuries later scarcely differ in principle from those of the Assyrians.

Glass-making flourished exceedingly in Roman times, when it was centred on Sidon and Alexandria in the east, and Italy and the Rhineland in the west, from which places glass vessels were exported to all parts of the Roman Empire. Finds of ancient glasses make it clear that Roman glass-workers had full command over every technique of glass-making and glass-decoration, and Roman products were no whit inferior to those of Venice in its hey-day. The Romans sometimes used glass panes as window-lights, and it is probable that at all periods some Christian churches had glazed windows.

Development of the Mediæval Glass Industry

Windows of coloured glass are alluded to after A.D. 800. It is, however, probable that stained glass windows date from the fifth or sixth century, as witnessed by glass surviving at Ravenna. These were probably made by the methods set out by Theophilus (pp. 72–4). During the so-called Dark Ages

(c. A.D. 500–1000) one of the main centres of glass-making was at Constantinople, but ornamental glass-ware of a higher order was manufactured under Moslem rule in Syria. It has been supposed, on no very strong evidence, that when this region was partly conquered by the Crusaders some of the secrets of its high technique were transmitted to Venice; but it is known that the making of glass had been practised there at least as early as A.D. 1090, and it may not owe much to the Islamic technique. Venetian glass became famous in the thirteenth century, at the end of which period the manufacture was for-bidden in the city owing to the danger of fire and was trans-ferred to Murano, a site which, moreover, being on an island, was a difficult one for the glass-workers to leave.

At this era there were, of course, many glass manufactories in different parts of Europe, as is witnessed by the wonderful stained glass to be found in every European cathedral. Never-theless Venice retained a virtual monopoly of the manufacture of the finest and clearest glass (*cristallo*). We continually hear of efforts to persuade Venetian craftsmen to come to other countries and found a glass industry, and of the stringent regulations of the Venetian Government to retain them. In fact some of these workmen migrated to Germany in the fifteenth century, and to England in the sixteenth, and taught these countries the higher arts of glass-making.

Mediæval glass was made from the whitest sand that could be obtained, but this was rarely altogether free from iron, so that the glass was commonly of a green or brownish tinge. The usual alkali was ashes made from ferns, though other vegetable ashes could be used. The Venetian glass-makers used rocchetta, the ash of the *salsola soda*, imported from Egypt and the Levant (*v.* p. 75), though Spanish barilla (*ibid.*) was even more esteemed.

The transformation of such apparently unpromising materials into colourless glass was a foretaste of the wonders of chemistry. As Chaucer says:

> But netheles some saiden that it was
> Wonder to maken of ferne ashen glas
> And yet is glas nought like ashen of ferne . . .
>
> (*Squires Tale*, l. 254)

Our best account of mediæval glass-making is given us by Theophilus, who compiled his *Account of various arts* some time during the tenth century, using documents which were in some cases of the eighth century or even older. The treatise of Theophilus is not illustrated, but Plate IV, B, taken from a model in the Science Museum, London, shows the plan of his furnace, while Plate V, which purports to show the Tyrian glass-works described in the *Travels* of Sir John Mandevile, gives the general appearance of the small glass-house of two or three centuries later. Theophilus described a glass-works as having three furnaces, one for melting, one for working the glass, and one for annealing. These were shallow rectangular chambers built of stones and clay. The fire was in a sunken hearth. Openings were provided for charging and emptying the furnace and for working the glass. There is no mention of a chimney to increase the draught. His materials were ashes of beech-wood and clean sand; these ashes would contain sufficient lime for making a stable glass; his crucibles were of white clay carefully fired.

Theophilus is chiefly interested in the making of church windows, and he gives special attention to the making of glass plates for this purpose. Here is his account of the way it was to be done:

Take the iron tube and place the end of it in a vessel of glass, and when it has adhered to it turn the tube in your hand until there is conglomerated about it as much glass as you wish; then withdraw it and put your mouth to it and blow gently and at once remove it from your mouth and hold it near your cheek, for fear that you may happen, if you draw in your breath, to draw the flame into your mouth. You must also have a flat stone in front of the furnace window, on which stone gently strike the glowing glass so that it may hang equally from every part, and at once blow frequently and with haste, as often removing it from your mouth. And when you see it hang like a long bladder, bring the end of it to the flame and at once a hole will appear in the melted part, and taking the piece of wood made for this work, make the hole as wide as it is in the middle. Then join the mouth of it, that is to say the upper part to the lower part, so that from either part of the join there shall appear a hole. And at once with a wet piece of wood touch the glass close to the blowing tube and shake it a little and it will be separated. At once heat the tube in the flame of the furnace until the glass which is joined to it liquefies, and rapidly place it upon the opening and the vessel of glass joined together and it will stick. Take it up at once and put it in the flame of the furnace until the hole, from which you formerly separated the tube is melted; and taking the round piece of wood dilate it like the other end and folding together its mouth in the middle, and separating it from the tube with the wet wood, give it to the boy, who by putting into it a piece of wood will carry it to the cooling furnace which should be moderately hot. . . .

How the glass sheets are dilated.

. . . make a large fire in the furnace in which they are to be dilated and made flat. When it is glowing, take the hot iron and splitting one part of the glass, put it on the hearth of the glowing furnace, and when it begins to be softened take the iron tongs and the flat piece of wood, and opening it in the part in which the split is, you will dilate it and flatten it with the tongs as you will. And when it has been altogether flattened, at once take it out and place it in the cooling oven, moderately heated; and so that the plate may not lie down but stand against the wall, next to which you will put another, similarly flattened, and a third, and so all the rest. When these have become cold, use them in making windows by separating them into pieces as you wish.[1]

The account is not perfectly clear, but the process is probably as illustrated in Fig. 16. Another method of making flat glass was to blow a bulb and cut it into ' gores ' with a hot iron. The curved ' gores ' were reheated and pressed flat. A quite different method of making glass panes was the crown-glass process. A bulb was blown, keeping most of the glass at the top end: it was then opened and the glass on the blowing-iron was reheated. By twirling the iron the glass was made to expand into a wide disc which could be used as a large circular pane or could be cut into smaller panes. The antiquity of the crown-glass process is difficult to estimate; it seems to have been used as early as A.D. 700 in Palestine, and we may conjecture that it dates back to Roman times. A third method of making flat glass, which also goes back to the latter period, is the simple one of pouring or pressing the hot glass into flat open clay moulds.

Theophilus is somewhat obscure concerning the colouring

[1] Theophilus. *Schedula Diversarum Artium.* Book II. Chaps. VI and XI. This work is given in English and Latin in *An essay upon various arts, in three books, by Theophilus, called also Rugerus . . . , translated with notes by Robert Hendrie.* London 1847 '. But this edition is incomplete. The translation in Appendix A of ' An Inquiry into the difference of style observable in Ancient Glass Paintings ', by Charles Winston, Oxford and London, 1867, is more satisfactory.

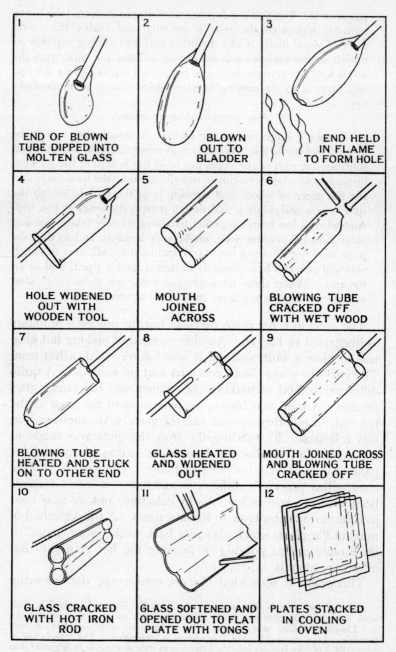

1 END OF BLOWN TUBE DIPPED INTO MOLTEN GLASS	**2** BLOWN OUT TO BLADDER	**3** END HELD IN FLAME TO FORM HOLE
4 HOLE WIDENED OUT WITH WOODEN TOOL	**5** MOUTH JOINED ACROSS	**6** BLOWING TUBE CRACKED OFF WITH WET WOOD
7 BLOWING TUBE HEATED AND STUCK ON TO OTHER END	**8** GLASS HEATED AND WIDENED OUT	**9** MOUTH JOINED ACROSS AND BLOWING TUBE CRACKED OFF
10 GLASS CRACKED WITH HOT IRON ROD	**11** GLASS SOFTENED AND OPENED OUT TO FLAT PLATE WITH TONGS	**12** PLATES STACKED IN COOLING OVEN

FIG. 16. The making of glass plates as described by Theophilus.

of glass, but it is clear that in the Middle Ages blue glass was made with zaffre, an impure cobalt mineral (p. 78). A green colour was imparted by means of cupric oxide, while burnt copper (cuprous oxide) under reducing conditions gave a red. Violet was obtained by the use of native manganese dioxide. A deep yellow resulted from the use of iron, and a beautiful golden tint from metallic silver. All mediæval materials were, chemically speaking, impure, and it is probable that many of the beautiful shades then obtained were due to the modifications of the colours of the pure metallic silicates by traces of other materials capable of colouring glass.

The Methods of Neri

Agricola gives a good account of the glass furnaces (Plate VI, A) and of glass-blowing technique (Fig. 17), but it is not really his subject. The classic work on glass-making is Antonio Neri's *De Arte Vetraria*, published in 1612 and translated into English as *The Arte of Glass* (1662). Neri does not give us the details about furnaces which we find in Agricola, but he furnishes precise information about the materials to be used.

We find in the work of Neri the first deliberate purification of the alkali in order to arrive at a perfectly colourless glass. His preferred starting point is ' polverine ' or ' rochette ', which was the ash of a plant that grew in the Levant or Syria, probably *salsola soda*: he also commends ' barilla ', the ash of the same plant but brought from Spain. These were well-known materials, being widely used by the makers of hard soap (p. 133).

James Howell, in 1618, thus describes the production of barilla for making crystal glass.

> This Barillia is a strange kind of vegetable . . . a thick earthy shrub that bears berries like barberries. When ripe they dig it by the roots and stack it in cocks like hay to dry. When dry they place the shrubs in a trench and set fire to them. The pit is closed and when, after some days, it is opened the Barillia juice is found turned into a blue hardstone.

The background of Plate V probably represents the growing shrubs and the pit in which they were burned. The ' blue hardstone ' contained up to 20 % of sodium carbonate together with common salt and various impurities. Other alkalis used were fern ash, the ashes of beans, rushes, cabbages or straw,

FIG. 17.   Glass-blowing as illustrated by Agricola (1556).

also salt of tartar, made by calcining the tartar deposited in wine casks. All these contained potassium carbonate as their active constituent.

Neri thus describes the purification of the polverine and barilla. They are to be powdered, sieved and boiled with water: a little tartar, burnt black, is added to the boiling liquor; the charcoal contained in this probably acted as a decolorizing agent. The liquor was allowed to settle and the clear part ladled off from the sediment and boiled down till it crystallized. The crystals were drained, dried and powdered. The ashes yielded about 27–30 % of the salt, which must have been fairly pure sodium carbonate. This is not the first instance of recrystallization as an industrial process, for the method was employed in making saltpetre, alum and blue-vitriol; but it is perhaps the first deliberate and conscious attempt to remove impurities by recrystallization. Neri describes a process of purification even more like that of the chemical laboratory: the ashes were dissolved in water contained in glass-bodies (*i.e.* large wide-necked glass flasks), the liquid was filtered and then evaporated in glass vessels, thus avoiding all danger of metallic contamination. Neri also describes the use of lead oxide as a base for making the most brilliant glass.

The silica he recommends is a white quartz which he describes as ' marble '. He has an adequate test by which to know material suitable for glass-making; for, he tells us, " those stones which strike fire with a steel are fit to vitrify . . . and those which strike not fire with a steel will never vitrify." This test would distinguish silica from most materials resembling it. It is true that pyrites strike fire with steel, but no sensible man would think of using pyrites to make glass!

Curiously enough, Neri, like the earlier writers, says nothing about the lime he must have added to his mixture of soda and quartz at some stage of the proceedings, for his purified materials cannot have contained more than a minute proportion of it.

Having made these pure materials, he fired 200 lb. of the silica with 130 lb. of the soda and so obtained a ' frit '. To make glass, the frit was melted with a little manganese dioxide and the molten glass poured into water; this glass was again melted and maintained in a state of fusion, the scum being taken off, and when a test portion appeared perfectly clear it was worked with the blowpipe. To make the brilliant lead-glass used for paste gems, etc., lead oxide was mixed with the frit before it was fused the first time.

Neri gives us a full account of the substances to be used in colouring glass.

Manganese dioxide he knew as a common mineral, which (when reasonably pure and free from iron) had the valuable property of removing greenness from glass, and in greater quantity gave a good amethyst. Neri recommends that from Piedmont.

Blue glass was made from zaffre, a material containing cobalt. Cobalt preparations have been used for colouring porcelain and glass since ancient times, and we may suppose that these consisted of various minerals of cobalt (cobalt arsenide, or sulpharsenide, with various other metallic sulphides), roasted so as to remove sulphur, arsenic and other volatile matter. Agricola tells us how bismuth is made from its ore and leaves behind a residue which glassmakers use to give a blue colour: we may suppose this to have contained cobalt with traces of nickel, and probably copper and iron, and to have given shades differing to a variable extent from that given by the pure cobalt. Combinations of zaffre and copper compounds (e.g. calcined brass) gave a sea-green.

Copper compounds alone could give either greens or reds. The most usual form in which copper was added to glass was *ferretto*, burnt copper (cuprous oxide). This was made by a recipe which goes back to classical times.

Copper was heated with sulphur and the black mass (copper sulphide) was roasted until it was converted into the red ferretto. Alternatively, copper could be calcined with vitriol or copperas, by which copper sulphate is here probably intended. The resulting material would probably contain a good deal of basic copper sulphate. *Calcined brass* or *brass-makers' scales*, the mixture of oxides of copper and zinc formed when brass was heated, was also a useful colour. *Crocus Martis* (red oxide of iron), made by the same process as ferretto but using iron instead of copper, was also much favoured. This word evidently covered many reddish compounds of iron, e.g. ferric acetate, nitrate or chloride, made by treating iron filings with vinegar, *aqua fortis* or *aqua regia*.

Thus the glassmakers' colours were very few, and great skill was needed to decide the proportions to be used and to mix them so as to get the best effect.

Yellows were obtained by means of iron, as *crocus martis;*

blues from zaffre; greens from zaffre, copper and iron in various proportions. Black was obtained from zaffre and manganese, while opaque white was produced from tin oxide and a little manganese. Deep red could be obtained from iron with a little calcined brass, but the fine reds were made with copper or gold. To do this a lead-glass containing copper was fused with a small proportion of tartar, which reduced the copper to the cuprous state. On reheating the work a fine red was induced. The best red, then as to-day, was obtained by adding to the frit a little gold chloride, made by dissolving gold in *aqua regia*.

Glass in the Eighteenth Century

So admirable was Neri's textbook that it remained a standard work until well into the eighteenth century. Nevertheless there were not a few changes and improvements. The Venetian secrets of glass-making became widely diffused through Europe, and ornamental as well as useful glass was made in most countries. In England the firing of glass-furnaces by coal was initiated in 1610. The coal fire was said to produce ' sulphurous fumes ' which made it necessary to use covered crucibles instead of open pots.

In England the Glass-Sellers Company began, about 1664, to try to find means of rivalling the Venetians. In 1673 they engaged George Ravenscroft (1618–81) to experiment, with the help of an Italian, on making better glass. He substituted calcined flints for the Venetian quartz pebbles: but the flint was difficult to fuse, wherefore he used a greater proportion of alkali (a purified potash substituted for Venetian rocchetta). This caused the glass to be ' crisselled ', *i.e.* obscured by fine internal cracks, and to remedy this lead oxide was added. The result was a new type of glass of great clarity and fire, and during the first quarter of the eighteenth century this *flint-glass*, consisting of potash, lead oxide and calcined flints, with or without sand, was rapidly developed. This product had a dispersion and play of colour to be compared to that of the diamond. This was enhanced by cutting the glass into prismatic faces, a practice which had been adopted by the Romans and Arabic glass-workers, but which had fallen into disuse. Cut glass, then, began again to be made about 1730, and it was at its best between 1750 and 1800.

The ordinary soda-lime glass continued to be used for windows and for common ware of all kinds. This was termed crown-glass. The existence of these two kinds of glass, having different powers of refraction and dispersion, made possible a notable advance in the design of optical instruments. Since the time of Newton it had been thought that a given refractive index was always associated with a corresponding dispersion. This was now realized not to be so. The correction of the chromatic aberration of one lens without reducing the net refraction to unity was seen to be possible and enabled Dollond in 1758 to devise his achromatic combination, composed of two lenses, one, of the soda-lime type, used for crown-glass, the other, of the potash-lead type, used for flint-glass.

CHAPTER SIX

Pigments

Pigments in Antiquity

PAINTING is an art which reached its first peak at least 10,000 years before the Christian era. The wonderful representations of animals in the caves of Spain and France witness a highly developed painting technique, though the range of colours available to the primitive artists was but a small one. Vessels containing their pigments have been found: thus we know that kaolin furnished their white, burnt bones their black, while powdered iron and manganese ores gave a range of reds and yellows. The earliest pigments were native materials such as these, and the first artificial colour was powdered blue frit, used in Egypt and Mesopotamia (p. 60).

The Egyptians executed enormous numbers of paintings, but their range of colours was small and unchanging. It has been thought that the seven colours employed by them may have been sanctified and fixed by religious usages. Artists in Mesopotamia used several good colours which do not appear in Egypt, though they must have been known to its inhabitants. The Roman and Greek palette had a wider range. Thus Pliny records five different red pigments, two greens and four blues. After the fall of the Roman Empire the knowledge of pigments probably persisted in many parts of Europe but was preserved in especial fullness in Constantinople. Traditional recipes for artists' materials and methods were collected in such books as the *Mappæ Clavicula* and the *Compositiones ad Tingenda*, which were copied and continually augmented from the eighth to the thirteenth centuries. These works served to hand on the special knowledge of the Byzantine artists to the illuminators and painters of the Middle Ages and Renaissance, who in their turn further developed the preparation of pigments and raised it to a high art. The rise of chemistry in the late eighteenth and nineteenth centuries led to the manufacture of a far wider range of colours which, unhappily, does not seem to have led to a corresponding improvement in the pictures to which they have contributed.

Preparation of Pigments

Whatever the source of the coloured material, it has to be brought to the requisite fineness of division. It does not follow that the pigment should be as finely ground as possible, for very fine grinding can diminish the lustre of a crystalline pigment and unduly lighten its shade. The painter who ground his own colours or had them ground in his workshop knew just how fine to grind them, though he could not impart this knowledge in writing or in any other way except by personal training. The material was normally first ground in a mortar, then rubbed on a porphyry slab with a rounded stone, called a muller. Lapis lazuli required peculiar treatment, of which more will be said on p. 87.

Black Pigments

The typical black pigment is, of course, carbon. The prehistoric painters used burnt bones: the Egyptians used carbon in the form of fine soot, such as lamp-black. In the ancient world eye-paints were much in fashion. It is often supposed that antimony sulphide was then, as later, the usual black eye-paint: but in fact galena (lead sulphide) and native manganese dioxide were the chief cosmetics of this type.

Blacks were wanted not only for painting and cosmetics but also for ink. The ancient ink was, like Chinese ink, a suspension of carbon, and was imperishable unless it was rubbed off; the modern type of ink, made from galls and ferrous sulphate (*atramentum*, found as an incrustation in copper mines), came into use in late classical times. Iron inks slowly lose their blackness but fade to a yellowish-brown which is substantially permanent.

The mediæval and Renaissance painters used two types of carbon-blacks. One was the deposit of carbon-black from smoky flames—as of bees-wax, tallow, oil, incense or pitch— and the other was charcoal. The finest form of the latter was made from vine tendrils or the stones of peaches and almonds, calcined in earthen pots; it seems that the black made by heating bones or ivory was no longer used.

Brown Pigments

The prehistoric painters and those of later times employed various minerals containing iron and manganese. A brown ochre, *i.e.* a clayey oxide of iron, was used in Egypt. Mediæval miniaturists and painters had little use for brown: they used brilliant colours and when a brown was needed they mixed black and red and yellow. Some of their copper-greens have become altered to brown in the course of centuries and give us a false idea of their tone-range—as, of course, does the all too common coating of varnish added in later years and discoloured by time.

White Pigments

The prehistoric painters used kaolin (white china clay), while the Egyptians used gypsum, or calcium carbonate, *i.e.* whiting or chalk. The Assyrians also used tin oxide. The major invention in this field was the preparation of white lead or ceruse, basic lead carbonate, which is still regarded as one of the finest of white pigments, though having the disadvantage that it is blackened by hydrogen sulphide and is also very poisonous.

White lead was made, at least as early as the fourth century B.C., by a process which lasted, in a modified form, until the twentieth century. Several authors give similar but not identical accounts of the process as carried out in Græco-Roman times; the oldest of these is given by the Greek Theophrastus in his work on minerals (*c.* 320 B.C.):

> Lead is placed in earthen vessels over sharp vinegar, and after it has acquired some thickness of a kind of rust, which it commonly does in about ten days, they open the vessels, and scrape it off, as it were, in a kind of foulness: they then place the lead over the vinegar again, repeating over and over again the same method of scraping it, until it is entirely destroyed: what has been scraped off they then beat to powder and boil for a long time, and what finally subsides to the bottom of the vessel is the ceruse.

The process involves the conversion of the lead into basic lead acetate, which was then converted by the carbon dioxide and moisture of the air into basic lead carbonate—white lead. This process remained in use for nearly 2,000 years before it was much improved, but in the seventeenth century an important advance was made, namely, the application of heat. The pots containing the lead suspended over the vinegar were heated in a dung-bed, and the dung-beds and pots were arranged in vertical stacks. The fermenting dung provided heat, which greatly accelerated the reactions and also maintained a high concentration of carbon dioxide and water vapour. Here is a contemporary description:

A Relation of the making of Ceruss, *by Sir* Philiberto Vernatti.[1]

First Pigs of clean and soft Lead are cast into thin Plates a yard long; six inches broad, and to the thickness of the back of a Knife. These are rolled, with some Art, round; but so as the surfaces no where meet to touch: for where they do no Ceruss grows.

Thus roll'd, they are put each in a Pot just capable to hold one, upheld by a little Bar from the bottom, that it come not to touch the Vinegar, which is put into each Pot, to effect the conversion.

Next a square bed is made of new Horse-dung, so big as to hold 20 Pots abreast, and so to make up the number of 400 in one Bed.

Then each Pot is covered with a Plate of Lead; and lastly all with Boards, as close as conveniently can be. This repeated four times makes one heap, so called, containing 1600 Pots.

After three weeks the Pots are taken up, the Plates unrolled, laid upon a Board, and beaten with Battledores till all the Flakes come off. Which, if good, prove thick, hard and weighty: if otherwise fuffy and light; or sometimes black and burn'd, if the Dung prove not well order'd; and sometimes there will be none.

From the Beating-Table the Flakes are carried to the Mill; and with Water ground to almost an impalpable fineness. After which it is moulded into smaller parcels, and exposed to the Sun to dry till it be hard and so fit for use.

The modern stack-process differs from the above chiefly in the use of spent tan-bark as a fermenting medium. This has the advantage of not producing the hydrogen sulphide which often discoloured the pigment produced in the dung-bed.

Lead-poisoning, which was prevalent among white-lead makers, was known and dreaded even in the Middle Ages. Vernatti describes its effect with an accuracy which demonstrates its familiarity.

The Accidents to the Workmen are, Immediate pain in the Stomack, with exceeding Contorsions in the Guts and Costiveness that yields not to Catharticks. . . .

Next a *Vertigo* or dizziness in the Head with continual great
pain in the Brows, Blindness, Stupidity, and Paralytic Affections;
. . . and these chiefly in them that have the charge of Grinding,
and over the Drying Place.

But it does not appear that anything was done about it.

The other white pigment in use in the Middle Ages and
Renaissance was calcium phosphate, in the form of bone-white,
made by calcining bones until the carbon was burnt off. It
was not so white as white lead nor had it the same covering
power, but it had the advantage that it did not become
blackened and that, unlike white lead, it could be mixed with
verdigris (basic copper acetate, p. 88) or orpiment (arsenic
trisulphide, p. 88) without discolouring them.

Red Pigments

The reds used by the prehistoric painters and by the
Egyptians and Assyrians were native iron compounds—clayey
iron ores (ruddles or ochres), some of which are of quite a
strong and bright colour. By the Græco-Roman period a
much wider range of red pigments had become known. In
addition to those already mentioned there was cinnabar or
vermilion (mercuric sulphide), red lead, a sort of cochineal
lake (*coccum*), and the resin derived from the dragon's-blood
tree.

Methods of making or preparing all these were doubtless
handed down to the men of the early Middle Ages. Their
favourite pigment was vermilion, made by grinding mercury
and sulphur so as to produce the black form of mercuric
sulphide, ' Aethiops mineral ', and subliming this to convert
it into the scarlet form. Vermilion is extremely brilliant but
has the disadvantage of darkening in sunlight and is therefore
unsuitable for outdoor work. It was also very costly. Red or
orange lead, made by gently roasting white lead, was also used,
but was not very permanent.

The other important red colours were lakes. The word
lake seems to be derived from *lacca*, a resinous colour made
from ' hedera ' (presumably ivy, but possibly some other
creeper) by a process now unknown. This lacca was not a
lake in the modern sense, but the true lakes were so named
because they resembled it. Lakes are soluble colours precipitated in a solid insoluble form by means of alum: they are very

transparent and, where this transparency was objectionable, they were often mixed with some opaque white pigment. The most favoured of them was crimson lake, made by a rather odd process from an insect allied to but not identical with the modern cochineal insect. The dried insects, known as ' grain ' (pp. 121–2), were used to dye wool or silk. The colour was then extracted by boiling the red wool or silk with lye (a solution of wood-ash, containing potassium carbonate). A solution of alum was then added and the dyestuff was precipitated as a compound with aluminium hydroxide.

Brazil [1] (a wood from Ceylon) was another source of red lakes. It was scraped to powder, extracted with lye and precipitated with alum. This lake was of a fine rose colour which seems to have been fairly permanent. Madder (p. 121) gave another rose lake, which was not, however, much used in the Middle Ages.

Blue Pigments

The Egyptians used the finely-ground blue copper-ore azurite, basic copper carbonate, as a pigment, and this continued to be popular all through the Middle Ages. It is permanent and has a peculiar crystalline lustre. The Egyptians also used their famous blue frit (p. 60): there seems to be no evidence of the use of ground cobalt glass. The Assyrians also used powdered lapis lazuli, a material which they held in great esteem, but we do not know whether they prepared it by the complex method mentioned below. The Romans may have used all of these, and they also knew of indigo.

In the Middle Ages azurite was much used, and also indigo, brought from India, or the similar blue pigment made from woad (p. 119). Another popular blue was turnsole, the juice of the seed capsule of *crozophera tinctoria* soaked up in little bits of cloth treated with lime. The colour was soaked out of the cloth before use. Its shade depended on the acidity or alkalinity of the medium, so that it could afford both blues and purples. Smalt, finely-powdered cobalt glass, was known and was made by heating the sulphide ores of cobalt (p. 78) with

---

[1] The country of that name was so called because this wood was (incorrectly) supposed to abound there. See also p. 123.

sand and alkali. The cobalt formed the dark blue silicate, while the sulphides of nickel and most other metallic impurities formed a layer of ' speiss ' beneath it. The ordinary cheap blue pigments were made from copper solutions, lime and ammonia, in the form of stale urine. These were not permanent, gradually losing ammonia and fading to a pale green which might later become brown through the action of hydrogen sulphide in the air.

The most precious and lovely of blue pigments was the true ultramarine, made from lapis lazuli. It is not enough merely to powder the native mineral, because it contains so large a proportion of other minerals that the resulting powder is not of the true ultramarine but grey or blue-grey. The method used was, indeed, to powder the mineral finely but then to incorporate it with wax, oil and resin, forming a soft cake. This cake was then kneaded for hours or days in weak lye; the blue ultramarine found its way into the liquid and later settled out, while the impurities remained in the wax. The principle seems to be the same as that of the oil-flotation used for separating concentrates of pyritic ores in modern mineralogical practice. We have no idea who discovered it, but the world of artists owes him a great debt.

In 1704 a new blue pigment was accidentally discovered, namely, Prussian Blue. Diesbach and Dippel, the discoverers, kept the process secret, but in 1724 Woodward described the curious process of strongly heating potassium carbonate with dried bullock's blood (so obtaining potassium cyanide), mixing a solution of the product with a solution of green vitriol and alum, and treating the resultant precipitate with hydrochloric acid. Artificial ultramarine, prepared by heating clay, sodium sulphate, sulphur, silica, etc., was discovered by Guimet and Gmelin independently in 1828; both may have been anticipated by Köttig. This discovery, however, belongs to the period of scientific chemistry, for these workers knew at least the approximate composition of the lapis lazuli they were so successfully to imitate.

The mediæval purple pigments were usually a mixture of blue and red, but were also prepared from various species of whelk, which, like the famous Tyrian murex (p. 124), secrete colours of this shade. Turnsole and archil, a dye from lichen, also gave purples.

Green Pigments

The most ancient green pigment is malachite, a basic carbonate of copper. This was used from predynastic times in Egypt and remained popular up to the sixteenth century. Its colour could be brightened and improved by dyeing it with the yellow weld (p. 121) as described by Pliny. The only other ancient green colours seem to have been copper frits. The early mediæval recipe books (*c.* eighth to tenth century A.D.) mention two types of green pigment derived from copper. Verdigris (basic copper acetate) was made by packing copper plates in fermenting grape-skins, or more simply by moistening copper with vinegar and leaving it exposed to air. Salt-green was made from vinegar, copper and salt and may have been identical with atacamite, basic copper chloride. These greens have proved to be unstable and have turned to a dirty brown with the lapse of centuries. Green earth (*terre verte*), though not brilliant, was more reliable. Sap-green was made by evaporating the juice of buckthorn berries with a little alum, and iris-green by treating the flowers of the flag iris in the same way.

Yellow Pigments

The most ancient yellow pigment is the native yellow ochre, a clay coloured by iron, and almost no other pigment of this colour was used in Egypt. Orpiment (arsenic tri-sulphide) was known, but despite its fine golden tint it was somewhat rarely used in Egypt or Mesopotamia, though it became popular in Roman times. The Assyrians, on the other hand, were familiar with lead antimoniate (now known as Naples Yellow), which must have involved a good deal of chemical preparation. The mediæval painters sometimes used orpiment (arsenic tri-sulphide) but, as it was incompatible with white lead and verdigris, preferred to rely on the very permanent yellow ochres; they also used some organic pigments—saffron, Persian berries and weld. Much use was made of gold, which was reduced to the necessary fineness by grinding it with honey or salt, which prevented the particles from cohering and could be afterwards washed out with water. The so-called mosaic gold, tin disulphide, made by heating sal-ammoniac, tin-amalgam and sulphur, was known as early as the fourteenth century under the name of 'purpurina' but does not seem to have been widely used.

Crafts of the Artist

The artist of the Middle Ages and Renaissance required a very wide range of techniques—metallurgy, gilding, painting, lacquering, dyeing, enamelling, niello, the technique of glass and glazes, lustre, lapidary work, the treatment of textiles, parchment, the making of gesso, glues and inks. Some of these techniques are described elsewhere and some lie outside the range of industrial chemistry, however widely interpreted. We may note in passing the method of making the glue required for panels and gesso. The artist made his own, not as a rule from skins and refuse, as to-day, but by boiling ' lean cheese ' with lime and water: the resulting glue had a reputation for great strength. Gesso, which was used as a surface for wood to be painted and also for coating carved work to give a surface that could be very finely finished, was made of chalk or gypsum and this glue.

CHAPTER SEVEN

Mineral Acids

Mineral Acids

THE mineral acids known before the mid-seventeenth century were:

(1) Nitric acid, or *aqua fortis*.

(2) The mixture of nitric acid with hydrochloric acid or a chloride, known as *aqua regia* or *aqua regis*. This is also sometimes called *aqua fortis*: it is probably the *green lion* of alchemy.

(3) Sulphuric acid, which was known in the form of (*a*) *oil of vitriol* or *spirit of vitriol*, and (*b*) *oil of sulphur*; these were not identified as the same substance until the seventeenth century.

(4) Hydrochloric acid (*spirit of salt* or *muriatic acid*), which was not discovered until the early seventeenth century.

It does not follow that these were recognized as forming a class of ' acids ', for the notion of such a class is a fairly modern one; indeed, we do not hear of ' acids ', as a collective term, until the latter part of the seventeenth century.

Discovery of the Mineral Acids

The ancients were very well acquainted with vinegar (dilute acetic acid); this is discussed, however, in Chapter Twelve. The Hellenistic alchemists speak of preparing ' a very strong vinegar ', and it is tempting to suppose that this might be sulphuric acid distilled from green vitriol, which they knew well, but the evidence is insufficient for such a conclusion. We find no evidence of any knowledge of the mineral acids, nitric, sulphuric or hydrochloric, in the unquestioned works of the great Arabic alchemists, nor are they mentioned by the thirteenth-century Western writers on metals and chemical matters.

The first known mention of mineral acids is in the *Summa Perfectionis*, attributed to Geber but probably compiled at the beginning of the fourteenth century. Here we find the description of the making of nitric acid. Saltpetre is, of course, the source of the acid; and saltpetre was, in all probability, unknown in Arab and Western countries before about 1250. We may reasonably suppose then that the discovery of nitric acid and *aqua regia* belongs to the period 1250–1300.

Geber's recipes are worth quoting. In the seventeenth-century translation of R. Russell they read:

> Son of Doctrine, search out Experiments, and cease not; because in them you may find Fruit a Thousand-fold. For We writ this Book only for you, which we are willing to compleat with certain Waters and Oyls, very necessary in Our Magistery. With these We shall conclude our Book of the Invention of Perfection. And first we shall begin with Our Dissolutive Water, of which We made Mention in Our Summe of Perfection, when We speak of Dissolution with the Accuity of Waters.
>
> First of Vitriol of Cyprus, lib. I of Salt-peter, lib. II and of Jamenous Allom one fourth part; extract the Water with Redness of the Alembeck (for it is very Solutive) and use it in the before alleadged Chapters. This is also made much more acute, if in it you shall dissolve a fourth part of Salammoniac; because that dissolves Gold, Sulphur, and Silver.

In modern language, ferrous sulphate, alum (or more probably aluminium sulphate) and potassium nitrate are to be mixed and heated to redness. The sulphates liberate water and sulphur trioxide, which form sulphuric acid. This reacts with the potassium nitrate, forming potassium sulphate and liberating nitric acid, which distils over and is condensed. When ammonium chloride is dissolved therein a certain amount of chlorine is formed and remains dissolved in the acid: this chlorine will react with gold, as nitric acid will not, forming the soluble ' gold chloride '—actually chlorauric acid.

If the ferrous sulphate and alum used had not been freed from their water of crystallization, the distillate would have contained much water; so we may suppose that, as in later recipes, these salts were to be at least partly dehydrated at a moderate temperature before they were mixed with the saltpetre.

This recipe is the first mention of mineral acids, and it is likely that for some years they were used for alchemical experiments rather than for industry.

Industrial Use of Acids

The first useful work that is known to have been performed by the aid of mineral acids was the separation or ' parting ' of gold from silver (Chapter Two). Nitric acid was, in fact, known by the German writers as *Scheidwasser*, ' the separating water '. The gold-bearing silver was heated with nitric acid until the silver was converted into soluble silver nitrate, while the gold remained undissolved in a brownish powdery form (p. 34). We know that this process was used as a test by assayers in the sixteenth century, and there is evidence, moreover, that the separation was carried out in Venice as early as the fifteenth century and it may be even earlier. The *Probirbüchlein*,[1] which is the earliest work on assaying and dates from about 1510, refers to the separation of gold and silver by means of *Scheydwasser* or *Starckewasser*, but does not describe the preparation of this substance.

Manufacture of Nitric Acid

The writers on assaying of the middle sixteenth century, Lazarus Ercker and Agricola, describe the making of nitric acid on a fairly large scale. The process was essentially that described by Geber, the heating of saltpetre with iron sulphate from which all or most of the water of crystallization had been removed by previous heating. Alum was sometimes added and, if the acid was required to dissolve gold, salt also. The mixture was heated at first slowly and finally to redness. A mixture of nitrogen tetroxide and nitric acid was evolved and led into a receiver containing a little water.

The distillation apparatus was made of glass or pottery or iron (for the latter metal is not attacked by concentrated nitric acid). Glass apparatus was apt to break under the heat, which when distilling acid was, to say the least of it, inconvenient. To minimize this possibility the glass was coated with various mixtures, *e.g.* of clay, ashes and horse-dung, moistened with blood. Even so, Ercker tells us that the glass flask or ' body ' from which the acid was distilled could only be used once: he therefore commends pottery, but prefers iron as the most satisfactory. In glass retorts about 8 lb. of the mixture could be distilled at a time, but in iron retorts 20 lb. If the con-

[1] Probirbüchlein/auff Golt/Silber/Kupffer/und Bley/Auch allerley Metall/wie man die zunutz arbeyten und Probieren Soll. (No author or date.)

densed acid proved to be too weak the superfluous water was distilled off until brown fumes began to appear : this would

FIG. 18. Distillation of nitric acid (Ercker, 1574).

indicate that the final product was of the strength of the present commercial nitric acid (68%). Nitric acid of greater strength was probably unknown at this period. The acid was often purified (from chlorides) by adding a little silver.

The chief demand was for nitric acid (*aqua fortis*), free from chlorides, for the parting operation; but nitric acid containing hydrochloric acid (*aqua regis*) could also be used as described below. *Aqua fortis* was valuable for dissolving the silver out of an alloy and leaving the gold, but it would not attack alloys containing more than about 25 % of gold. If more gold than this was present in the metal, it was often alloyed with more silver to make it susceptible to attack. Alternatively, however, the alloy could be dissolved in *aqua regis* giving a solution of gold chloride and a precipitate of silver chloride. The former was decanted and distilled, whereupon the acid came over, leaving the gold chloride, which was heated on the cupel and converted into pure gold; the silver could easily be recovered from the silver chloride.

The discovery that a very strong volatile or fuming nitric acid could be made by distilling saltpetre with oil of vitriol was claimed both by Glauber and by Boyle in the middle of the seventeenth century, but the high price of oil of vitriol forbade its general use.

In the eighteenth century nitric acid was made from saltpetre by the action of quite a number of different agents. It was sometimes distilled in the ancient fashion with green vitriol or alum. In France nitre was often distilled with various types of clay or bole, which had the merit of cheapness. If these contained considerable quantities of sulphates, the residue, which contained both potassium and aluminium sulphates, could be lixiviated for alum. Nevertheless the use of sulphuric acid for making nitric acid rapidly gained ground as the price of the former fell, consequent on the adoption of the lead-chamber process. Thus the heating of a mixture of saltpetre and sulphuric acid, in England at any rate, became the standard method of making nitric acid by the year 1800.

Manufacture of Sulphuric Acid

In the sixteenth and seventeenth centuries sulphuric acid was a substance much less important than nitric acid. It was first introduced as a medicament; indeed, Ercker and Agricola do not mention it, because it was not of use to the metallurgist. It is difficult to say when it was discovered. Monardes in

1574 alludes to oil of vitriol as an invention of his own time, and the pharmaceutical writer Valerius Cordus (*d.* 1544), in his *De Artificiosis Extractionibus*,[1] commended oil of vitriol as a medicine. He regarded it as a mixture of alum and sulphur, the first giving it its ' sharpness '. He selected large crystals of blue or green vitriol (cupric or ferrous sulphate) and heated 12 lb. of them in an earthenware pot until all the water had been driven off: the anhydrous salt was then powdered and heated again until it became reddish: 6 lb. of it should remain. So large a reduction of weight would indicate that not only the water but that some sulphur dioxide and trioxide had been driven off. The powder was charged into a retort,

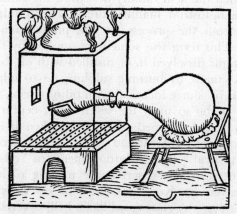

FIG. 19   Distillation of oil of vitriol (1554).

preferably of Venetian glass well luted with clay, and this was set in an upright stove-like furnace. The powder was then distilled, with a gradually increasing fire, for two days or more, the vapours being led into a large glass receiver containing about 18 oz. of water. The liquid in the receiver (dilute sulphuric acid) had then to be distilled. Water passed over and what was left behind in the flask was oil of vitriol—still, however, of a brownish colour. This was then distilled from a retort and pure oil of vitriol resulted. At a generous estimate a week's skilled work would yield about 2 lb. of sulphuric acid, which was therefore a somewhat precious material.

---

[1] This work was published in a collection of works of Valerius Cordus in 1561, but since Cordus died in 1544 at the age of twenty-nine, we may reasonably date the recipe as *c.* 1540.

This process remained in use for centuries: it had the advantage that if only a very little water were placed in the receiver the result would be a solution of sulphur trioxide in sulphuric acid, the ' oleum ' of modern chemical industry. The process was in later years carried on at Nordhausen, in the Hartz mountains, and persisted until 1900, when it was finally displaced by the contact process (p. 424), which was capable of producing oleum at a much lower price.

' Oil of vitriol ' made as described above was at first much cheaper than the ' oil of sulphur ' made by burning sulphur as described below. But the making of oil of vitriol had great disadvantages. It was slow and it required a high temperature, at which the acid rapidly destroyed the stills. In consequence the industrial manufacture of cheap sulphuric acid developed from the process for the preparation of ' oil of sulphur '. This term was sometimes applied by the pharmacists to sulphur dissolved in or distilled with oil, but normally to the ' oil ' made by burning sulphur, *i.e.* to sulphuric acid. This oil was of course identical with oil of vitriol, but was not recognized to be so until the seventeenth century. ' Oil of sulphur ' was used as a medicament and, taken up on a feather, was used to touch venereal and other ulcers in order to stimulate them to heal. P. A. Mattioli mentions ' oil of sulphur ' in 1535 but does not describe the making of it, which is, however, given by Konrad Gesner in his *Euonymi Philiatri Thesaurus* (1554). A glass vessel like a bell, covered with a lute of clay, was hung up about 18 inches from the ground by a wire. Under it was placed a somewhat wider glass dish: at the centre of this was set a cup on which was placed some sulphur. This was set alight and more was added from time to time. The gases and vapour rose, and the sulphur trioxide combined with the moisture of the air to form sulphuric acid, which condensed on the bell and dripped off into the dish. The process was very inefficient, for only a very small proportion of the sulphur was converted into the trioxide, which with the moisture of the air formed the sulphuric acid, while all the rest of the sulphur was converted into the suffocating gas sulphur dioxide, which escaped into the air. Later an alembic was substituted for the bell-jar, the acid dripping from its nose.

This process was developed, and larger and larger bell-jars and alembics were employed. In the 1740's, indeed, the

PLATE V

Mediæval Glass House (see pp. 72 ff.).

PLATE VI

A.—Sectional Model
Glass Furnace. *A*
Agricola (see p. 76)

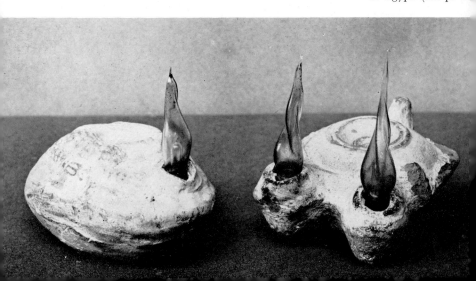

B. — Roman Lan
from Temple of Ph
in Egypt (see p. 10

quack doctor Joshua Ward, who was manufacturing in bell-jars of 66 gallons capacity, made the essential improvement in the process, namely, the addition of saltpetre to the sulphur. He patented this in 1749, though he may have used it earlier. No one then knew why this addition caused a much greater proportion of the sulphur to be turned into sulphuric acid, but Ward observed the fact and took advantage of it to bring the

FIG. 20. Making of sulphuric acid by the bell (early seventeenth century).

price of the acid down to 1s. 6d. or 2s. 6d. a pound. The process was soon improved, and for some years it was carried out in the following way. Glass globes, holding 40–50 gallons each, were made with short necks like those of a bottle; they were suspended with their necks horizontal and a gallon of water was put into each and kept hot. Then a pottery ladle, attached to a stopper that fitted the neck of the globe, was filled with sulphur and saltpetre, which were set alight. The fumes filled the globe and dissolved in the water. After a number of charges had been burned in the globe, the water contained about half its weight of acid. This solution was removed and the liquid was first heated to boil off the water and then distilled. This process brought the acid down to about 4*d*. a pound, at which price it could be used for such industrial purposes as making nitric acid and copper sulphate.

Meanwhile, in 1746, Dr. Roebuck, a Birmingham physician, had realized that there were necessary limits to the size of glass bell-jars and globes. He therefore began to burn his sulphur and nitre in leaden ' houses ' as they came to be called. These had at first about ten times the capacity of the globes and jars, being 6 feet long, 6 feet broad and 6 feet high; as the century went on they were made bigger and bigger until in the 1820's a size of about 45 × 15 × 15 feet was adopted.

In 1749 the situation was changed by a new industrial demand for acids. The British Isles had for many years made excellent linen, but they had not the art of bleaching it to perfection and it was sent to Holland for that purpose— whence the name ' holland ' for linen. To bleach a piece of linen took from March to September. It was soaked and boiled in solutions of alkali (of which more hereafter) and exposed for weeks on the grass to the sun and dew. It was then ' soured ' (soaked in weak acid), and the process was repeated half a dozen times as the year went on. The acid used for the ' souring ' was lactic acid—fermented buttermilk—and the process took from two to six weeks. When bleaching was undertaken in Scotland it was found that the use of dilute sulphuric acid instead of sour milk reduced the time for souring from two to six weeks to twelve to twenty-four hours, so halving the total time required for bleaching. Thus the demand for sulphuric acid increased: other manufacturers set up in business and, as the materials were very cheap and the acid was sold very dear, large fortunes were made.

In 1774 Scheele, the great Swedish chemist, discovered chlorine and noted its bleaching power, but it was not till 1785–86 that Berthollet experimented on its practical use for bleaching textiles. The news of the efficacy of chlorine soon got around, and within a couple of years bleaching by chlorine was in growing use in England and Scotland. Now, as chlorine could not be made without sulphuric acid, the demand for the acid increased; and after Charles Tennant, of Glasgow, discovered a safe and easy way of bleaching by turning gaseous chlorine into solid bleaching powder the demand increased very much further. More and more sulphuric acid works were set up. Successive charges of sulphur and nitre were burnt in ' lead houses ' of dimensions up to 60 × 18 × 15 feet, and the resulting sulphur trioxide continued to dissolve in the layer of water that lay at the bottom until it became fairly strong acid. It was then distilled in glass retorts until all the superfluous water had passed over. The breakage of these retorts was frequent and disastrous. To quote Samuel Parkes, himself a manufacturer of acid:

> When the acid is sufficiently concentrated (in retorts) the fire is usually taken out of the grates and the acid of the retorts is allowed to remain in the sandheats until the next day that the glasses may become sufficiently cool to be removed from their beds without danger of their being cracked by too sudden a change of temperature. A man then lifts the retorts one by one out of the sand, each retort containing 50 or 60 pounds of hot concentrated sulphuric acid, and this he pours into carboys that have been previously warmed to receive it. This is a frightful and a dangerous task; and instances have occurred of men being confined to their beds for several months together, with inveterate burns occasioned by these retorts, loaded with sulphuric acid, having burst in their arms and having thrown acid over their legs and other parts of their bodies.

Despite the progress of the sulphuric acid industry no theory of the reaction had yet been formulated. Thus the work of Clément and Désormes (p. 188) marks the beginning of the scientific sulphuric acid industry and must be taken up in another chapter.

Hydrochloric Acid

Hydrochloric acid was first prepared and recognized as a new substance by J. B. van Helmont before 1644: his method was to heat a mixture of common salt and dried potters' clay. Glauber greatly improved on this, probably before 1646, by distilling the salt with green vitriol and alum, and in 1658 he set out the standard method of preparation, *i.e.* from salt and oil of vitriol. Both van Helmont's and Glauber's methods continued to be used throughout the eighteenth century. Glauber's was much the more convenient, but the cheapness of the clay used by Helmont seems to have compensated for the prolonged heating needed to bring about the reaction. Hydrochloric acid was but little used at this period; but when the Leblanc process for making soda came into use in the early nineteenth century, vast quantities of hydrogen chloride were evolved as a by-product. This made hydrochloric acid the cheapest of mineral acids and it soon came into wide use in chemical industry.

CHAPTER EIGHT

Combustibles

A CHEMIST is traditionally a ' worker in the fire ', and the elucidation of the nature of combustion was the decisive step toward the foundation of modern chemistry. It is fitting, therefore, here to consider the technology of combustibles before the period of modern science. Under the heading of combustibles we may consider, first, the fuels used as sources of heat; secondly, fuels for use in lighting; and thirdly, the incendiary and explosive mixtures used in warfare.

Fuels in Antiquity

The use of fire seems to be of greater antiquity than our own species, *homo sapiens*; for indications of its use were found with the much older remains of Pekin man, *australopithecus sinensis*.

The most obvious and the chief primitive fuel is wood, yet it happens that the two greatest early civilizations flourished in Egypt and Mesopotamia, where wood was relatively scarce, and a number of other fuels were therefore adopted.

It appears that in Egypt, in addition to wood and charcoal, which were relatively expensive, the dried dung of cows and asses, and also straw, were used for domestic cooking. The papyrus plant, whose bark furnished the Egyptians with writing material and whose cabbage-like head was eaten as a vegetable, forms large knotty roots, and these were much used as fuel. Wherever metals were smelted, large quantities of fuel were required. Wood had to be brought, we must suppose, from some distance to the Sinai copper-mines. In Cyprus, a great source of copper from the Bronze Age onwards, the forests were entirely cut down in order to supply such fuel : indeed, in the Mediterranean region there seems to have been a general destruction of forests for charcoal-burning in later classical times, the consequence of which was the erosion of the soil, which has made much of the country barren or desert.

In later times glassmakers used enormous quantities of wood, both to heat their furnaces and to make ashes. Glass-blowers, indeed, frequently moved their furnaces from places where the wood was exhausted to new parts of the forest.

The Babylonians, like the Egyptians, lacked wood, so that this and charcoal were relatively expensive fuels. They cultivated reeds in their extensive marshes and used these for burning their bricks: they also burned the desert-thorn and dung and even date kernels. For industrial work, *e.g.* metallurgy and ceramics, they used well-seasoned logs, for no other known fuel would give the long hot flame required (p. 70).

Charcoal was the domestic fuel of choice in the classical world. We know little or nothing about the methods of the charcoal-burners of Egypt and Mesopotamia, but Pliny (*c.* A.D. 50) shows us that the methods of the Italian charcoal-burners of his time were very much like those of the seventeenth century (p. 104, Fig. 21 below). Small logs of wood were piled up into a dome-like structure, covered with earth and ignited, the supply of air being kept at a minimum. Sometimes a drain was provided to carry off the liquid products of distillation, chiefly wood-tar, which could be boiled down to give wood-pitch.

For heating rooms charcoal was burned in flat open braziers or pans, much as it is to-day in Southern Europe; the danger of carbon monoxide poisoning is not great if the hot charcoal forms a comparatively thin layer. The Romans had no chimneys except in bake-ovens. For metallurgical purposes, where a very high temperature was required, briquettes of charcoal and pitch were sometimes employed. The word ' pitch ' was used to denote both the resinous exudations from various coniferous trees and the semi-solid residue resulting from the boiling down of wood-tar. The modern coal-tar pitch was, of course, unknown.

In places where coal occurs near the surface the knowledge of it may be very ancient: thus coal has been found in a Bronze Age barrow in South Wales. It was not unknown to the Greeks and Romans, for Theophrastus (fourth century B.C.) speaks of it as being used by smiths. The Romans also used it in certain parts of the Empire where it occurred as outcrops. Thus coal cinders have been found in Roman sites in Northumbria and the Forest of Dean; it is quite likely that it continued to be used here and there as a fuel throughout the Dark Ages.

In the Middle Ages the chief domestic and industrial fuels were wood and charcoal; in the coal-bearing countries, however, coal was an important industrial fuel, but it remained almost unknown in Italy up to the fifteenth century. Thus

FIG. 21. Charcoal-burning in the eighteenth century; from the *Grande Encyclopédie*.

Marco Polo met with coal in China and thought it a wonder, and as late as the fifteenth century Aeneas Sylvius Piccolomini (Pius II) thought it worthy of mention as a thing not generally known.

Charcoal-burning was extensively practised in the Middle Ages, and indeed up to modern times. In the late nineteenth and early twentieth centuries the distillation of wood in retorts, primarily to make acetic acid, methyl alcohol and acetone, replaced it, but with the development of syntheses for the above products wood-distillation has been abandoned and charcoal-burning has once more become an industry.

The general way of making charcoal was to prepare a large circular mound of logs regularly arranged, with some sort of flue at the centre. The spaces were filled up, as far as might be, with smaller wood and the whole was then covered over with turf and rubbish. The fire was started by pouring lighted charcoal or wood down the centre shaft: this was then blocked and other vent-holes made nearer the circumference. These were later blocked and a new range of holes made, nearer the edge. By skilful management a smouldering fire was made to spread outward from the centre, and the whole mass was thus converted into charcoal. The process as operated in the eighteenth century is shown in Fig. 21: doubtless the ancient charcoal-burners also operated in some such fashion.

It seems that in the sixteenth century the liquid products were wasted, but in the early nineteenth century the heaps were often built on a paved circular hearth, sloping from the edge to the centre, whence a drain carried off the liquid products (tar and acetic acid) to a storage tank.

The Use of Coal

The word 'coal' (carbo) was applied in the Middle Ages to what we call charcoal as well as to what we call coal. The latter, in England, was usually distinguished as 'sea-coal', meaning the coal carried by sea from Newcastle and Durham to London and elsewhere. Land carriage of coal would have raised its price very greatly, so in fact it was used only in places to which it could be brought by water.

The uses of coal were at first limited. Chimneys [1] came into use but slowly, and until the sixteenth century only the houses of the wealthy were equipped with them. The normal practice was to make the fires against a wall and let the smoke escape through a hole in the roof. The atmosphere of the houses therefore became very smoky: wood-smoke was tolerable and considered to be healthy, but coal-smoke was very offensive to the otherwise insensitive mediæval nose and was thought to

---

[1] The word 'chimney' in mediæval usage meant a brazier, but it is here used to denote a flue, as today.

be poisonous. Thus the domestic use of sea-coal had to wait on the adoption of chimneys and became frequent only in the sixteenth century; even in London it ousted wood only in the period 1600–25. Even then the smoky atmosphere it engendered led to many complaints. John Evelyn's *Fumifugium* (1661) is the first condemnation of smoke-pollution—that ' hellish and dismal cloude of sea-coale '. It is notable that the disease of rickets first came to notice in seventeenth-century London. We may conjecture that for the first time in history smoke-pollution had cut off the ultraviolet light which makes vitamin D in the skins of children and so brought about this deficiency disease in the many who failed to get the vitamin from their diet.

Thus coal found little domestic use before the sixteenth century, but for at least four centuries before this it had been locally employed by smiths and lime-burners, who needed high temperatures, and by brewers and dyers, who had large vats of liquid to heat.

Coal could not at first, however, be used successfully for the smelting of metals, probably because the furnaces had no sufficient arrangements for draught. Thus they were often low, without flues and dependent for draught on a wind-hole. This was adequate for charcoal firing, but not for coal.

The Mining of Coal

We hear of the extensive use of coal in the thirteenth century in England, in the Ruhr and the Saar, in all of which localities it was obtained by mining outcrops or those parts of the coal seams which lay near the surface. In Scotland the first records of a coal trade date from about 1200, and coal-mining became general throughout that country in the course of the next fifty years. In London there was a Sacoles (*i.e.* sea-coal) Lane in 1228. Coal was soon so widely used by brewers and dyers that a Royal Proclamation forbade its use in 1306, but the practice was certainly very little checked by it. In 1353 the lime-burners and smiths employed on the works at Windsor Castle had loads of sea-coal brought, presumably by river. So much coal was used that resort had to be made to deep mining practice, the system adopted being that of the shaft and adit. The adit was a drift or tunnel driven into the side of a hill to meet the shallow shaft; the adit was driven slightly to the

E*

rise—that is, slightly upwards—so that the water from the mine could run downwards into the valley beneath. This inclination of the adit also favoured the transport of coal from the mine. Where two adits or two shafts were connected together the ventilation of the mine was also improved. By the end of the fifteenth century there was need to mine deeper than adits could drain, and we hear of pumps operated by horses, and windlasses for raising water in buckets—probably very much like those illustrated by Agricola as in use in the sixteenth-century German mines. Ventilation became more difficult with increasing depth, and in the seventeenth century there were many explosions and fatalities in mines.

At this period the use of coal was greatly extended; as we have seen, it became the usual domestic fuel in London, and it was also brought into use in glass-works and iron-works, though somewhat slowly. The making of coke was introduced in the first half of the seventeenth century, but did not become normal practice until the eighteenth. After 1700 the steam-engine began its further demands, which were enormously augmented in the industrial revolution.

Fuels for Lighting

The most primitive mode of lighting is the fire on the hearth; but in Egypt and Mesopotamia, where wood was scarce, there must have been need for other—and cooler—methods. The oil-lamp, in the form of hollowed stones, shells or animals' skulls, in which were burned fats or fish-oil with wicks or moss or vegetable fibre, dates back to the Palæolithic period. Thus primitive lamps used by the cave-painters of ancient France have been found on these sites. All ancient lamps were shallow in form because the various vegetable oils used were of low capillarity and would only rise in the wick a little way above the level of the oil in the receiver. It appears from the account of Herodotus that the Egyptians used salt in their lamps, presumably to support the wick and to soak up the oil and prevent it from being spilt. Greek and Roman lamps were shallow dishes with floating wicks or vessels of the well-known form shown in Plate VI, B. They smoked excessively.

Petroleum was known to the ancients though not widely available; the Babylonians used it in lamps, as did the inhabitants of Agrigentum (Girgenti), in Sicily, where there was a petroleum spring.

Candles were probably known in Greek and Roman times; their liturgical use is recorded as early as A.D. 258. They were made by dipping a wick, of fibrous material, in melted wax or tallow, allowing it to cool and then dipping it again, the process being repeated until it was thick enough—a method still employed for making church candles of bees-wax. The taper and the rushlight, the pith of a rush dipped in fat, are variants of the candle. Torches derive from the resinous splinter, which must be of the utmost antiquity and was still used when Dr. Johnson visited the Hebrides in 1773: these splinters developed into wooden sticks wrapped at one end with fibrous material and dipped in wax, resin or fat. These were used in antiquity, but not, apparently, in Egypt. A lantern intended to have glass or horn panes has been found at Pompeii.

These, with various small improvements, were the only means of lighting up to the time when the invention of gas was brought into use in the first decade of the nineteenth century (p. 208). The various types of candle used in the Middle Ages and Renaissance hardly fall within the scope of chemistry; suffice it to say that animal and vegetable oils, resins, fats and waxes remained the sole sources of artificial light.

Incendiary and Explosive Mixtures

The use of fire as an offensive weapon dates back at least to the Assyrians, who had access to bitumen, asphalt and petroleum (naphtha), all of which occur in quantity in that part of the world. The use of fire to destroy ships and siege-works was much favoured in the ancient world. Burning materials difficult to extinguish were propelled by means of arrows or lances, or hurled in pots by ballistæ or similar engines of war. The typical incendiary mixture was made up of sulphur, pitch, resin and naphtha. It seems that at the siege of Constantinople (A.D. 660–670) the Byzantines used some new type of incendiary (Greek fire) by which the Muslim ships were set alight. It may have been a mixture of quicklime, sulphur and naphtha which caught on fire when wetted. There are also indications, hard to interpret, of the projection of inflammable matter from tubes, directed at will. There is not sufficient evidence to enable us to know what was done, but we have no reason to suppose that any true explosive was used, nor that saltpetre was added to the mixture.

Saltpetre and Gunpowder

The greatest step in chemical warfare was made when saltpetre was brought into use and the first explosive, gunpowder, was discovered. Like so many mediæval inventions, the use of saltpetre cannot be certainly traced to any individual or, indeed, locality. All we can say is that we cannot find any trace of it anywhere in the world before 1200. Saltpetre is first mentioned by the Arabic author Ibn al-Baithar about 1248,

FIG. 22.   Fire-pots and incendiary arrows as illustrated by Biringuccio (1540).

under the name of ' Chinese snow'; but we have no other evidence that it really came from China. It was certainly brought in a crude state from India; but neither China nor India seem to have had gunpowder as early as the West.

Saltpetre was made by extracting with water the soluble salts from earth in which nitrifying bacteria had been active. Nitrification was, in fact, most rapid where soil saturated with animal refuse or excrements was exposed to heat with free access of air. Thus the soil in and around Indian villages was the best source of saltpetre, though, as will be seen, it could also be obtained from European sources, natural or artificial. As first extracted it contained much common salt, and to make it fit for use in fireworks and gunpowder it had to be recrystallized; *i.e.* heated with water and allowed to cool, whereupon fairly pure potassium nitrate crystallized out. In the thirteenth century the crude saltpetre was apparently recrystallized but once; a second recrystallization was later adopted (we do not know when) and was the normal practice in the sixteenth century.

The question of Roger Bacon's connection with saltpetre and gunpowder is a vexed one. He certainly knew of gunpowder, but the question whether he knew of it as early as 1248 depends on a decision as to whether he wrote the *De Secretis Naturæ* and, if so, when he wrote it; and whether the supposed cryptogram in this work has been correctly deciphered. For our purpose it is perhaps enough to know that gunpowder of a sort was known in Europe before 1270. There was for a long time no agreement about the most suitable proportions of the ingredients. Early gunpowder contained less saltpetre than the modern kind: moreover, the ingredients were merely mixed as powders and not corned (*i.e.* moistened, formed into small pieces and dried).

The making of gunpowder soon became a considerable industry. The fifteenth-century illustrations that appear as Plates VII, A and VII, B show the processes of pounding and mixing. It is notable that the pounding is timed by a sandglass, perhaps the earliest example of timing an operation of chemical industry.

The best composition for gunpowder was worked out in the sixteenth and seventeenth centuries, when the first crude apparatus was devised for testing the force of the explosion. The ballistic pendulum of Benjamin Robins (1742) gave the first accurate means of testing the force of powder.

Firework Compositions

Gunpowder makes its first appearance as a filling for crackers, more than fifty years before it was used in a gun. We do not know anything about mediæval fireworks, except that they were in use as early as the end of the thirteenth century, but in the second half of the sixteenth century there appeared several books on pyrotechny, and fireworks were then evidently a very popular entertainment. The chief of them were the rocket, the cracker and the squib or fizgig. The method of making rockets was remarkably like that employed to-day. The firework materials were saltpetre, charcoal, sulphur, iron filings, and later stibnite and orpiment, the native sulphides of antimony and arsenic. The use of coloured stars and fires seems to have come in during the eighteenth century, when copper salts were used to give a green colour to the flame. The red fire given by strontium salts was not discovered until the early nineteenth century.

Manufacture of Saltpetre

The essentially chemical feature of the making of gunpowder and fireworks was the recrystallization of saltpetre, which, after alum, was the first pure chemical to be manufactured: sulphur, which had been known from very early times, also assumed a new importance.

Saltpetre is potassium nitrate, and nitrates are formed by the action of nitrifying bacteria upon ammonium salts. Where large quantities of putrefying organic matter, especially urine, are contained in the soil and the products of their nitrification are not washed away by rain, nitrates may collect until they form a crystalline efflorescence on the soil.

Thus around Indian villages the rapid nitrification of sewage-saturated earth produces a crust very rich in nitrates, from which crude saltpetre was extracted by water. Thus saltpetre was at all periods exported from India, but its price was high owing to the numerous middlemen and the cost of transport; and consequently it was profitable to make saltpetre in Europe. Earth from old dry sheep-stalls and stables or the material of old walls and cellars in the cities was collected, and was known as saltpetre-earth.

In the eighteenth and early nineteenth centuries nitre-beds were much in use. They consisted of heaps of a mixture of dung with light porous chalky earth, watered occasionally with urine and the drainings of dunghills. Calcium nitrate was formed and appeared as an efflorescence on the surface, which was periodically scraped off and sold for conversion into saltpetre as described below. The home production of saltpetre was an obvious necessity if the state's armies were to have an uninterrupted supply of gunpowder. In Sweden the peasants were compelled to maintain nitre-beds, and in many countries saltpetre-makers were privileged to take saltpetre-earth wherever they could find it, a practice that led to many abuses.

In France the rights of collection of saltpetre were farmed out for many years. Dissatisfaction with the corruption and inefficiency of the private corporation responsible led to the setting up of a *Régie des Poudres*, a Government agency for the manufacture of powder. Lavoisier did extremely valuable

FIG. 23.   Nitre-beds in the sixteenth century (Ercker).

work in promoting the scientific study of powder manufacture and so improved its quality that grave concern was expressed in England at the improvement in French fire-power. Lavoisier's connection with this powerful agency brought him the splendid facilities for research at the Arsenal which he used so well, but unhappily also contributed to the case put forward by those who sent him to the guillotine.

To extract the saltpetre, alternate layers of saltpetre-earth and a mixture of wood-ash and lime were filled into a vat and water was allowed to trickle through it. The potassium carbonate in the ash reacted with the calcium nitrate of the saltpetre-earth, giving insoluble calcium carbonate and a solution of potassium nitrate. Thus the liquor issuing from the bottom of the vat contained the saltpetre together with a good

FIG. 24.   Sulphur refining (Agricola, 1556).

deal of common salt and some other saline impurities: if it was not strong enough (as judged by the taste) it was run through another and similar vat also containing alternate layers of saltpetre-earth and ashes. The resulting solution was then boiled down in a copper cauldron and earthy matters allowed to settle out. The supernatant liquid was then mixed with a little lye (p. 129) and alum and boiled down. At the boiling-point of the solution common salt is much less soluble than saltpetre, and it therefore crystallized out first and settled to the bottom. The hot solution was run off into vats in which rods were hung and the saltpetre crystallized out on them.

Refining of Sulphur

Sulphur, of course, was known to the ancients, who refined it, though they do not tell us how they did so. In the sixteenth century the ore—a mixture of sulphur and earthy matter—was heated in an earthenware pot with a spout through which the vapour passed into another and larger pot. The sulphur vapour condensed and liquefied in the second pot, the liquid sulphur being discharged through a spout near the bottom. The principle is the same as that of the large-scale Sicilian refining furnace used up to the end of the nineteenth century.

CHAPTER NINE

Dyeing

Ancient History

THE great difference between ancient and modern dyeing resides in the very small number of dyestuffs in use before the nineteenth century. Even of these only a few were in use at any particular place and time, and we may think of any prescientific dyer as operating with less than a dozen dyes yet producing a variety of fine colours by combining them.

No doubt all kinds of coloured plants were used from the most ancient times to stain skins or textiles, but only a very small proportion of these plants yield a colour that will stand even a moderate exposure to light, air and washing. We know that dyeing was practised in the remotest periods of civilization, and some of the methods then employed persisted for thousands of years. Indeed, it was perhaps the most static of arts, for the innovations introduced between Roman times and the middle of the nineteenth century were few compared with the body of unchanged technique.

The two chief methods of dyeing are mordanting and vat-dyeing.

Vat-dyeing

Vat-dyeing is a process by which the dyestuff, itself insoluble in water, is converted into, or used in the form of, another chemical compound, soluble in water. The fabric is dyed in this solution, which is often without colour, and is then exposed to the air, when the dyestuff itself is formed on the textile. This process was used for dyeing with indigo and woad.

Mordants and Alum

The process of mordanting consists in boiling [1] the fabric with a solution of a mordant, usually a metallic salt, and

Cold solutions were sometimes used, *e.g.* for silk.

particularly alum. The fabric is then washed and boiled with the solution of the dye-stuff. The result is that the colour is permanently fixed on the fabric: the shade produced is often different from that of the dye-stuff and the use of different mordants can give different shades or even quite distinct colours. Alum, discussed below, has been the mordant *par excellence* from antiquity, and the history of its manufacture and use has been admirably set out by Dr. Charles Singer in his sumptuous work *The Earliest Chemical Industry*.[1]

This is perhaps the most suitable place to discuss the manufacture and use of alum, the chief mordant used by dyers.

By the word 'alum' the chemist of to-day means a *class* of salts, the double sulphates of a tervalent and a univalent metal, crystallizing with 24 molecules of water, while the ordinary man means by it the hydrated double sulphate of aluminium and potassium. But nothing was known of the composition of alum before the eighteenth century, and to the men of earlier times the word meant 'a white astringent salt' or even 'an astringent mineral substance'. It is not surprising then that we cannot always identify the substances referred to by the ancients when they used the word *alumen* in Latin and *stypteria* in Greek.

The use of alum in dyeing was known in Egypt in Græco-Roman times, and it is probable that the mordanting of madder with alum dates back to about 2000 B.C. Alum was produced in Egypt in considerable quantities, and in Græco-Roman times it was extracted from alum-rock in many districts, and especially in the islands of Stromboli and Melos, probably by the method described on p. 117. The alum made in these islands was the substance to which we give the name to-day, but many other astringent salts (*e.g.* the double sulphate of aluminium with magnesium or iron, also hydrated aluminium sulphate) were sometimes called *alumen*. These substances could all be used as mordants and also as astringents or styptics in medicine. Inflammable substances, such as the wood of ships or engines of war, were sometimes fireproofed by immersion in solutions of alum.

The mediæval dye trade required alum in quantity for mordanting various colours. In the twelfth century it was still made in Melos from the native alum-rock, but something called

[1] *The Earliest Chemical Industry.* Charles Singer. London 1948.

FIG. 25. Alum making (Mercati [1541–93]; *Metallotheca*).

alum (perhaps native aluminium sulphate) was being imported from Yemen, in Arabia. Other kinds of ' alum ' were brought from Syria and Egypt.

From ancient times up to the later Middle Ages alum was made from the mineral alunite or from other minerals which yield aluminium sulphate when roasted. The roasted rock was weathered and then boiled up with water, successive charges of the rock being added to the same solution until it was strong enough to crystallize on cooling. It was then cooled in vats or casks and the crystalline salt knocked off the sides and sold.

In the thirteenth century or earlier the conversion of native aluminium sulphate into what we now know as ammonium alum was described. The native mineral was treated with stale urine and evaporated until it formed crystals: these were much more convenient for the dyer than was the native aluminium sulphate.

The alum trade was highly profitable and new sources of alum were eagerly sought. The alum-producing regions up to the fifteenth century were Turkey and the Greek isles, but when the Turks conquered this part of the world an alum famine resulted. In that century, however, it was discovered that the mineral which we call *trachite*, where it has been exposed to sulphurous volcanic fumes, is converted into alunite or alum, and the greatest mass of this mineral was found in papal territory at Tolfa. Hence grew up the enormously profitable papal monopoly in alum. Despite very strenuous efforts, this monopoly was not effectively maintained, and in the sixteenth century the Protestant countries made great efforts to develop an alum trade.

Alunite was not to be found in quantity in their territories, but shales which when roasted yielded aluminium sulphate were not uncommon. To these roasted shales potassium or ammonium salts had to be added in order to form the alum.

In England the shale found in east Yorkshire was utilized from the seventeenth century onward. It was quarried and then calcined by burning it with wood—which incidentally provided some potash. During this process the iron pyrites, which abounds in the shale, was oxidized to ferrous sulphate. This decomposed at a higher temperature and converted the aluminium silicate of the shale into aluminium sulphate. This was extracted by solution in water; to this solution kelp, wood-ashes or stale urine were added, so providing the potassium or ammonium salts necessary to convert the aluminium sulphate into alum. The liquors were then boiled down and crystallized.

Similar processes were carried out all over Europe. In these processes the yield of alum was small, perhaps 1 % of the weight of the mineral. It was not until the nineteenth century that the chemistry of alum manufacture was properly understood and more effective methods introduced.

The active portion of alum, in its function as mordant, astringent, precipitant, etc., is the aluminium ion, the potassium sulphate being quite inert in these respects. In recent years, therefore, aluminium sulphate has increasingly replaced alum for all these purposes.

Centres of the Dyeing Industry

We know that in ancient times the Egyptians and Assyrians were skilled dyers; a special industry, however, sprang up in the dyeing of the purple of the ancients (p. 124), for which fresh marine molluscs had to be used. Purple-dyeing was therefore carried out in maritime towns, of which the Phœnician Tyre and Sidon were the most famous. The Greeks and Romans were also highly skilled dyers. After the fall of the classical civilizations (c. A.D. 400) the secrets of dyeing became the property of the Byzantines and the Jews of the Levant; throughout the Middle Ages cloth was sent to Constantinople by the Italians, experts as they were, for the dyeing of certain colours which they could not themselves produce. From the thirteenth to the sixteenth centuries the dyeing experts of Europe were the Italians. The Genoese were the first, later the Bolognese and Pisans: in the fifteenth century, however, the Florentines led Europe in this craft. This does not mean that dyeing was not done elsewhere, for, in fact, dyeing was carried on both as a home industry and as a trade in every civilized country: the Italians, however, had the art of dyeing the most brilliant and even colours and furnished the most luxurious fabrics.

Some Eastern countries had secrets that were not quickly learnt by Europe. Thus the Indians knew how to dye the brilliant madder-reds with the help of oil, and ' Indian red ' fabrics were imported for many years. In the eighteenth century the Turks learnt this art, and the colour still bears the name of Turkey-red. Later in the same century the knowledge of the process passed to Europe.

In the seventeenth century the Dutch became important dyers, especially after Cornelius Drebbel's discovery of dyeing the brilliant cochineal scarlet with a mordant of tin chloride. In the eighteenth century England's dye industry developed proportionately with her textile trade.

The Natural Dyes

These are perhaps best discussed under their colours rather than in order of discovery.

Blue Dyes

The only truly blue dye known before the nineteenth century was indigotin. Indigotin, however, is derived from a large number of different plants of the genus *Indigofera*, the indigo-plants, and also of the genus *Isatis*, woad. The former grow only in tropical countries, while the latter can be cultivated anywhere in Europe. Thus solid indigo was imported from India to Europe, but indigo-blues could also be dyed in Europe direct from the woad plant. The indigo-content of woad is, however, much inferior to that of the *Indigoferæ*.

Indigotin itself is an insoluble solid which cannot be used as such in a dye-bath, but has to be reduced to the soluble indigo-white. This process was accomplished by allowing the plants, whether of indigo or woad, to ferment in the dye-bath. Fabrics could then be dyed by steeping them in the liquor and hanging them in the air, whereby the indigo-white was oxidized to the dark-blue indigo, on and in the fibre. Alternatively, the liquor of the indigo-vat could be exposed to air, whereupon the colouring matter separated out as a dark-blue powder, in which form indigo was exported from India to the West. These processes are very ancient, but as their theory was not understood until the nineteenth century indigo-dyeing remained an empirical craft. The Egyptians knew how to dye with indigo as early as 1500 B.C., but in the Græco-Roman period the true indigo seems to have been used only as a pigment, and their blue fabrics were dyed with woad.

In the earlier Middle Ages woad was the chief means of

dyeing blues and was a very important crop though, it is said, most destructive to the fertility of the soil. Indian indigo had come into use by the fifteenth century, at which time it was reduced and brought into solution for dyeing by boiling with honey and lime (*i.e.* glucose and alkali). In the sixteenth century the importation of indigo from the East was bitterly opposed by the growers, but its use steadily increased. From this period it was usual to introduce the indigo into a vat of fermenting vegetable matter (which might be woad), lime and water, so that the fermentation should reduce it to the soluble indigo-white with which the cloth could be dyed.

Indigo was an excellent colour, so fast that specimens of Egyptian fabric dyed with it still retain their colour. Synthetic indigotin is still an important dye, and indeed the manufacture of woad has only recently ceased.

In 1744 Barth discovered that indigo could be brought into a soluble state by heating it with the Nordhausen fuming sulphuric acid. The resulting indigosulphonic acid was used as a wool dye under the name of Saxe Blue.

Black Dyes

The only truly black dye known before the nineteenth century was the gallo-tannate of iron, dyed by boiling the fabric first in a solution of galls and then in a solution of ferrous sulphate (*atramentum sutorium*) which was found in copper-mines and resulted from the oxidation of iron pyrites. Alternatively, a black could be obtained by superimposing two or more dark colours.

Green Dyes

No satisfactory green dye was known before the nineteenth century, and it was usual to produce a green by dyeing the cloth first with yellow weld (p. 121) and then with blue woad or indigo. Buckthorn berries with alum gave a green pigment (sap green), and they were sometimes used for dyeing skins green. Other vegetable greens, *e.g.* sloe-berries, were used but were probably not fast to light. Copper greens were dyed on fabrics by boiling them with verdigris and alum.

Yellow Dyes

The most ancient yellow dye seems to have been safflower

(*carthamus tinctoria*), a small annual of the composite family. This dye has been identified on ancient Egyptian mummy wrappings of the XII Dynasty (*c.* 2000 B.C.), and it remained in use until modern times. It yields both a yellow and a red dye which until recent years was used for dyeing the proverbial red tape of the British Government. Safflower must not be confused with saffron, the stigmas of the saffron crocus, which, though much used in antiquity, was not employed as a dye. It has, however, long been in use in India for dyeing the yellow robes of Buddhist priests.

The most important yellow dye of the Middle Ages was weld (*reseda luteola*, dyers' weed), a plant allied to mignonette. It gave a pure yellow on cloth mordanted with alum. *Fustic* (known to-day as young fustic) is a Mediterranean shrub and gave somewhat browner yellows. Other yellow dye-plants were introduced in the sixteenth century, namely, old fustic (from America), turmeric (from India) and, in the late eighteenth century, quercitron, the wood of the American oak (*quercus nigra*). The Egyptians seem to have dyed fabrics an iron-buff by boiling them with green vitriol (ferrous sulphate). Mention may also be made of the Indian cutch, a brown dye, still used for the sails of small craft.

The resources of the dyer in yellow were therefore fairly considerable.

Red Dyes

The most ancient of these seems to be madder, derived from various species of *rubia* which grew wild in the Mediterranean region and Near East. It was used in Egypt as early as 1500 B.C. Madder mordanted with alum gave a fine red, rather on the bluish side.

From Greek and Roman times onward crimson, and also the more brilliant reds inclined to scarlet, were dyed with one of the species of coccus, known as *coccus*, *vermiculus*, kermes, grain or cochineal. These are all insects, parasitic on various plants. Cochineal, derived from *dactylopius coccus* (Costa), gives the most colour, but is of Mexican origin and did not reach Europe until the sixteenth century, though used much earlier in America by the Aztecs. The most ancient of the coccus dyes is derived from the insect *kermes ilicis* (Linn.), parasitic upon the holm-oak. The swollen bodies of the immobile females look like little bladders or eggs. These were collected and crushed and the product was used for dyeing with an alum mordant. A kind of coccus was said by Ctesias (400 B.C.) to have been imported from India, and this was probably different from the Western type. Coccus was used in the Græco-Roman period and, very widely, in the Middle Ages. The Arabs called it *kermes*, whence comes the word ' crimson '. On the other hand, the dye was also known, from the seventh century at least, as *vermiculus* (the ' little worm '), and this word became transformed to ' vermilion ', which was also used to describe the scarlet pigment mercury sulphide (p. 85). In the later Middle Ages there were two articles of commerce, identical with or very like kermes, known as *coccus* and *grana*. Though both were red dyes derived from insects, they were evidently not the same, for they are often mentioned in the same list and their prices were different. *Grana* gave rise to the English colour-name ' grain', surviving only in the phrase ' dyed in grain ' and the word ' ingrained '.

A recipe for dyeing with kermes (taken from the treatise known as *Plictho* [1540] as translated by Singer) may be taken as typical of mediæval methods:

> *Venetian way of dyeing scarlet.* Weigh the cloth, and for each pound prepare 6 ounces of mordant, to wit roche alum 1 part, white tartar 2 parts, dissolved in clear water. Boil the cloth for 1 hour. Wash in running water. Prepare the cauldron with 4 parts of strong fat water [that is fermented bran-water] and when boiling add grana. Put in the cloth and give 5 turns with the winch (Fig. 26). Take out and let cool. Wash in running water. Pass through two or three bran-baths, each containing 1 pound of roche alum and of tartar. If the colour is heavy, give another bran-bath with 1 pound of roch alum, boiling for $\frac{1}{4}$ hour.

The exact shades represented by mediæval colour-words must remain somewhat obscure. Actual specimens of fabrics are always faded: moreover, we cannot judge of them from the costumes shown in mediæval pictures, for painters could only represent these by means of their pigments, which could not always render the colour of dyed cloth or silk; furthermore, many mediæval pictures have much faded. Doubtless many of the reds used by painters to depict garments were compounded of the very permanent vermilion and the more fugitive madder, brasil or folium (p. 123), in which case the latter would have faded, leaving the bright scarlet vermilion. We could probably discover much by dyeing fabrics with the old materials (many of them, however, no longer articles of commerce) and by the old methods—as far as the often obscure recipes reveal them. I suspect that such an investigation would show that the fabrics of the Middle Ages were not of the vermilion-scarlet and ultramarine blue beloved of the nineteenth-century painter of historical subjects, but of a much more sober range of crimsons, clarets, roses and indigos. Thus, for example, when the cardinals assumed their red dress in 1464, it was of the colour we call crimson, dyed with kermes and alum, and not of the brilliant scarlet of to-day, which was then unknown. It was not until the early seventeenth century that someone, probably Cornelius Drebbel, discovered the dyeing of true scarlet from cochineal by the use of a solution of tin-salts as a mordant. Thereafter the word ' scarlet ' came to be applied to this colour, and finally to it alone, the word ' crimson ' being kept for the old colour derived from kermes and alum. The tin mordant was first used in Holland, but it was soon introduced into England and elsewhere and the resulting scarlet remained the most brilliant of colours until the advent of aniline dyes.

A third important red was brasil, or brazil, from which the South American country took its name. Brasil is the wood of the tree *caesalpinia echinata*, from Ceylon and the East Indies; it dyed a red or reddish-brown with alum mordant. When South America was discovered, another ' brazil tree '—a different species of *caesalpinia*—was discovered there, and its name was given to the country.

A fourth red was given by *lac*, a resin mentioned on p. 85, and a fifth by *archil*. Archil is an ancient dye made from lichens growing by the sea. The lichens were powdered and mixed with stale urine and lime; they formed a reddish-violet paste which dyed a reddish-violet with alum mordant. The Greeks and Romans called it *fucus* (sea-weed), and it was much used both as a cosmetic and as a means of imitating the true and very costly purple (p. 124). It was employed till very recently for dyeing in conjunction with indigo. The plant *rocella tinctoria*, growing near the sea in Mediterranean lands, seems also to have been termed archil, though it was a totally different material.

The chief addition to these red pigments after the discovery of America was log-wood, an extract of which survived for a long time as a red ink and which, as hæmatoxylin, still affords a useful microscope stain. This is probably the only natural dye at present in regular industrial use.

None of these reds was fast to light, and consequently it is doubtful whether the still beautiful colours of red mediæval vestments give us much idea of their appearance when they were new.

Purple Dyes

The word ' purple ' is here taken to signify the range of colours between blue and red. The word was used in the Middle Ages to denote some shades we would call red, *e.g.* that of the crimson robes of a cardinal. We know, however, what the purple of the ancients was like, for specimens have survived and it has been reproduced in modern times. The colour of these fabrics is of a very dark brownish- or blackish-violet—a tint to which the modern eye does not accord the same measure of approval as did the ancient.

Purple is derived from a number of species of shell-fish of the genera *murex, purpura* and *helix*. These possess a gland filled with a creamy liquid which, when exposed to air and light, changes through yellow, green and blue to the typical dark purple, the active principle of which is 6-6'-dibromindigo. Like indigo it is insoluble in water and very fast to light and washing.

Centres of the purple industry can be recognized by the accumulation of shells, and the earliest we know of was in Crete, about 2000 B.C. The dye has not been identified on any ancient Egyptian fabrics, but in Greek and Roman times the dyeing of purple was a large industry centred on the Phœnician towns of Tyre and Sidon. The shell-fish are found throughout the Mediterranean and many minor centres of purple-dyeing sprang up.

The usual technique of purple-dyeing was to crush and boil up the fresh shell-fish and dye with the extract. It seems that the dye-material was taken up in some state prior to the formation of the insoluble 6-6'-dibromindigo and that the dye itself developed on removal of the fabric from the bath. Different shades were produced by using two or more different species of shell-fish, and other dyes such as archil and kermes were combined with it. Many shades were thus produced, but if any of our surviving specimens ever contained archil or kermes, doubtless these fugitive colours have long ago faded. The smell of decayed shell-fish associated with purple-dyeing was bad enough to have excited mention in an age not so sensitive as our own.

Fabrics dyed in purple commanded very high prices: the dye was regarded as a precious material comparable with gold and silver, and in the earliest alchemical works of the first or second centuries of the Christian era we find numerous recipes for imitating it with less precious and stable dyes, such as archil. Purple continued to be dyed at Byzantium until its conquest by the Turks in 1453, but thereafter it became a lost art.

The Secrets of Dyeing

Dyeing was always something of a mystery. In the Middle

Fig. 26. Dye-vat and winch (*Plictho*, Venice, 1540).

FIG. 27.   Dyeing skeins (*Plictho*, Venice, 1540).

Kingdom of Egypt it was a temple industry, and in Ptolemaic times a royal monopoly.   The dyer might not be highly thought of, for he was stained and often stank abominably, but he was a craftsman of great skill who usually kept his secrets to himself.   Very little has been recorded about dyeing methods and the recipes that remain are often very obscure. There are, however, a few useful records.   Thus we have an account of how the fifteenth-century Florentines obtained various colours by mixing dyes:

Dye	Colour
Kermes	Blood red or peach.
Kermes and brasil . .	Royal scarlet, Parisian red, old rose.
Fine kermes . . .	Scarlet.
Weld	Yellow.

Dye		Colour
Orange and fine kermes	.	Orange.
Fine kermes and weld	.	Golden yellow.
Orange, kermes and fustic	.	Dull orange.
Kermes and fustic	.	Quince.
Fine kermes and fustic	.	Yolk yellow.
Fustic and weld	.	Sulphur yellow.
Weld and woad	.	Sea blue.
Weld and fustic	.	Lemon.

Despite the general air of mystery there are one or two manuscripts and early printed books which give useful records. The most interesting is a fifteenth-century manuscript from Bologna, by Cennino Cennini, which has been more than once printed. The recipes that appear there are very clear and practical.

In addition to the more famous dyes here described, not a few plants were used by country people as distinguished from professional dyers. Thus, for example, heather and white clover flowers (which contain small quantities of quercitrin) can be used to dye wool in various shades of yellow and brown; doubtless many other plants were used in this way.

CHAPTER TEN

Cleansing

WE are rightly inclined to think of the last hundred years as being those in which the value of cleanliness was first adequately appreciated. It is true that the connection of cleanliness with health was first elucidated by the sanitarians and bacteriologists of the nineteenth century, but in every age—even in the Dark Ages—there were means of cleansing human beings and their clothes, for reasons of beauty, comfort and health. In the nineteenth and early twentieth centuries the cleansing agent *par excellence* was soap, which has, however, been supplanted for most purposes, other than that of washing the skin, by many chemically-prepared detergents. In the Middle Ages and earlier periods many other cleansing agents were employed.

Detergent Alkalis in Use before the Nineteenth Century

Alkalis can be used as detergents, and the most ancient seems to be the kind of soda which mineralogists call ' natron ' but which the Romans called *nitrum*. This was obtained from the natron lakes of Egypt, which still yield large quantities of the material. It consists of sodium carbonate with some bicarbonate, sulphate and chloride, and may be thought to have had much the same efficacy as modern washing-soda. The ' nitre ' referred to in the Bible as a detergent is this same *nitrum*. It seemed to the Egyptians to be a divine and purifying substance and was used by them in the process of mummification.

The other chief source of alkali was the ashes of plants. The ashes of wood and of most land-plants contain a proportion of potassium carbonate, which when extracted with water and evaporated to dryness is called potash.

The ashes of certain salt-marsh plants, notably the shrub *salsola soda*, already alluded to on p. 75, contain a

PLATE VII

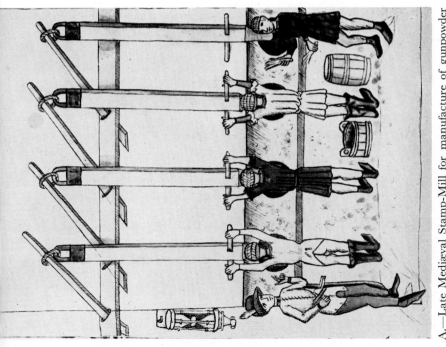

A.—Late Mediæval Stamp-Mill for manufacture of gunpowder (see p. 109).

B.—Filling bombs and soaking fuses in saltpetre (see p. 109).

PLATE VIII   A.—Woad Mill at Parson Drove, Wisbech (see p. 119).

B.—Eighteenth Century Pharmacy, Interior (see p. 143).

notable proportion of sodium carbonate—up to 20%. This material may have been known to the Egyptians, and it was certainly a very important article of commerce from the early Middle Ages till the early nineteenth century. It was then known as *rocchetta* or *barilla* and was the chief source of hard soap. Finally the fused ashes of sea-weeds—*kelp* or *varec*— contained both sodium and potassium carbonates and were extensively used in the eighteenth and early nineteenth centuries.

A practical distinction between these products was made from the earliest times, but it was not until 1739 that the Frenchman Geoffroy explained it by proving that barilla had the same base as common salt, whereas potash had not.

Another alkali available from early times was ammonium carbonate, contained in stale urine; ammonia (*i.e.* the solution of ammonia gas in water) was made by the Arab chemists, but up to the eighteenth century was used only for medicinal purposes. Solutions of alkalis were generally known as *lye*, which word properly represents a solution made by extracting the soluble parts of ashes with water.

Detergents in Egypt and Mesopotamia

Natron was an important article of commerce from the earliest times, for not only was it used as a cleanser and mummifying agent but also as an ingredient in the mixtures which, when fused, gave glass and glazes (pp. 60, 69). Natron was not the only detergent used in Egypt, and its severe action on the skin would militate against its general use for washing the body ; it is recorded, indeed, that pounded lupins were used for cleansing the hands after eating.

Did the ancient peoples possess soap? From Mesopotamia we hear of the use not only of alkalis but also of oil and alkali. Oil and alkali are both cleaning agents and it was natural to use them together. If the alkali were used as a very strong lye or if it were boiled with the oil, soap would result. In the later periods of the Egyptian culture a material called *antchir* was used for personal washing, and the Copts, who preserved in their language many ancient Egyptian forms, later used the word to denote what we call soap. The Ebers papyrus, which is concerned with medical matters and was written about 1550 B.C., several times mentions the boiling of oil or fat with alkalis, so that the discovery of some sort of soap is at least possible. In Græco-Roman Egypt, however, there does not seem to be any mention of true soap, but we hear that the washers of textiles used a mixture of castor-oil and lye. We seem, indeed, to have no evidence of the existence of solid soap, as distinguished from mixtures of oils and alkalis, in Egypt or Mesopotamia; we must therefore consider the possession of soap by these civilizations as a question not yet settled.

Detergents used by the Greeks and Romans

The Greeks and Romans before the Christian era seem to have been without soap. Oil was much used for cleansing the skin, and the Greeks supplemented it by mechanical detergents, such as bran, sand, ashes and pumice-stone. The cleansing of clothes and woollen textile materials was carried out by treading the material or beating it with stones or a wooden mallet, in presence of fuller's earth together with an alkali, which was either natron or potash lye, or more usually ammonia, in the form of stale urine. The latter was collected by the Roman fullers, who put out pitchers at the street corners. Repellent as it seems to us, stale urine was used for cleansing clothes from Roman times right up to the nineteenth century, when it was still in use on sailing-ships for that purpose: it is still used by the Eskimos.

The Greeks and Romans also used soap-root (the modern *gypsophila struthium*) as a detergent. This plant contains the complex organic substances known as saponins, which lather like soap and are excellent media for washing delicate textiles. The use of saponin-rich plants for this purpose continued throughout the Middle Ages and later; thus Gerarde's *Herbal* (1597) speaks of 'saponaria or fullers-grasse'. In India use was and is still made of soap-nuts or berries from *sapindus* species. Soap-bark, the modern source of saponins, is from *quillaia*, a South American genus.

The Origin of Soap

True soap is mentioned by several authors of the first century onward. It was regarded as a Gaulish invention and was thought of as a cosmetic for making the hair yellow; but since there is no evidence that soap bleaches the hair, perhaps the yellowness was not so much produced as revealed. It is thought that soap (*sapo*) is a Teutonic or perhaps a Tartar word. The Scythians seem to have used a kind of soap for washing or anointing the head, and it may well be that soap was a Tartar invention. Most of the references to soap in classical authors are to its use in medical preparations, but Galen has a passage that seems to show that in his time (*c*. A.D. 150) it was a normal means of washing. Dioscorides, a century earlier, speaks of the use of powdered and sifted earth or clay shaken from the roots of the nard plant (and presumably scented thereby) for cleansing the hands; so presumably soap was not used for that purpose.

At this point we may note that the only soluble non-volatile alkalis known to the ancients were carbonates of sodium or potassium. Oils and fats are saponified very slowly, if at all, by sodium or potassium carbonate, but very easily with caustic soda or potash, which can be obtained by heating the carbonates with lime. Mediæval soap-makers ' sharpened ' their lyes by adding quicklime to them and boiling, and this invention was essential to the soap industry. The ancients knew that lime made their lyes sharper and, since they made soap, we must think it at least probable that they, too, causticized their lyes with lime.

Mediæval Soap-making

No records of the methods of soap-making used by the ancients or in the early Middle Ages have survived, but from later records we may suppose that the process, in general terms, consisted of boiling lye with lime, taking off the clear liquor and then heating this with some kind of oil or fat. If the lye was made from wood-ashes it yielded a potash-soap— *i.e.* soft soap; if from barilla or rocchetta or from natron it yielded a soda-soap, *i.e.* hard soap. Hard soaps were preferred, as to-day, but were much more expensive than soft soaps.

The history of soap between classical times and the thirteenth century is obscure. In late classical times it was evidently produced on an industrial scale, for in A.D. 385 a ' saponarius ', a soap-maker, is mentioned by Theodorus Priscianus. The Arabs, who had access to soda-ash, manufactured hard soap, and at a later period scented soap was widely exported from Damascus as a luxury. In mediæval Europe soap is first mentioned in a French document dating from *c.* A.D. 800., the Carolingian capitulary *De Villis et Curtis*: here it is prescribed that some of the hands on the farms should be experienced in boiling soap. Evidently it was even then more than an article of luxury. In England it is mentioned in a ninth-century document and in the Saxon leechdoms or medical works.

The soaps that were made in the northern countries by the action of wood-ash lyes on animal fats and fish-oils were probably soft soaps of unpleasant odour. In the Mediterranean countries, on the other hand, soap was made with olive oil and the ash of the soda-plant, which process yielded a hard white odourless soap, exported as an article of luxury. This industry flourished in Spain as early as the twelfth century; Castile soap has indeed a history of some 800 years. In the fourteenth century Marseilles became the chief centre, and thereafter Venice, which imported great quantities of soda-ash (rocchetta) from the East for this purpose and also for the making of glass. Soap was exported to England from all these localities and also from Smyrna.

In England we hear of the soap-maker's trade being centred about Bristol as early as 1180. Coventry is also alluded to in this connection. The chief product seems to have been a soft or potash soap made from tallow and wood-ashes. This was known as speckled or grey soap. This soap was fairly expensive. In 1523 it sold at a penny a pound, equivalent at least to two shillings of modern money. Much soap was made from whale-oil, but this had an offensive smell. Thus, according to Stow, there were in Queen Elizabeth's reign three kinds of soap:

(1) Coarse soap, made with whale-oil.

(2) Sweet soap, made with Seville olive oil.

(3) Speckled or grey soap, made with tallow.

The Bristol manufacture remained important until Charles I ruined it by granting a monopoly to a company of soap-makers at Westminster. Much soap was doubtless made at home, especially in the country.

Mediæval Uses of Soap

Soap is generally written of in the Middle Ages as something used for cleaning textiles and clothes, and, indeed, it is difficult to say whether it was widely used for personal washing. We learn, for example, from his accounts that King John had a bath about once in three weeks, but there is no item recording the provision of soap. It may be noted that Queen Elizabeth I had a bath only about once in four weeks, and there is no reason to suppose much improvement in these matters before the middle of the eighteenth century. The earliest explicit record of the use of soap for personal washing seems to be in the time of Chaucer, when Robert, Marquis of Dublin, granted a licence ' to make tallow for washing the faces; and to set up a boiler in the city of Dublin and fill casks not more than twenty gallons.' This ' tallow ' was presumably soap. There is, however, a much earlier passage in a homily dating from *c.* 1175: ' She smeareth herself with face-powder, which is the devil's soap.' It seems unlikely that such a phrase would have been used if soap were not then recognized as a normal means of washing the face.

We know that hard soap, which was pleasant to use for toilet purposes, was being imported from Genoa across the Alps in the thirteenth century. We may suppose, then, that in the Middle Ages hard soap, made from the olive oil and soda-ash of Spain (p. 75) and the Levant, was imported for toilet purposes into the northern countries that had no soda; while the soft potash-soaps for industrial and household uses were manufactured in these northern countries, including England, from indigenous fats and locally-burned ashes. This was evidently a large industry, for in the fifteenth century, when Britain became the world's great manufactory of woollen cloth, it was necessary to import ashes from the Baltic countries to satisfy the demands of the fullers and soap-makers for lye. These were known as Dantzic ashes.

Soap-making from the Sixteenth Century

No clear account of the way that soap was made has survived from the mediæval period. An early recipe is contained in that interesting book *The Secrets of Master Alexis of Piedmont*, written about 1547:

Take strong lye, with two parts of the ashes of the wood of the tree called in latin *cerrus*, which is a kind of tree like to a poplar, having a straight long stem bearing a kind of mast, rough without like a Chestin, and one part of quicklime, and make it so strong that it may bear a new laid egg swimming between two waters (*cf.* p. 135). Take eight potfulls of this lye very hot, a potful of deer's grease or suet well strained clean: mingle them and set them on the fire, but see that they seeth not. Put all in a great vessel leaded within having a large bottom, leaving it in Summer in the Sun, and stirring it four or five times a day with a stick, and note that you must set it in the day time in the sun and the night time in the air abroad, so that it rain not, continuing thus the space of eight days. Let it wax as firm and as hard as you will, so that it remain nevertheless in the form of paste, and the older it is the better it will be. Then afterwards take of this mass or paste, as much as you will, and put it in a vessel leaded, stirring it well with a stick, and add to the same as much fine Musk Rose water as you will: keep it eight days in the sun, stirring it from time to time, as is aforesaid; and if it wax too hard, put Rose Water to it, in such quantity, that it be neither too hard nor too soft, and fill as many little boxes withal, as you will.

This is a typical prescientific soap recipe, and the testing of the strength of the lye by floating a new-laid egg on it remained in use at least until the latter part of the eighteenth century.

The cold method here described was, however, less usual than the method of repeatedly boiling the fat with weaker lye until it was saponified, as described below.

We may perhaps date the awareness of the possibility of scientific soap-making from the seventeenth century, when the Royal Society turned its attention to this trade, as to so many others. Thus there exists in the British Museum a hitherto unpublished account of soap-making dating from the latter part of the seventeenth century. This recipe contains the first record of the important operation of salting-out. In this process, which is still in use, salt is added to the hot soap solution formed by the boiling of the oil and the lye. The soap is thrown out of the solution and comes to the surface, where it solidifies on cooling to a mass containing only some 30% of water. This can easily be separated from the lye and glycerine below it, and the process is thus very much shortened. The seventeenth-century recipe referred to above is part of a manuscript book of technical recipes collected by the physician Theodore Turquet de Mayerne (1573–1655) and 'Jo. Colladon', whom I have not been able to identify. It is not dated, but other dates in the book indicate that it is earlier than 1675. The spelling and punctuation are modernized.

To make soap of tallow

Take strong lye and melt your tallow therein and when it is melted make it to boil and presently put in a good quantity of more lye and let it stand without boiling for the space of one hour. Then with a knife or stick try whether it rope [*i.e.* draw out into a thread]; if it rope not about a yard long, then put in more lye, letting it stand as before. And when it ropeth so long, take up a little upon a slate, and when it is cold taste it with your tongue and if it be very sharp then boil it no more: but if it be not sharp, then put in more lye and boil it and be still tasting of it with your tongue until it be as sharp as you please; then strew in salt and take up a little of it upon your slate, and if the lye part from the tallow, then there is salt enough in, but if they part not, put in more salt until that they do part, then boil it as fast as you can, at the least one hour, and then if you dip in a skimmer and hold the one side downwards, you shall perceive the soap run down the skimmer like flakes of snow. Then put both soap and lye into a tub and when it is cold, melt it upon a small lye, keeping it ready to boil and be still putting in of lees, until it be as hard as you please . . . coffin the lye and soap together, so they will be but one body, but beware in your boiling that you boil it not too much.

Salting-out came into general use in England in the eighteenth century, but does not seem to have been adopted in France until near the beginning of the nineteenth century. The reason for its slow adoption in both countries may have been the heavy duties on salt, the removal of which in the early nineteenth century was a great encouragement to chemical industry.

A good account of French eighteenth-century soap-making is given in the *Encyclopédie* (Tome XIV. 1765). The soap-makers took Alicante soda (barilla) and broke it with hammers. An equal bulk of quicklime was slaked, mixed with the soda and charged into a vat. Water was allowed to percolate through it and form a lye, which escaped through a hole at the bottom. This lye was tested by floating a fresh egg on it: the lye which floated the egg on its side was said to be strong; the next portion in which the egg still floated, but vertically, was called medium; and that in which the egg sunk so as to rest ' between two waters ', *i.e.* above the stronger lye but below the weaker, was the ' weak ' lye. In the boiling-vat was first placed a little weak lye and then the whole of the oil. The mixture was heated till the lye boiled, and then weak

lye was added until there were signs of coagulation. Then the
medium lye was added until the consistency of the mixture was

FIG. 28.   Soap works from the *Grande Encyclopédie* (eighteenth century).

fairly thick, and last of all some of the strong lye. The mixture
was then allowed to cool and formed a paste above with liquid
below. The paste was removed and boiled with more lye

until it became of the consistency of honey. It was then cooled and transferred to large wooden chests or boxes with perforated bottoms, where the watery solution drained away from the soap. When the soap was hard enough it was cut up into blocks.

The chemistry of soap-making was not understood until 1811–23, when it was cleared up by the researches of Chevreul. Thus in the eighteenth century soap was considered to be ' composed of oil and alkaline salt, united in such a way that both substances can dissolve simultaneously in water and form a homogeneous mixture where there appears no sign of either.' It was not, in fact, recognized as a chemical compound.

CHAPTER ELEVEN

Pharmacy

Prescientific Pharmacy

THE ancient pharmacy consisted for the most part in the collecting of natural animal, vegetable and mineral materials believed to be active in the cure of disease; and, if necessary, preparing and mixing these so as to produce a medicine suitable for administration or external application. There was little in these processes that was strictly chemical: rather were they a sort of arcane cookery. The essentially chemical processes of pharmacy—namely, the making of new substances and the extraction of pure substances from complex mixtures—were, it is true, employed even in ancient times, but became an important feature only in the period of enthusiasm for mineral medicines which began in the sixteenth century. In this brief account we shall not be considering pharmacy in its true function, the provision of medicines for the cure of disease, but only in so far as it contributed to chemistry. From this point of view, we see in pharmacy four chief stages:

(1) The gathering and treatment of herbs and animal products.

(2) The preparation of ' spirits ' or distilled products.

(3) The preparation of active extracts.

(4) The preparation of new chemical compounds.

Pharmacy in Egypt and Assyria

The Egyptians and Mesopotamians used a great variety of materials in the preparation of medicines, but it is not often easy to identify them. Plants, animal products and minerals were all employed: the majority were probably inactive and were perhaps adopted on account of some supposed magical virtue. The Greeks and Romans remarked on the profusion of drugs known to the Egyptians, but the Sumerians and Assyrians seem to have employed a still wider range, for over 500 drug names are found in their texts. It is probable that the Assyrian pharmacopœia was the source of much of the Greek knowledge about drugs.

It seems that the pharmacists of Egypt and Babylon used almost exclusively natural products or the by-products of other arts, *e.g.* of metallurgy or the making of pigments, and they do not seem to have prepared new substances for use in pharmacy. Their processes of preparation included boiling, roasting, straining, expression, filtration, pounding, grinding and fermentation. The Egyptian pharmacists or physicians weighed out their drugs with some accuracy, but the Assyrians do not generally specify quantities.

We may think, then, of the most ancient pharmacology as having contributed some chemical technique but as being only on the margin of the chemical art.

Greek and Roman Pharmacy

A great deal was written about drugs in classical times, but perhaps the most informative and influential work was the *De Materia Medica* of Dioscorides. There is still, however, very little chemistry in it. The chief recourse of the physician was still the products of plants and animals. These were variously prepared by grinding, boiling and so forth; an advance is perhaps to be noted in the number of materials administered as ' wines,' *i.e.* as solutions made by steeping the solid drug in wine. We must not suppose that the men of the time were aware that they were extracting an active substance from the crude drug, for they were much more likely to think in terms of an ' influence ' or ' virtue ' passing from the drug to the wine.

The most interesting part of the work of Dioscorides is the account he gives of the products of minerals and metals, amounting to about a hundred different preparations. The use of mineral remedies was, of course, prevalent in Egypt and Assyria; moreover, we are told that Crateuas, from whose work that of Dioscorides [1] may largely derive, used mineral remedies before 100 B.C. Most of these were not truly chemical preparations but native minerals or industrial products, such as pigments or metallurgists' residues; in a few cases, however, preparations are described. Thus he tells how to make copper sulphide (' burnt copper ') by heating ships' nails with sulphur

[1] Galen. XV. 134.

and salt; verdigris by exposing copper to the fumes of vinegar; 'vermicular verdigris' by grinding copper with vinegar, alum, salt, etc.; 'washed lead' by grinding water in a leaden mortar and filtering off the black deposit. He gives the earliest description of sublimation in his account of the making of mercury (p. 51), and of a sort of distillation in his preparation of oil of pitch by heating pitch and condensing the vapour in fleeces.

We may judge from the works of Dioscorides that the pharmacist of the first century not only compounded simples but actually made a few of them.

Early Poisons

The poisoner was certainly well enough known in antiquity. Apparently vegetable alkaloids (*e.g.* the hemlock draught of Socrates) were used, and also the poisons of serpents. We must think it improbable that any very recondite poisons were used before the era of modern chemistry. The preparation of white arsenic was known to the alchemists of the early centuries of the Christian era, who employed it in the colouring of metals: this drug does not seem to have been known to the pharmacists of the period and it may have been employed as a secret poison, being well-nigh tasteless and, in the days before chemical analysis, impossible to detect. The inability to detect poisons worked both ways for evil. Not only did the poisoner remain undiscovered but many who died from natural causes must have been supposed to be poisoned.

The Arab Pharmacists

The Arabs were highly-skilled physicians and possessed a wide range of drugs, including some tropical plants not known to the Greeks. An interesting text which throws light upon the more chemical side of Arab pharmacy is 'The Dispenser's Book' (*Liber Servitoris*) of Khalaf ibn 'Abbas al-Zahrawi, usually known as Albucasis (*fl. ca.* 1000): this work was translated into Latin at an early period and had a considerable influence on the mediæval pharmacist. It is of particular interest because its purpose is to tell the reader how to prepare the 'simples' from which were compounded the complex drugs then generally used. The author deals, of course, with medicines from plants and animals, but he also gives methods of preparing litharge, white lead, lead sulphide (burnt lead), burnt copper, cadmia, marcasite, yellow arsenic and lime, the various vitriols, salt, natron, *crocus martis*, etc. Some of his recipes derive from Dioscorides. He also gives a considerable number of recipes for distilled products, though not alcoholic ones; thus he distils ' waters ' from plants, and a peculiar ' oil of bricks ', which was the product of the dry distillation of pieces of brick saturated with old vegetable oil; the red volatile product probably contained a good deal of acrolein.

The greater pårt of the mediæval pharmacy is of little interest to the chemist, consisting as it does of preparing mixtures of dozens or even hundreds of vegetable and animal drugs. The beginning of distillation as a means of preparing drugs is perhaps the most significant feature: further details of this trend and its results are given in Chapter Twelve.

Chemical Remedies

A new current in pharmacy started from Paracelsus and his followers. By what means this strange man convinced himself that mineral remedies were much more valuable than the prevalent Galenicals is not altogether clear. He believed, of course, in the correspondence of the metals with the planets and tried to extract from the metals a volatile quintessence. His process would seem to have resulted, it is true, only in dilute solutions of acids containing no metal, but he had started an idea. Moreover, Paracelsus hailed from the region of the world where practical chemical operations were in progress, namely, the mining districts of Central Europe, and he had a knowledge of the many and remarkable compounds of metals. His followers, especially Andreas Libavius, followed him in this respect. Mercurial medication for syphilis gained a great reputation in the sixteenth century. *The Triumphal Chariot of Antimony* (1604), attributed to the supposed fifteenth-century monk Basil Valentine, but probably written by the German salt-manufacturer Thölde, described the preparation of physiologically active compounds of antimony. Others, such as J. R. Glauber, described simple inorganic compounds not previously known, and, to cut a long story short, the use of inorganic compounds as remedies, internal and external, steadily gained ground. In the sixteenth and early seventeenth centuries they were still felt to be unorthodox but were begin-

Fig. 29. Pharmacy, as illustrated by Jerome Braunschwe.g, c. 1510.

ning to be recognized. Thus the London Pharmacopœia of
1618 recommends several, but the Cologne Pharmacopœia of
1627 gives hardly any of them. A hundred years later they
had taken their place as the most favoured of official remedies.

Beginnings of a Fine-chemical Industry

Of what use were these inorganic salts in medicine? Not
very much perhaps; but, as a class, they were at least as
valuable as the herbal remedies that were their alternative.
Very few of either have survived into the modern pharmacopœias. Be this as it may, this interest in chemical remedies
was the means of encouraging the study of inorganic chemistry
and the rudiments of chemical manufacture. A large number
of inorganic compounds had to be prepared in quantities.

The official pharmacopœias and dispensatories always gave directions for the making of such chemical remedies as they included. Originally these remedies were made by the individual druggist, and in some countries legislation forbade their wholesale manufacture and sale. This prohibition began to be relaxed about the end of the seventeenth century, and it is certain that by 1700 in England certain firms of pharmacists were preparing chemicals on the large scale and selling them to the local apothecaries, physicians and farriers. These firms may be thought to be the root of the fine-chemical industry, as the alkali manufacturers were of the heavy-chemical industry. None-the-less the local druggist generally continued to make mineral drugs until the close of the eighteenth century. The finished drugs were evidently not thought of as materia medica; thus a collection of 1,032 specimens of materia medica dated 1729, and now in the Museum of the History of Science, Oxford, does not contain such drugs as tartar emetic, *crocus martis*, Epsom salts, magnesia, etc., but simply the materials from which such drugs could be made. These were the metals steel, tin, copper, brass, silver, gold, mercury, spelter and bismuth; various metalliferous minerals and products of other industries, such as chalcitis, stibnite, cinnabar, cadmia, verdigris, red lead, white lead, plumbago, litharge, pyrites, marcasite, iron slag, copper ore, spodium, tutia, hæmatite, calamine, rock alum, plume alum, sal-ammoniac, borax, common salt, rock salt, white arsenic, orpiment, realgar, green vitriol, white vitriol, blue vitriol, tartar, nitre and sulphur.

These are all products of other industries or native minerals; it would be the task of the pharmacist, retail or wholesale, to work them up into the drugs described in the succeeding sections.

Chemical Remedies in Use in the Eighteenth Century

Let us now survey the variety of drugs used in medicine and farriery in the middle of the eighteenth century. We will leave aside the many vegetable and animal materials, for all that was done to these by the chemist was to prepare extracts, *i.e.* oily, vinous, acetous or alcoholic solutions of them, or to distil from them volatile products. We shall therefore rather glance at the main types of inorganic medicines.

Salts of the Alkali Metals

In the early eighteenth century the notion of forming a salt by neutralizing an acid with an alkali was firmly established (Chapter Thirteen).

The sources of potassium salts were wood-ashes, tartar and saltpetre. By extracting the first with water and evaporating the solution, 'pearl-ash', a fairly pure potassium carbonate, was made: 'salt of tartar', an even purer potassium carbonate, was made by calcining tartar until the carbon had burnt off it. By letting salt of tartar deliquesce in moist air a strong solution of potassium carbonate, 'oil of tartar', was obtained. This could be 'sharpened' to a very powerful caustic by heating it with lime. Solid caustic potash was made by boiling Russian potash and quicklime with water, evaporating the clear solution, till the liquid solidified on cooling. This was used as an actual caustic.

Up to about 1750 it was common to prescribe the 'salts' of various plants; thus salt of wormwood was the extract from ashes of the wormwood plant: about this period, however, it was realized that all the salts of plants were identical with pearl-ash in a more or less impure condition, and that this was the same substance as salt of tartar, which discoveries went far to simplify the pharmacist's art.

The acetate of potash (or soda) was 'diuretic salt': the chloride was 'coagulated spirit of salt'. About this time saltpetre was realized to be identical with the salt formed from *aqua fortis* and potash.

Potassium sulphate appeared under a host of titles. A whole series of products were made by deflagrating nitre. With charcoal it gave 'fixed nitre' or sal prunellæ, which was mainly potassium carbonate; with various quantities of sulphur it gave sal polychrestum and sal enixum. These were no more than mixtures of potassium sulphate with unchanged nitre, and when they were purified they became identical with the salt made by mixing salt of tartar with vitriolic acid, and known as 'vitriolated tartar'. This again soon came to be identified with 'vitriolated nitre', the product of the action of sulphuric acid on excess of nitre strongly heated.

Among sodium salts, soda (sodium carbonate) was well enough known in the impure forms of natron, barilla and kelp, as also was caustic soda made by 'sharpening' solutions of these with lime. Sodium sulphate (Glauber's salt) was made by distilling common salt with oil of vitriol, adding sea-salt or kelp, and strongly heating the residue. It was distinguished from magnesium sulphate by the fact that it gave no precipitate with soluble carbonates (fixed alkali).

Borax was known as a native product (tincal or tincar) but its nature was not understood. Boric acid was made from it by the action of acids, but was thought to be a salt, which was called *sal sedativum* because it appeared to have a calming effect on maniacs.

Sodium nitrate, known as 'cubic nitre', was made by dissolving chalk in nitric acid, adding Glauber's salt, filtering off the calcium sulphate and crystallizing the filtrate.

Common salt was familiar enough, but various kinds were distinguished. The name *sal gemmæ* was given to rock-salt; sea-salt, containing magnesium chloride, etc., was prescribed for many purposes.

Ammonia and ammonium compounds had been known since the Arabic period. Ammonium chloride (sal-ammoniac) was made by burning cow-dung, and also by mixing bittern (the residue of the brine of sea-water from which salt had been crystallized) with stale urine, evaporating it to dryness and subliming the volatile salt. In the eighteenth century ammonia was often made by heating sal-ammoniac with lime, but was also still made by distilling horn or bones or other animal refuse, whence its name of *spirit of hartshorn*. Ammonium nitrate (*nitrum flammans*) was made by neutralizing ammonia with nitric acid. Various preparations of ammonia, alcohol and spices were used as smelling salts and cordials.

Salts of the Alkaline Earth Metals

Of the compounds of the alkaline earth metals only those of magnesium and calcium were known. Joseph Black's researches of 1751–5 established admirably the relations of the oxides, hydroxides and carbonates of calcium and magnesium, which were previously obscure.

The magnesium compound of greatest interest was the sulphate, *sal catharticus amarus*, bitter purging salt, or Epsom salt. It was first of all prepared by evaporating the Epsom waters, but later was made from bittern, the mother liquors from the crystallization of sea-salt. The basic carbonate, magnesia alba, was called *miraculum chemicum*, ' because from two pellucid liquors a coagulum is formed '. Thus to make it Epsom salts were dissolved in water and a solution of pearl-ash added. The white precipitated carbonate was boiled with water, washed and dried. By calcining it, burnt magnesia (magnesium oxide) was obtained.

Of the calcium compounds, lime, in the form of quicklime, was used to make caustics, and it was also made into lime-water. That very familiar compound calcium carbonate appeared in many curious forms in medicine, chiefly as an ' absorbent ' for other drugs. The popular forms of calcium carbonate were the finely-ground tips of crab's claws, and also the so-called ' crab's eyes ', concretions from the stomachs of craw-fish, imported in large quantities from Russia; the wealthy used coral and pearls levigated. None of these had any greater efficacy, of course, than common chalk, which was also in use. The only other calcium compound used in pharmacy was the chloride, prepared by dissolving chalk in spirit of salt.

Compounds of Mercury and Antimony

The heavy metals were much in request, particularly mercury and antimony. The vigour of their physiological effect was not open to question, and mercury was clearly a specific remedy for syphilis. Yet outside this field they were probably of little or no value, and sometimes positively harmful.

Mercury was used in a great number of forms. The metal was administered internally and externally in a ' mortified ' form, *i.e.* ground up with powders or fatty substances until its particles became invisible, as in the ' grey ointment ' of to-day. Mercuric oxide was used in two forms, not at first recognized as identical. The first, *mercurius calcinatus*, was made by heating metallic mercury below its boiling point in a glass flask with a small air-hole. The process required months for its completion: to avoid the trouble of maintaining a fire for so long, the glass was often stood in the cooler part of some oven or furnace kept going for another purpose. The second, *mercurius corrosivus ruber*, was made by dissolving mercury in nitric acid, evaporating and heating till the mass became dry and finally bright red.

Corrosive sublimate (mercuric chloride) was well known and was made by several methods, of which the best, used in the eighteenth century, was to convert mercury into mercuric sulphate with sulphuric acid and sublime the product with salt. By subliming corrosive sublimate with metallic mercury, calomel (mercurous chloride) was obtained. This was used as a cholagogue purgative, and it was necessary to free it from the very poisonous corrosive sublimate by repeated washings.

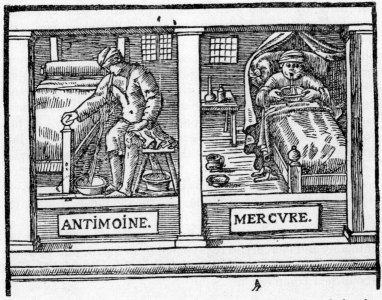

FIG. 30. Antimony as emetic and purge: mercury as antisyphilitic pushed to the point of salivation (Barlet, 1653).

The test for complete removal was to rub it on gold, which is whitened if any corrosive sublimate be present.

Other mercurials prepared in quantity were *yellow emetic mercury* (turbith or turpeth mineral), made by heating mercury with oil of vitriol and washing the white mass with water till it became bright yellow, and *white precipitate*, made by dissolving corrosive sublimate and ammonium chloride in water and precipitating the solution with a fixed alkali.

Antimony likewise was much in use. Before the nineteenth century the word was correctly applied only to the black mineral stibnite (antimony trisulphide, Sb_2S_3), while the metal was called *regulus of antimony*. By calcining the mineral until it first became grey, then melted to a liquid which solidified to a glass, a preparation called *glass of antimony*, an oxysulphide, was obtained. Antimony tetroxide was obtained as a fine powder, *flowers of antimony*, by heating the metal in air. A purified form of glass of antimony was called *cathartic antimony*. By dissolving glass of antimony in madeira wine, antimonial wine, a strong emetic, was obtained. This wine contained some *tartar emetic* (potassium antimonyl tartrate), which was also made by boiling glass of antimony with cream of tartar (purified potassium hydrogen tartrate). Tartar emetic was the chief antimonial medicine and has kept its place in the pharmacopœia till modern times. It is no longer used as an emetic, it is true, but has been found efficacious against the tropical disease kala-azar. *Crocus of antimony* was made by deflagrating stibnite with nitre and a little salt; it contained potassium sulphantimonate, potassium sulphate, etc. The volatile antimony chloride, *butter of antimony*, was made by heating antimony sulphide with mercuric chloride: it was used as a caustic. By treating antimony chloride with an excess of water the famous medicine *mercurius vitæ* or *powder of Algaroth* (antimony oxychloride) was precipitated as a white powder.

It will be seen that a considerable range of compounds of antimony and mercury were prepared by or for the pharmacists and clearly characterized, though little or nothing was known about their composition.

Compounds of the Heavy Metals

The heavy metals other than mercury and antimony were less popular with the prescribers. Copper compounds were little used. *Blue vitriol* (copper sulphate), made from copper pyrites in Sweden or Germany, or from copper and sulphuric acid, was sometimes used as an emetic, also as a mild caustic or escharotic. The only compound of silver used was the nitrate, either solid or dissolved in nitric acid. This was the famous *lunar caustic*, still occasionally employed. Gold was always thought to be a potent medicine, and 'potable gold' finds a place in nearly every recipe book. The only known soluble compound of gold was the 'chloride' (chlorauric acid) made by the action of *aqua regia* on the metal. This was dissolved in a mixture of an essential oil and alcohol, whereupon the organic compounds reduced the gold chloride and gave rise to purplish liquids which, in fact, contained colloidal gold.

Zinc was used in the form of *calamine*, the carbonate, native or precipitated, which was considered efficacious for skin diseases, as to-day. *White vitriol* (zinc sulphate) was used as an emetic and also as an application for the eyes.

In the eighteenth century bismuth, by which word the native sulphide of bismuth was then signified, was made into the insoluble subnitrate by dissolving it in nitric acid and pouring into an excess of water. The efficacy of the subnitrate in relieving indigestion was not yet known and its only use was as a face-powder, for which purpose it was perhaps less harmful than the alternatives, white lead and calomel!

Lead compounds were used, for the most part externally. Litharge, red lead and white lead had been known from antiquity, but the chief compound used in medicine was lead acetate, recommended by Thomas Goulard in 1751. This very poisonous compound, made by the action of distilled vinegar on white lead, had long been known as *sugar of lead*: a solution made by heating a quart of vinegar with a pound of litharge was *Extract of Saturn*, while *Water of Saturn* (Goulard's Water) consisted of 100 drops of the extract in a quart of water together with a little brandy. These preparations were used externally, but *Saturnine tincture* was administered internally to consumptives. It was made by macerating equal parts of lead acetate and green vitriol in spirit. Fortunately there was enough green vitriol to precipitate all the lead as the insoluble sulphate, so that the clear liquid taken contained ferrous acetate and no more than traces of lead: it was in fact a means of administering iron.

Iron was given as filings, or as ferric oxide in the form of rust or of *crocus martis*. *Martial flowers* were made by subliming ferric oxide with sal-ammoniac and consisted of ammonium chloride coloured yellow by the volatile double chloride of ammonium and ferric iron. Iron was also given as tartrate in ' chalybeate wine '. Mixtures of ferrous and ferric chlorides made by the action of spirits of salt on iron or iron oxide were dissolved in spirit of wine and administered as tincture of iron.

This survey of the inorganic drugs produced in quantity by the pharmacists of the middle of the eighteenth century must indicate at once the considerable range of their practical chemistry and the still rudimentary condition of the science. About the only chemical principle realized was that acids and bases form salts: the nomenclature of bodies was still without system and was based on the method of preparation rather than on the composition of the substances in question. All this was soon to be transformed by the *révolution chimique*.

CHAPTER TWELVE

Sugar, Alcohol and its Products

Sugar

FROM the most ancient times man has used a large number of carbohydrates as food-stuffs, but has not, as a rule, subjected the raw materials to any chemical treatment or purification; sugar is, however, an exception to this rule, for it presents one of the earliest examples of separation of a fairly pure chemical compound by crystallization.

The sugar-cane seems to have been native to the South Pacific and to have been distributed by man to every region where it will grow. It is recorded in Western India in 325 B.C., but is not mentioned in Chinese literature until A.D. 286, though it may have been grown there for several centuries before. There are records of the production of a hard white sugar in India as early as A.D. 375.

The Greeks and Romans knew of the existence of sugar, but there seems to be no evidence that it was an article of commerce before the rise of Islam. After the conquest of most of the Mediterranean region the Arabs began the cultivation of sugar-cane, which remained profitable until, in the sixteenth century, it was made uneconomic by the competition of the plantations of Madeira, of the Canaries and of the New World. Sugar was cultivated in the Middle Ages not only by the Arabs but also in Palestine, Sicily, Spain and the Greek islands, and it was an article of commerce in mediæval Europe, though honey remained the ordinary culinary sweetening agent well into the seventeenth century.

The voyages of exploration of the fifteenth and sixteenth centuries led to the establishment of sugar-plantations in the new colonies. There is controversy whether the sugar-cane was grown in the New World before the arrival of the Europeans, but the best-informed opinion is inclined to the view that it was introduced from Europe.

The simplest treatment of the juice of the sugar-cane is to boil it down to a solid mass; an advance on this is to boil it down until it sets on cooling to a semi-solid mass and then to press out of this as much of the liquid as possible. It is difficult to know the earliest date at which the crude sugar was further refined by recrystallization, but the process was probably known to the Arabs. In the fifteenth century raw sugar was imported into Venice and there refined, and in the sixteenth and seventeenth centuries the practice spread over most of Europe.

There exists no detailed account of sugar-refining earlier than the eighteenth century. At this period the raw sugar was dissolved in lime-water, and a little egg-white or blood was added; the liquid was heated and the scums were taken off. The liquid was then strained and transferred to the boiling-pan, where it was evaporated until it crystallized satisfactorily. It was then cooled and the semi-solid mass was transferred to conical clay moulds, perforated at the tip to let the mother-liquor drain off. Wet clay was laid on the sugar, whereby a little water was allowed to percolate through the mass in order to wash away the coloured mother-liquor. Finally the moulds and sugar were dried, the sugar was knocked out and formed the well-known sugar-loaves.

Many improvements followed in the late eighteenth and early nineteenth centuries. The decolorizing of syrups by wood-charcoal may date from 1794, while the more efficient animal-charcoal was introduced about 1812. The use of the vacuum-pan for evaporation was patented by the Hon. Edward Charles Howard in 1812: multiple-effect evaporation seems to have been invented by Rillieux about 1832 and put into practice in 1843. In that year also the centrifuge was first applied to the drying of sugar-crystals.

The discovery that the beet contained sugar was made by Marggraf about 1747, but it was his pupil, F. C. Achard, who worked out the practical extraction of sugar from that root. The first beet-sugar factory was erected by him, under the patronage of Frederick William III of Prussia, and began to operate in 1802. The industry had many difficulties. By 1839, however, beet-sugar constituted a twentieth of the world's output; a hundred years later this had risen to two-thirds.

Ale and Beer

The words ' ale ' and ' beer ' have been used in different senses at different periods; before the sixteenth century the word ' beer ' is rare, and ' ale ' meant the drink made from fermented malt. In the sixteenth and seventeenth centuries the word ' beer ' was brought into use to denote ale flavoured with hops. In modern times the terms ' beer ' and ' ale ' are almost synonymous. In this section ' ale ' is used to denote fermented liquor made from grain and not flavoured with hops, while ' beer ' denotes the usual hopped liquor.

The practical use of the alcoholic fermentation is of unknown antiquity. No people, however primitive, have been found to be ignorant of it. Ale is probably the oldest fermented liquor. The Egyptians and Sumerians made ale of a sort even in the earliest period of their civilizations, before 3000 B.C., and the practice may well be much older. The method used suggests that the process developed in some way from that of bread-making. Funerary models showing brewers at work have survived (Plate IX, A). The ancient Egyptians have not left us any recipes, but a much later Egyptian, the alchemist Zosimos of Panopolis (Akhmin in Egypt), wrote a work about A.D. 300 on the making of ale, and some fragments of it have survived. It is interesting to see that even at that time the chemist thought brewing to be a fit subject for his pen.

Although the recipe is rather brief and the translation of some parts is not very certain, its meaning is quite clear.

Good clean white barley is steeped for a day, then taken out and left to lie in a heap till next morning. It is then steeped again for five hours. It is placed in a perforated earthenware vessel for steeping. It is then dried, first in a still place, then in the sun. Then this barley (which would hardly be sufficiently sprouted to be called a true malt) is ground and made into loaves with leaven. The loaves are lightly baked on the surface, then broken up, mixed with water and sieved. At this stage, presumably, the main fermentation occurred. This ancient process is much like that used to make the Russian *kvass*.

The Egyptians and Sumerians were great drinkers of ale, and many kinds of ale are described. The Egyptians flavoured it with various plants, among which, however, hops were not included. The Greeks and Romans despised ale, at any rate in the earlier times. It was the national drink of the Germanic and Gallic tribes, however, and it seems that they used something like the present-day process of malting. Thus malt is mentioned by classical authors of the fourth to sixth centuries A.D., but not, apparently, earlier. Ale, of course, remained the staple drink of the Middle Ages. Hops seem to have been introduced into Germany by the eighth century A.D., but were not used in England until the sixteenth. A good account of the brewing of ale in the middle of that century is given by the famous English physician John Caius (1510-73).

The barley is covered with water and steeped for some days, until it swells up and cracks and germinates at both ends; then all the water is let out of the cistern, being of no use, and the barley is taken out. It is spread thinly on the floor and turned twice a day, in such a way that all moisture escapes, and no corruption is generated in the heap nor does the barley become mouldy. When all the moisture has disappeared, which happens in a few days, a furnace is prepared with a chamber which admits the fire but does not return it. (He then describes the drying floors and the method of drying the malt and grinding it.) The quantities of malt and water depend on the strength of the ale to be made. It is boiled in water for three or four hours and the clear reddish liquor is run off through a strainer into the shallow wooden vats and is left to cool. While it is still warm it is run off into another deeper vat; groats and new ' flower of ale ' (*i.e.* yeast) are added and stirred up with it. Then after twenty-four hours it is run off into casks, where the yeast rises to the surface and is taken off. When this process has come to an end the casks are bunged.

Beer is to be made in the same way, but hops are boiled with the malt-liquor and no groats are used.

Wine

Wine is not much less ancient than beer. It was made in ancient Egypt (before 3000 B.C.) by treading the grapes and squeezing the crushed grapes by twisting them in a cloth, the juice being fermented in jars. In ancient Egypt wine is said to have been drunk by the upper classes only; much was imported in later periods from Palestine, Syria and Greece, in all of which countries it was the principal beverage.

The process of wine-making in classical times was but little less simple. The grapes were first trodden and then pressed in a simple type of wine-press, worked in earlier times by a long lever or by wedges, later by a screw. The juice ran off into large jars or into a stone cistern or sink in the ground, where it almost at once began to ferment. The fermentation lasted about nine days. In the earliest times the wine was stored in skins, but later and more commonly in earthenware vessels, usually coated with bitumen. Where wood was abundant, casks were used. Sometimes resin or pitch or salt water was added to preserve the wine: it was also 'plastered' with marble-dust or plaster to decrease its acidity. Fragrant plants or herbs were sometimes added.

In addition to wine and beer, the ancients used to drink date-wine, palm-wine, mead and cider. The methods of wine-making used in mediæval and later periods differed very little from the ancient. Chemistry, indeed, scarcely began to affect the making of fermented liquors before the latter part of the eighteenth century.

Distillation of Spirits

Although the chemist had little to do with the technique of fermentation, he played a very important part in the develop-ment of the products of wine, especially of spirits or, as we now say, alcohol. The distillation of spirits was apparently an alchemical invention, and the development of large-scale distillation apparatus and plant was almost entirely a response to the demand for spirits.

Aristotle recognized that when wine was evaporated it condensed to a modified kind of water, but there is no evidence that he was acquainted with anything that could be called a still, or that he collected the product of condensation of the vapour of wine in any quantity.

The history of distillation is by no means free from problems, but it may be said with reasonable certainty that distillation apparatus was invented in the first century A.D. by the Hellenistic alchemists, who used it to distil 'waters' or 'spirits' by which they hoped to accomplish the transmutation of base metals into gold. Still-heads (Plate X, A) of the fifth to the eighth century A.D. have been excavated in Egypt and Syria. They were probably articles of commerce, but we do not know their purpose. The evidence that the early alchemists distilled wine, *pace* Diels, is insufficient, and it is not until the twelfth century A.D. that we find the first reference to the distilling from wine of ' a water which burns '.

In the late twelfth and the thirteenth centuries *aqua vitæ* distilled from wine was discovered to be an active medicine— a remedy for the troubles of old age—and by the end of the latter century it was being commonly distilled, though not apparently on a large scale. The apparatus employed was normally the ordinary alembic (Fig. 31). To obtain a spirit as strong as possible the distillation was performed very slowly, thus obtaining some fractionation by condensation in the ' body ' of the still. Repeated redistillation gave a spirit well over proof.

The mediæval test of the strength of spirits—which remained in use for many centuries—was to moisten a linen rag with the liquid and set it alight. If the spirit contained much water the rag was left too wet to burn: but if the rag was fired the spirit was thought to be satisfactory. A later version of this test was to put a little gunpowder in the bottom of a spoon, cover it with spirit and set fire to it. If the powder fired after the spirit had burned off it was ' proof spirit ' or stronger. The result of the test must have varied with the quantities of spirit and gunpowder used, and proof-spirit to-day is taken to be that which contains almost exactly half its weight of alcohol, though its precise definition varies from country to country.

In the fourteenth century the medicinal virtues of alcoholic distillates were much extolled by the followers of Ramon Lull. *Aqua vitæ*, or its purified form ' *circulatum* ', was believed to be the fifth element or *quintessence* of the wine, carrying with it all the virtues thereof; moreover, as a kind of ' fifth element ', it was allied to the fifth element of the celestial regions and could very readily receive the supposed virtues of the stars, which were composed of that element. Moreover, this quintessence of wine would dissolve the essential oils of plants; thus it appeared to the men of the fourteenth and later centuries that it could extract the ' virtues ' from plants, and that the resulting liquid thereby acquired the virtues of those stars to which the plants corresponded. *Aqua vitæ* came to be called ' *cœlum philosophicum* ' (the philosophers' heaven), in which the virtues of the stars could be set and brought into use at any time to heal diseases. Thus resulted a great enthusiasm for preparations similar to the modern liqueurs—alcoholic extracts of plants, probably sweetened to make them more palatable. In the fifteenth century these alcoholic preparations were found to

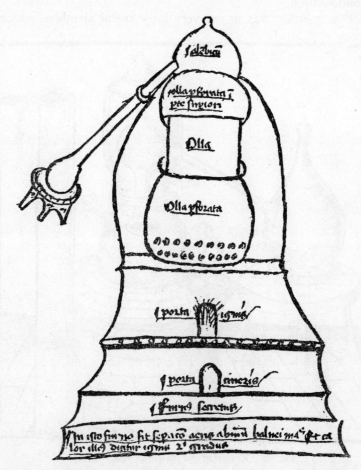

FIG. 31. Fifteenth-century still, heated by an air-bath over a charcoal furnace (courtesy of Mr. D. I. Duveen).

be very good to drink, and in the sixteenth this use of spirits and the like became widespread. Thus during these centuries the demand for alcohol much increased.

It was wasteful to use good wine for making spirits, and so the turbid residues from the bottoms of the nearly empty wine

and ale casks were commonly sold to the distillers. The glass
or pottery alembic was inadequate to condense the stream of
vapour from a large and quickly-heated vessel, and the chief
technical problem of the distiller was to secure adequate
condensation.

One solution was to use very large metal alembics, which

FIG. 32.   Rectifying still (Braunschweig, c. 1510).

gave a larger surface and one more readily cooled than glass;
another was to use a water-cooled metal tube as condenser.
This latter, the modern method of condensation, was certainly
used in the early fifteenth century.   Figs. 32, 33 show some
types of water-cooled condenser.

The idea of fractionation, *i.e.* removing some of the water
from the vapour by condensing a part of it before finally con-

densing the alcohol which was to be collected, is found in the sixteenth and seventeenth centuries, but there was, of course, no scientific theory of fractionation. Figs. 33, 34 show typical fractionating columns of this period.

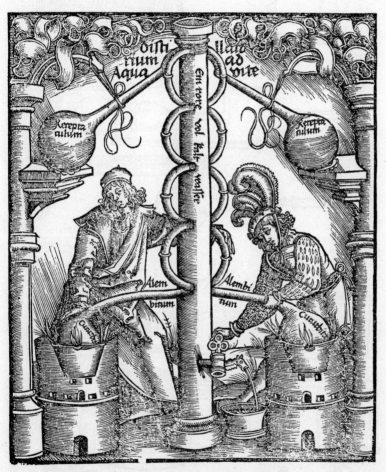

FIG. 33. Use of a fractionating column (Braunschweig, *c.* 1510).

In the seventeenth century the making of spirits had become a large-scale industry. We must, of course, distinguish the making of spirituous liquors for drinking from the making of pure alcohol. The former are required to retain the various volatile oils and esters which give them their aroma, nor need

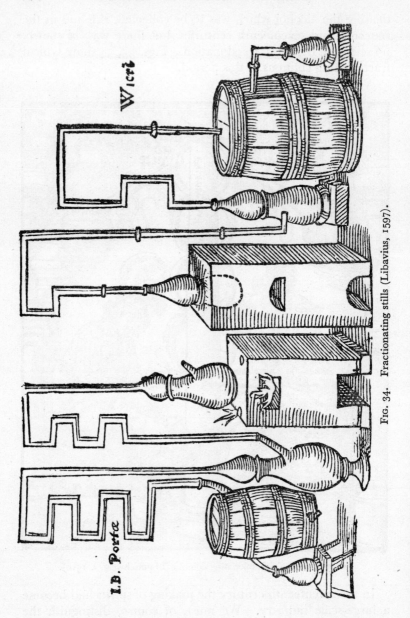

FIG. 34. Fractionating stills (Libavius, 1597).

they be freed from water; the latter must be freed from every-
thing except alcohol itself. The former were termed proof
spirits, while the purer alcohol obtained by redistillation of

PLATE IX

A.—Egyptian Funerary Model: Brewer Kneading Dough. The large vessels are presumably for fermentation, the small ones for water (see p. 153).

B.—Manufacture of Sugar: *Stradanus, c.* 1580 (see p. 152).

PLATE X

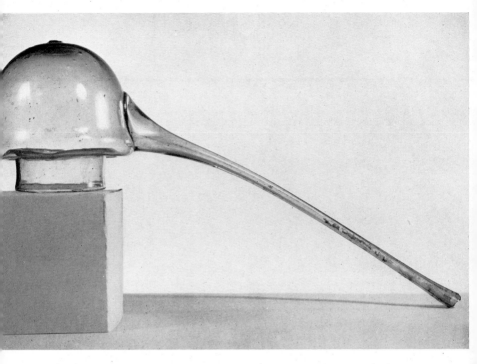

A.—Glass Alembic, Egyptian Fifth to Eighth Century (see p. 155).

B.—Apparatus used by Davy for Experiments on Soil Chemistry (see p. 172).

these was called rectified spirits, or spirits of wine. Only the most highly purified received the name of ' alcohol '.

Thus the makers of brandy and other spirits had no inducement to design efficient fractionating columns. The advances made by them were chiefly in the direction of more economical heating, *e.g.* the use of the liquor to be distilled as the cooling liquid for the condenser and the design of stills with a large heating surface. Stirrers were introduced, with the double purpose of preventing foaming and the adhesion of deposits to the bottoms of the stills.

It was not until the nineteenth century that totally new designs for stills were evolved, with a view to making distillation a continuous process capable of yielding alcohol of high strength in a single operation.

Ether

The actions of sulphuric acid and of nitric acid upon alcohol soon attracted interest and led to the discovery of ether. That the action of oil of vitriol on spirits produced a volatile substance was known to Valerius Cordus about 1544, but the practical distillation books of the seventeenth century do not mention it, and it did not attract serious attention until 1730, when Frobenius described the process in the Philosophical Transactions. Ether was at first made by mixing 1 part of sulphuric acid with five or six times its weight of alcohol, leaving the mixture for a few days and then gently distilling it. The preparation was soon improved and the continuous etherification process was set out by Cadet in 1774.

The word ' ether ' has a long and curious history. The Greek word *aether* was applied to the pure upper air—thus to the sky—and the influences supposed to descend from it. Thus a very volatile spirit could be thought of as an ' ethereal spirit '. The product of distilling alcohol with sulphuric acid was at first called ' sweet spirit of vitriol ' but was also called ' ethereal spirit '. The former name lasted well into the eighteenth century, but was gradually supplanted by the term ' aether' or ' ether' *tout court*, introduced in 1734.

Sweet Spirits of Nitre

Another new product derived from alcohol was the mixture of ethyl nitrite and nitrate known as ' sweet spirits of nitre '.

Nitric acid ('strong spirit of nitre') was dropped into three or four times its volume of rectified spirit of wine. After a few days the mixture was distilled and a volatile liquid passed over. This process seems to have been tried by the followers of Lull but, like the making of ether, to have attracted little attention before the eighteenth century.

Tartar

When wine is left to mature in cask it commonly deposits on it a hard pink to dark-red mass of *argol* or *tartar* (potassium hydrogen tartrate). This substance was of much interest to the early chemists. It was refined by recrystallization and then formed white crystals (cream of tartar).

The important substance, salt of tartar (potassium carbonate), was made by heating tartar to redness until the residue was quite white. This salt was often left to deliquesce, whereby it formed a strong alkaline solution called *oil of tartar*. A mixture of a little oil of tartar with much water was commended for the complexion; it might cleanse a greasy skin but we should to-day think it a drastic remedy.

Potassium carbonate, when added to alcohol containing some water, removes the latter, forming two liquid layers, the upper consisting of nearly pure alcohol and the lower a solution of the salt: this phenomenon was found to be a valuable means of obtaining nearly pure alcohol from rectified spirits.

Vinegar

The knowledge of vinegar must be almost as old as that of fermented liquors, which often sour spontaneously, but curiously enough it is not mentioned as having been made or used in Egypt before the Ptolemaic period. It was, however, known to the Jews, for it is mentioned in several places in the Old Testament. The seventeenth-century method of making vinegar on the large scale is given by Glauber as follows:

> Take two large open vessels, made in the manner of common hogsheads, in each of them place a wooden grate, within a foot of the bottom, as they stand upright; upon these grates first place a moderate layer of the green twigs, or cuttings of the vine, and upon this the stalks of the grapes, without the stones, till the whole pile reaches within a foot of the tops of the vessels, which are to remain open; then fill one of these vessels with wine to the

top, and only half fill the other; then with the liquor drawn out
of the full vessel, daily fill up that which was only half full before,
and do this alternately, without ever leaving a full vessel above
twenty-four hours. Thus on the second or third day there will
arise in the half filled vessel the motion of fermentation, with a
sensible heat, which gradually increases every day; and in the
full vessel, the motion and heat is at the same time checked, so as
almost to cease upon that day; and thus fermentation and heat
cease and renew alternately, first in one vessel, and then in the
other. The operation must be continued, till at length the heat
is extinguished, and the motion stopped in the half filled vessels;
which is a sign that this acetous fermentation is perfectly finished.
The vinegar thus prepared is to be kept in casks closely stopped.

That air played a part in the process was realized by the
vinegar-makers of the seventeenth and eighteenth centuries,
but they did not understand the part played by the *mycoderma
aceti*. They observed that an " incredible quantity of gross, fat,
oily or soapy matter " grows to the sides of the cask and the
twigs; this was not understood to take an active part in the
fermentation but was thought to be impurity thrown off by
the wine.

The strengthening of vinegar by distillation may have been
practised by the early alchemists, but there is no unequivocal
reference to the process. In the sixteenth century, however, it
was found that vinegar, when distilled, separated into a
watery part and a less volatile and more strongly acid part,
but it was not yet realized that an acid formed a small proportion of the vinegar and could be separated therefrom.

In the eighteenth century vinegar was rectified by a double
distillation, but the purest acetic acid was made by dissolving
verdigris in vinegar, so obtaining crystals of copper acetate.
These were then distilled. Water came off first, but on further
heating there distilled over a mixture of products of which the
chief was acetic acid. This was considered to be the strongest
acid of vinegar and the ' right acid for dissolving pearls '.

Other Fermentation Industries

Apart from the various alcoholic fermentations, the most
important is the lactic, which with the subsequent action of
moulds and bacteria converted milk into cheese. Cheese
dating from the First Dynasty (*c.* 3000 B.C.) has been found,
and its manufacture was presumably known to all subsequent

cultures. The chemical principles of cheese-making were, of course, unknown until the nineteenth century, but very good cheese was made without them. Gorgonzola was made in the Po valley in A.D. 879. The cheese of Roquefort is said to have a continuous history since Roman times, but was certainly well known by A.D. 1070. We do not know, alas! how many fine cheeses have been lost to gastronomy: I especially regret that which Margery Mylkeducke bartered with Eleanor Rummynge [1] for ale about 1510:

> . . . A Cantell of Essex chese
> Was well a fote thycke,
> Full of maggottes quycke;
> It was huge and greate,
> And mighty stronge meate
> For the deuyll to eate;
> It was tart and punyete.

But the history of mediæval cheeses, fascinating as it would be, must be thought to lie outside the field of chemical industry.

[1] John Skelton. The Tunnynge of Eleanor Rummynge (ll. 429–35). This coarse and richly comic poem throws light on mediæval brewing.

PART II

THE
SCIENTIFIC
CHEMICAL INDUSTRIES

CHAPTER THIRTEEN

From Craft to Science

Chemical Theory and Industrial Practice

THE reader will not have failed to notice that the chemical industries and crafts that flourished up to and during the eighteenth century were almost entirely empirical. The makers of glass or metals or soap knew what to do and did it, but the chemistry of the time, such as it was, did not afford them any indications of methods by which they might improve their processes or devise new ones.

By the middle of the nineteenth century, on the other hand, the majority of the industrial processes in use could be given an explanation in terms of chemical reactions. The understanding of a process in these terms led to the ability to distinguish the features of it that were essential and inessential; it made possible the calculation of the correct proportions of the ingredients; in some cases it indicated the best conditions (*e.g.* of volume, composition and temperature) for its rapid completion; often it indicated the best methods of separation of the products; above all, it enabled the manufacturer to devise new means of attaining his ends.

The growth of a theory of chemistry capable of giving assistance to industry began early in the eighteenth century and was greatly accelerated in its closing years. This gradual comprehension of the nature of the reactions of industrial chemistry falls into two parts, qualitative and quantitative, the former of which was, naturally, the first to develop.

Most of the chemical processes which we have already described in Part I are to be classified as relations between acids, bases and salts, or as oxidations and reductions; accordingly the comprehension of the nature of these classes of reactions was of the first importance for the chemical technologist.

The Relation of Acid, Alkali and Salt

That there were classes of substance to which the terms 'acid', 'alkali' and 'salt' could be applied is a conception difficult to date, and which may perhaps be carried back to antiquity; but the formation of a general theory of acids and alkalis as 'hostile' substances that, when brought together, neutralize each other's properties and form salts dates back only to the seventeenth century. We may attribute the fundamental notion to Otto Tachenius about 1666. He supposed, for example, that all metalliferous minerals were compounds of acids with metals and regarded the smelting of these as fusion with alkali, which removed the acid and set the metal free—at least a half-truth. The central notion of his theory—that many well-known bodies were compounds of acids and alkalis—is well expressed by him in the turgid language of the time. Hippocrates, he tells us, set up the two principles of fire and water as the combatants which by their strife or concordance accounted for all things ; but he, Tachenius, called these principles ACID and ALKALI,

> because all things in the Universe are made up of those two universal principles . . . to which a third doth inseparably adhere. . . . These two, either perpetually burn in Love one towards another, or else are at perpetual variance, are multiplied, and one is contrary to the other; so that the death of one is the life of the other, and that which one produces the other destroys; that so from this another more noble thing may again arise.[1]

It would take a long time to sort out the truths and errors in the works of Tachenius, but from his period the classification of bodies as acids, alkalis or salts, and explanations in these terms, became popular. Robert Boyle, indeed, protested that the terms 'alkali' and 'acid' were ill-defined and that there were many chemical phenomena which their interaction could not possibly explain. This was true, but none the less Tachenius had started a valuable and fruitful idea. It was made much more definite in the eighteenth century, especially after Rouelle had defined the term 'salt' (previously somewhat indefinite) as a compound of an acid and a base.

During the whole of the eighteenth century attention was

[1] Otto Tachenius: His Clavis to the Ancient Hippocratical Physick or Medicine . . . (English Translation), London, 1690.

Otto Tachenius.
his
Hippocrates Chymicus
Discovering
The Ancient foundation of
the late Viperine Salt
with his Clavis thereunto
annexed
Translated by J.W.

London Printed & are to be sold by
W Marshall at the Bible
in Newgate street
1690

FIG. 35. Frontispiece of the English translation of the *Hippocrates Chymicus* of Tachenius.

given to the enumeration of the different kinds of acids and alkalis from which the known salts were derived, and at the same time many new salts were made by neutralizing the known acids with the known alkalis.

In the seventeenth century alkalis were divided into the volatile (*i.e.* ammonia) and the fixed: in the eighteenth the chemical individuals contained in the various fixed alkalis of commerce began to be distinguished. Thus Pott, and later Marggraf, separated the ' earth of alum ' (alumina) and described it as an alkali different from other earths and capable of forming alum with acids. In 1758–59 Marggraf prepared a fixed alkali from common salt by converting it into the nitrate and deflagrating this with charcoal. He showed that this was the same as the mineral natron but different from the alkali made by heating tartar or from wood-ash. Soon after this Joseph Black (1755), in a brief but most influential paper,[1] showed the difference between lime and magnesia and between caustic and fixed alkalis. This work of Black led to an understanding of the nature of several industrially important processes concerned with alkalis. Among these were processes that led to the setting of plaster and mortar; thus Bryan Higgins, who studied these from 1774, tells us that he had learnt from the ' chaste and philosophic productions of Dr. Black ' the relation between limestone, or chalk, and lime; and this understanding led him to the experimental study and commercial production of what he regarded as the best cement yet produced (a lime-mortar containing bone-ash). From the same work of Black was derived the understanding of the familiar process of causticizing barilla and potash by boiling them with lime.

First Applications of the New Chemical Theory

We find in the chemical writings of the seventeenth and earlier eighteenth centuries a predominant interest in medicine or pharmacy, and very little concern with the manufacture of glass, ceramics, soap, metals, etc. It is true that in the 1670's and '80's the Fellows of the Royal Society had contributed many ' histories of trades ', but these were later abandoned,

[1] *Experiments upon Magnesia alba, Quicklime, and some other Alcaline Substances.* Published in *Essays and Observations, Physical and Literary, read before a Society in Edinburgh and published by them.* Edinburgh, 1756, ii, 157–225. Reprinted as *Alembic Club Reprint No.* 1.

probably because the science of the time could do so little to interpret the traditional crafts or suggest improvements. As the eighteenth century wore on, the chemical theory of some of these industries could be dimly glimpsed, and in its later years chemists turned their attention to them. Trades again came into fashion; in France the *Grande Encyclopédie* had given excellent accounts of many industries, which were thereby introduced to the notice of the savants, while in England the industrial revolution was already beginning to make men rich.

Torbern Bergman (1735–84) is an example of one of those who applied the new knowledge to a few of the industrial processes. Thus he attempted a detailed explanation of the chemical theory of alum manufacture. He understood that sulphuric acid from the pyrites in shale attacked the clay which is the base of alum, but he still supposed alum to be simply vitriolated clay, *i.e.* aluminium sulphate, and thought that the alkalis added, potash or urine, are simply to precipitate impurities (though he at least considers the possibility that alum may be a ' triple salt '). Here we see at least a partially successful consideration of an industrial process in terms of chemical ideas.

Bergman also understood in a general way the important process of double decomposition as exemplified in the process of making Epsom salts from ferrous sulphate and the magnesium chloride of bittern, and in the making of butter of antimony (antimony chloride) from native antimony sulphide and mercuric chloride.

In Bergman's time the compositions of various salts in terms of the particular acids and bases were beginning to be known and their industrial preparation understood, and the interest and usefulness of this work called for more and more accurate analyses of substances that might prove to be salts. Thus he knew, for example, that asbestos was made up of ' siliceous, magnesian, calcareous and argillaceous earths ', but this qualitative analysis could not yet lead him to a formula which should characterize the mineral. Such analyses of minerals were much pursued in the eighteenth century, so that by its close the chemists had a fairly accurate knowledge of the constituents of most of the known minerals and had been led to the discovery of a number of new elements (Chapter Nineteen). The intense interest in the manufacture of porcelain (p. 67) was operative in this direction; thus Pott, the Berlin porcelain-maker, was the first of the eighteenth-century mineralogists. The analysis of soils became possible at the end of the eighteenth century. Sir Humphry Davy's Royal Institution lectures, published as *Elements of Agricultural Chemistry* (1813), may be thought of as the first essay towards the founding of this subject of study.

In the British Isles Joseph Black's lectures at Edinburgh were the centre of chemical interest, and it is clear that he made continual allusions to the interpretation of industrial processes in the light of science.

Oxidation and Reduction

A large part of industrial chemistry, and especially of metallurgy, could only be understood in terms of oxidation and reduction. To understand the unhappy position of industrial chemistry in the earlier part of the eighteenth century we have only to remind ourselves that the significance of oxygen in combustion was not comprehended until the work of Lavoisier, from 1774 onwards, had made it clear. The rôle of air in promoting combustion was recognized in practice but not understood in theory. Metallurgists applied their bellows, but they did not understand that the air entered into reaction with the matter in their furnaces. The conversion of metals into calces, as in the cupellation of silver or the making of calx of tin for enamels, was familiar enough, but the meaning of these changes remained virtually unexplained.

The Phlogiston Theory

The eighteenth century adopted a theory of combustion and of the formation of calxes (oxides) of metals which took little or no account of the action of air—namely, the theory of phlogiston. The phlogiston theory first appears in the *Physicæ Subterraneæ* of J. J. Becher, published in 1669 at Frankfurt. This is an obscure and alchemical work, but out of his discussion of the first principles of things there appears the notion that metals contained ' a fat earth, improperly called sulphur ', which gave them their fusibility, their colour and the inflammable character in virtue of which they could be reduced to ashes (*i.e.* oxides) in the fire. This principle interested G. E. Stahl, not so much as a way of explaining the special properties of metals but rather as a means of explaining combustion. How was it that fire, so to speak, lay hid in matter? How did it transform one kind of matter into another? In his *Specimen Beccherianum* (1703) he wrote:

In brief, to the act of mixtion [chemical combination] there concurs as an instrument and is most effective, a Fire, flaming, fervid, hot; to the *substance* of the mixed body, entering (in ordinary language) as material principle and constituent part of the whole compound, there concurs a Matter and Principle of Fire, not fire itself: I henceforth shall call this *Phlogiston*, namely that first Principle which is susceptible of fire, inflammable, directly and eminently fitted for receiving and cherishing heat; especially if it concur with other principles in any mixed body.

Stahl applied this idea to what we call the oxidation of metals and the reduction of their oxides. The first example he gives concerns antimony. Antimony metal, he tells us, is despoiled of phlogiston by nitre and so loses its fusible and volatile character, due to that principle, and is converted into a white powder (antimony oxide). This forms a very hard glass when melted and is scarcely at all volatile, whereas antimony itself is soft and easily volatile. This white powder, when heated with charcoal, which contains much phlogiston, takes this up and forms metallic antimony once more. The relations of other metals with their calces (oxides) are described by him in the same sort of way.

The phlogiston theory hung fire for two or three decades but rose to popularity in the 1740's, only to be relinquished after a sway of some thirty years. We must confess that the hypothesis made sense of combustion and imparted the true notion that the essence of the phenomena which we now call oxidation and reduction was the *adding or removing of something*. It thus enabled a great many chemical phenomena to be grouped together as phlogistications or dephlogistications, and that classification remained untouched when these changes later came to be understood in terms of removal or addition of oxygen. The weakness of the phlogiston theory was that it could not explain the changes of weight which were known to accompany the transformation of calces to metals and *vice versa*, and that it did not recognize the essential character of the part played by air, whether in these processes or in the combustion of fuels.

The work of Lavoisier in the 1770's did not so much disprove the phlogistic theory as provide another and better. Combustion and oxidation were seen to be combination with the oxygen of the air: the reduction of calces to metal to be the removal of oxygen from them.

Accordingly, after Lavoisier had given his explanation of the oxidation of metals and the reduction of their oxides, metallurgical processes were correctly understood, at least in a qualitative fashion. Such an understanding at once revealed the need for rapid and copious supplies of air if high temperatures were to be attained: coinciding with the invention of the blowing-engine, this knowledge led to rapid improvements in the blast-furnace. Many problems of metallurgy remained insoluble in chemical terms, but in the words of M. J. A. Chaptal [1]:

> The mining industry is also founded on the principles of chemistry; and chemistry alone indicates and directs that series of operations which are performed on a metal from the moment of its extraction until that of its employment.

This was true enough, but in fact improvements in metallurgy came but slowly and belong for the most part to the middle and later years of the nineteenth century.

Recognition of Industrial Chemistry as a Subject of Study

M. J. A. Chaptal's book *La Chimie appliquée aux Arts* (1807) was perhaps the first work to be specifically and consciously directed to the study of industrial chemistry. It was certainly influential, not only in its country of origin but also in England, where a translation appeared in the same year. In it we find a clear realization of the rising importance of the application of chemistry to the arts. His brief account of what had then been accomplished is worth quoting:

> But the chemistry of the arts is not confined to the elucidation of what is already known, or to the improvement of what is already practised. It daily creates new arts: and within the period of a few years we have seen it teaching new methods for the bleaching of cloths, manufacturing ammoniacal salt, alum and copperas; decomposing marine salt for the purpose of extracting soda; enriching the art of dyeing with new mordants;

[1] Elémens de Chimie. Montpellier. 1790. Preface p. lvii.

forming saltpetre, and refining it by the simplest processes; compounding powder by most certain and expeditious methods; reducing the tanning of hides to its genuine principles and abridging its operations; improving the extraction and working of metals, simplifying the distillation of wines, economising the means of producing heat; establishing the combustion of oil, and lighting our habitations on new principles, and furnishing us with expedients to soar aloft in the air, and to consult nature three or four thousand fathoms above the surface of the earth.

And if all this seems small beside what has since been accomplished, it marked a great advance from the static and traditional state of chemical industry that had so long endured. The years round 1800 mark the turning-point of the chemical industries, the epoch when traditions of craft gave way to the direction of practice by theory and the results of informed experiment.

Quantitative Chemistry

Second only to the understanding of the qualitative aspect of the fundamental chemical processes was the ability to calculate the correct proportions in which to mix the substances which took part in any chemical change. This depended first on the recognition that definite chemical individuals were of at least approximately constant composition. It had, indeed, always been tacitly assumed that such was the case, but the formulation of this principle as a law had to wait till 1799. The determination of the proportions in which certain metals and compounds react began to be studied in 1783, but it was not until after the turn of the century that the idea of equivalents began to attract attention. Dalton's atomic theory (1803–8) excited further interest in the combining proportions of bodies, but it was J. J. Berzelius who, from 1810 onward, did most to show how the equivalents and atomic weights of elements could be used to make quantitative chemical predictions.

The Atomic Theory

The essence of the progress of the theory of chemistry, in the years 1800–60, was the attainment of an understanding of chemical changes in terms of the rearrangement of atoms, and also the establishment of the chemical formula and the chemical equation together with their quantitative interpretation;

furthermore, this part of chemical theory was immediately applicable to industrial processes.

The ancient hypothesis that matter consists of *particles*—discrete bodies with size, shape and mass—had been generally adopted by men of science since the early part of the seventeenth century. The simplest particles were assumed to be indestructible and unalterable and were called *atoms*: these were supposed to form associations or clusters of a relatively permanent nature which were called *molecules*. These ideas were not very important in the seventeenth and eighteenth centuries, because they had not been used to explain and predict chemical phenomena. The majority of theoretical chemists, indeed, continued to think in terms of the old Aristotelean continuous theory of matter, with its elements [1] of earth, air, fire and water, to which might be added the three principles of Paracelsus, namely, salt, sulphur and mercury; while chemical craftsmen did not bother their heads about such matters and continued to perfect their rules of thumb.

The idea of an element was made more precise in the 1780's by Lavoisier, who brought into use Boyle's notion that those bodies that could not be decomposed into two or more simpler bodies should be reckoned as elements until such time as they should be so decomposed. He thus gave chemists the means of distinguishing those bodies which might be supposed to be elementary; furthermore, he made a list of them which helped to display the practical importance of the distinction between elements and compounds. Lavoisier was an atomist, but he did not solve the problem of stating the composition of compounds in terms of the number and kind of atoms they contained. This problem was first successfully attacked by John Dalton, who between 1803 and 1808 showed in principle how it should be solved but left loose ends which it took half a century to tie up.

Dalton made certain assumptions about atoms and the way in which they combined to form chemical compounds. The essence of these may be expressed by saying:

(1) That the chemical elements consist of indivisible atoms: that all the atoms of any one element are precisely identical,

---

[1] These elements were thought of as consisting of only one 'species': they could not be decomposed, but unlike the later elements, they were thought to be transformable one into another.

and especially in weight, but that different elements have atoms of different weights.

(2) That chemical compounds are formed by the association of atoms in simple numerical proportions.

Thus the elements A and B might form one compound whose smallest particles might all be represented as

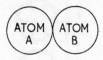

another whose smallest particles would be all

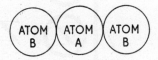

another

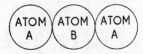

and so forth. He introduced a system of arbitrary symbols for the elements and combined them into formulæ, but these formulæ were not intended to show the spatial arrangement of the atoms, but only the number of each present in each molecule of a particular compound.

Dalton's version of the atomic theory explained (1) the fact that chemical compounds were limited in number, that there are, for example, only two compounds of copper and oxygen; (2) that they were of fixed composition—that, for example, every sample of carbon dioxide contained three-elevenths of its weight of carbon, never less or more. His theory, moreover, suggested that (3) in any two compounds made up of the same elements the proportions of the elements must be simply related: thus in ' carbonic acid ' there should be just twice as much oxygen per unit of carbon as there was in ' carbonic oxide '; and experiment showed this to be the case. There was no alternative theory that could explain these facts, so Dalton's ideas were readily accepted, and, indeed, broke on the chemists of the day as a dazzling light. Since Dalton's time the atomic

ELEMENTS.

		W.t				W.t
⊙	Hydrogen	1	⊕	Strontian	46
⊖	Azote	5	⊛	Barytes	68
⬤	Carbon	5	Ⓘ	Iron	50
○	Oxygen	7	Ⓩ	Zinc	56
⊗	Phosphorus	9	Ⓒ	Copper	56
⊕	Sulphur	13	Ⓛ	Lead	90
◐	Magnesia	20	Ⓢ	Silver	190
⬙	Lime	24	Ⓖ	Gold	190
⦶	Soda	28	Ⓟ	Platina	190
⦀	Potash	42	❋	Mercury	167

FIG. 36. Dalton's diagrams, symbols and atomic weights.

theory has seemed to chemists to be almost self-evident:
chemical nomenclature and formulæ have been based upon it,
and indeed the chemist has found it difficult not to treat the
theory as observed fact.

But Dalton did not show how we were to discover the numbers of each kind of atom that were contained in one molecule of a given compound. Thus water was known to be made up of the elements hydrogen and oxygen and nothing else. Let us adopt a convention later than that of Dalton and call a hydrogen atom H and an oxygen atom O. We know that 1 part by weight of hydrogen and 8 parts by weight of oxygen make up 9 parts by weight of water. Is water to be represented in this fashion,

which is the simplest possible? Dalton adopted this hypothesis. But when water is broken up into its elements (as was possible even in Dalton's time) exactly 2 volumes of hydrogen are obtained for every volume of oxygen; so we can, if we choose, suppose that the same volume of every gas contains the same number of particles, and so conclude that water contains two particles of hydrogen to one of oxygen, thus:

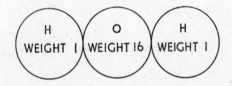

Now this formulation of the molecule of water (in the modern convention, H_2O) led at this period to just the same practical results as the simpler one (HO) given above; for in the former we take an atom of oxygen to be eight times as heavy as an atom of hydrogen, and in the latter sixteen times. Both formulæ gave the same result in chemical calculations, and indeed many analysts went on using the formula HO for thirty years after H_2O had been generally accepted as correct.

So even the slight degree of development of the atomic theory attained by Dalton was quite enough to allow analysis to be done, and formulæ and equations to be written which, if not always correct, were at least comparable and capable of showing the general relationships between the simple inorganic compounds. It was just these simple inorganic compounds with which the chemical industry of the first half of the nineteenth century was concerned, and even the feeble light that the chemical theory of the period was able to shed was enough to enable wonderful work to be done.

CHAPTER FOURTEEN

The Rise of Scientific Chemical Industry, 1788-1860

The New Industrial Chemistry

A FAIRLY compact period of industrial chemistry lies between the chemical revolution of 1788 and the great development of chemical theory in the 1860's.

From the point of view of knowledge it is distinguished from all that went before by the existence, for the first time, of a true and fruitful theory of chemical change. The formulæ of the common inorganic compounds were known, the chemical reactions which led to their preparation could be formulated, and new processes could be thought out from theoretical considerations.

At least equally important for the shaping of the chemical industries was the vastly increased demand for chemicals, a demand which could be satisfied only by production in tons of what was formerly made in pounds. Thus industrial chemistry gradually ceased to be large-scale laboratory work and became a department of engineering. Chemical engineering, like all other engineering, was made possible by the development of the steam-engine. This alone made it possible to construct large-scale plant and to mine and transport many of the raw materials of chemistry at a low cost. The steam-engine also brought about a huge development of the textile industry, which required the production of great quantities of the chemicals employed in cleansing, bleaching and dyeing. Thus the manufacture of alkalis, acids and metals were the principal chemical industries of the early nineteenth century. The production of cheap and good alkali was, perhaps, the prime need, and the acid industry developed in order to supply the needs of the alkali industry.

The Alkali Industry

The importance of 'alkali', by which was meant the carbonates or hydroxides of potassium or sodium, should appear from what has been said in Chapters Five and Ten. The chief uses of alkalis were for scouring, soap-making and glass-making. Before the nineteenth century the sole large-scale source of supply was the ashes of plants. The majority of plants yielded an ash whose chief soluble constituent was potash (potassium carbonate) ; but certain salt-marsh plants and sea-weeds yielded an ash which contained a proportion of soda (sodium carbonate). Potash could not be used to make hard soap, and for this purpose some form of soda was required, as also for most kinds of glass.

Potash was made exclusively from wood-ashes until 1861, when the mineral deposits of Stassfurt, etc., came into production. In the early nineteenth century the old producers of potash, Russia and Germany (p. 128) were overshadowed by the U.S.A. When forests were cleared the abundant brush-wood and small timber were burned; the ashes were transferred to large tubs with perforated bottoms covered with straw. Water was allowed to percolate through the ashes, and the resulting crude solution of potash was boiled dry; the residue of potash was then heated to redness and packed for export.

The means of obtaining sodium carbonate was much less satisfactory. The Spanish barilla, whose manufacture is described on p. 75, was the best product obtainable, but it contained only 12–20% of sodium carbonate, while kelp or varec, made by burning sea-weed, contained only 5–8%. None the less they were very profitable manufactures, for the textile industries could not get enough of them. The Scottish kelp-burners became rich, and at the end of the eighteenth century Lord Macdonald of the Isles was making £10,000 a year out of his kelp shares. The Spanish continually raised the price of barilla, and the price of soda became so high as to encourage several chemists to work out possible processes for making it artificially from common salt.

The first step was taken in 1736, when Duhamel proved that common salt was a compound of the base of soda and spirit of salt (hydrochloric acid). A further step was made by Joseph Black in 1755, who showed the relation between the mild and caustic alkalis, and thus showed that ordinary soda and potash were compounds of carbon dioxide with caustic soda and caustic potash respectively. It was, however, by no means easy, even with this knowledge, to devise a method of converting salt into sodium carbonate or caustic soda. In 1775, however, Scheele solved the problem, after a fashion, by strongly heating salt and lead oxide, so obtaining caustic soda and lead oxychloride, a useful yellow pigment; the process was used on the manufacturing scale at the beginning of the nineteenth century but was too costly to survive. Meanwhile the price both of potash and of Spanish barilla was rising and the French Academy offered a prize of 12,000 francs to the author of the best process for making soda from sea-salt. In 1774 Father Malherbe, a Benedictine monk, came near to a solution. He turned salt into sodium sulphate by means of sulphuric acid, and melted this with charcoal and iron. The resulting mass, consisting of sodium sulphide, sodium oxide and iron sulphide, was left to deliquesce in the air, and the resulting liquid became converted by the action of atmospheric carbon dioxide into a solution of soda. The process was worked on the large scale in 1779 and again in 1828 but did not come into general use because sulphuric acid was still expensive and the product was very impure. De la Méthérie, who seems to have been an armchair inventor and not to have tried out his process, suggested that sodium sulphate should be made from sea-salt as in Father Malherbe's process and reduced to sulphide by heating with charcoal; the sodium sulphide was then to be turned into sodium acetate by means of vinegar and the product heated to redness in order to turn it into the carbonate —which is soda. Variants of this process were employed from time to time. Bryan Higgins in 1785 suggested a similar process, but suggested the use of lead oxide or iron to remove the sulphur from the sodium sulphide.

This by no means exhausts the processes that were suggested or tried; their number witnesses the need. All these processes, except Scheele's, depended on the availability of reasonably cheap sulphuric acid. The progress of the acid industry is discussed on pp. 90–100, but it may be said that the requisite low cost was attained in the period round 1800, and thus made large-scale alkali manufacture a practical proposition.

Nicolas Le Blanc, who was physician to the Duke of Orleans, improved on all the above processes by using calcium carbonate, in the form of chalk, to remove the sulphur from the sodium sulphide and introduce the carbon dioxide. He thus solved the problem in so perfect a fashion that his process remained in use with little modification for over a century. He treated salt (sodium chloride) with sulphuric acid, obtaining hydrochloric acid (which he used for making sal-ammoniac) and sodium sulphate. He heated the latter with charcoal and chalk, so forming calcium sulphide and sodium carbonate, which latter only required to be dissolved out of the mass by water. Scarcely anyone has done so much for industry and received so little reward as did Le Blanc. In 1789 he and a pair of partners, who do not seem to have contributed much to the invention, made agreements with the Duke of Orleans for obtaining the capital to start a soda-factory. Le Blanc applied for a patent, but just as the process was coming into production the French Revolution broke out. The factory's capital was from a suspect source: its funds were seized and Le Blanc had perforce to surrender the factory and allow his secret to be published for the good of his country. It was not till seven years later that the factory was given back to him as compensation for the publication of the secret, but even then he had not the resources to get the process working again. In 1806 he died by his own hand.

England's great textile industry demanded a new and better source of alkali no less than did that of France. The Le Blanc process was used by Losh at Walker-on-Tyne in 1814, and at Tennant's works at St. Rollox in 1818, but the prohibitive excise duty on salt prevented the process from being widely used until 1825, when that ill-considered impost was repealed with the effect of reducing the price of salt ultimately to a fiftieth of its previous cost. In the same year James Muspratt introduced the process on a really large scale in the first alkali works at St. Helen's. Like previous manufacturers he began by selling the black-ash, *i.e.* the crude mixture of calcium sulphide and sodium carbonate. Previous makers had produced a black-ash containing only 17–20% of sodium carbonate—not much better than barilla. Muspratt made a product containing 41% of sodium carbonate, and in 1830 he went further and began to make ' white-ash ', *i.e.* anhydrous sodium carbonate. The soap manufacturers did not at first realize that this contained no less that six times as much alkali as the best barilla: Muspratt gave away tons of it, free of charge, in order to popularize it, but once its worth was appreciated he sold it so fast that it was loaded red-hot from the furnaces into iron carts and so dispatched to the manufacturers. Crystal soda, made by dissolving the soda ash in water and crystallizing it, became available by 1830.

The first part of the Le Blanc process, then, was the reaction of common salt and sulphuric acid to form normal sodium sulphate and hydrogen chloride. Thus, for every ton of soda made, about three-quarters of a ton of intensely acid hydrogen chloride gas was discharged into the air, destroying every green thing within miles as well as doing injury to buildings and external metal-work. It was not until 1836 that William Gossage patented a method of dissolving the gas in water and so producing hydrochloric acid, and it was only in 1863 that this condensation was made compulsory. The hydrochloric acid so made was used for producing chlorine for bleaching. By 1860 barilla was no longer used and the kelp still made bore a very small proportion to the output of artificial soda.

It may come as a surprise to learn that caustic soda was not produced on the industrial scale in 1850. If a solution of caustic soda was needed, e.g. by the soap-boiler, he still had to buy some form of sodium carbonate and ' causticize ' it with lime. But in 1851–52 solid caustic soda began to be made, and in 1853 William Gossage took up the process. He causticized the ' red liquor '—the impurest part of the Leblanc liquors— boiled it down and ran the melted caustic into iron drums. The product, though efficient, was impure and dark coloured; but in the next decade white caustic was made. This process was the only means of making caustic soda until 1890, when the electrolytic process began to be used, and after 1910 became the principal method of making alkali. None the less caustic continued to be made from Le Blanc soda-liquors up till at least 1920.

The Le Blanc process had many disadvantages. It wasted all the sulphur contained in the sulphuric acid used, for all this remained as insoluble calcium oxysulphide, or ' alkali- waste '. Vast heaps of this material, on which nothing would grow, disfigured the neighbourhood of the chemical works, and none of the processes for recovering the sulphur from it proved at this time to be a success. Furthermore, the soda produced by the Le Blanc process contained some 5% of impurities, including an appreciable proportion of sulphides.

The ammonia-soda process had none of these disadvantages, but it was slow to establish itself. The essence of the process is to saturate brine with ammonia and pass in carbon dioxide, so forming ammonium bicarbonate, which reacts with the sodium chloride, precipitating solid sodium bicarbonate and leaving ammonium chloride in solution. The sodium bicarbonate, when heated, gives pure sodium carbonate; the ammonia is recovered by heating the residual liquid with lime. The ammonia is therefore used time after time, and the only materials used up are salt, carbon dioxide and lime. The success of the process depends on complete recovery of ammonia, which is largely a question of chemical engineering. The reaction was known as early as 1822, and in 1836 John Thom was making soda by it on a small scale. In 1838 H. G. Dyer and J. Hemming patented the whole process in principle, and it was several times worked, but always given up on account of the loss of ammonia, which was then relatively costly. It was not till 1863 that a Belgian, Ernest Solvay, patented what is in essence the present method and made a success of the process. In 1872 Ludwig Mond introduced the process at Northwich. By using natural brine instead of solid salt he greatly lowered the cost of the product, and thenceforward the ammonia-soda process steadily gained on the Le Blanc. The latter, however, was kept alive by the value of its by-products, hydrochloric acid and the sulphur recovered from the alkali-waste by the process brought to success by A. M. Chance and C. F. Claus in 1894. Nevertheless the Le Blanc process, which reached its maximum development in America, at least, in the '70's and '80's, became extinct in the decade 1920-30.

The improvements in the alkali industry had their influence on the glass industry. The foundations of the chemistry of glass were understood in the 1830's. Berzelius had shown that silica was an acidic oxide, and glass was thereafter understood to be a mixture of salts, the silicates of various metals. The technique of glass-making had, however, changed but little since the time of Ravenscroft (p. 79). Kelp and barilla continued to be used as alkalis up to about 1830, but thereafter sodium carbonate or sodium sulphate from the Le Blanc process was brought into use. The new alkali was much purer than the natural products and of constant composition, and thereby contributed to the making of consistently colourless glass. At the same time cheap transport enabled the glass-works to bring purer sand from a distance instead of using the local and often inferior product.

The greatest technical improvement in glass-making was the tank-furnace, made possible by the regenerative principle introduced by Siemens (p. 201). Glass could be produced in far greater quantity than before and with far less expenditure on fuel, and the high temperature attained made the glass more fluid, whereby uncombined sand-grains, air-bubbles, etc., could more easily sink or rise, leaving the glass clear and homogeneous. The technique of glass-working remained traditional until the 1860's, apart from the casting and polishing of plate-glass, begun in France about 1680 and in England about 1773. In the twentieth century, however, machinery for blowing bottles and drawing sheet-glass has revolutionized the industry.

Coloured glasses continued to be made from the old materials, and uranium yellow was the only important improvement in this field.

Advances in the making of optical glass originated from Michael Faraday and M. Vernon Harcourt, both of whom made many new types of glass. The industry did not, however, take up this work, and the most important advances resulted from the researches of Abbe, who devised new types of glass for optical instruments, which glasses were made by Schott of Jena and utilized by the firm of Zeiss from 1884.

The Acid Industry

In Chapter Nine we have traced the growth of the sulphuric acid industry to about 1750, at which time Roebuck was burning large charges of sulphur and nitre in ' lead-houses ' of only about a couple of hundred cubic feet.

The improvement of the process came about not only through advances in technical engineering, allowing of bigger and better types of plant, but also through an understanding of the chemical reactions that took place. The extent of the improvement is mirrored by the fall in cost of the acid from £30 to £35 a ton in 1790–1800 to £3 10s in the 1820's and to £1 5s. in 1885.

In the early eighteenth century the process was not understood at all but simply carried out empirically. Lavoisier's discovery (1772–77) that sulphuric acid consisted of sulphur, oxygen and water showed the direction that improvement should take. Thus the nitre which was mixed with the sulphur did not appear to enter into the product. It seems that the nitre was sometimes thought of as a means of making the flame of the sulphur very hot, and sometimes it was considered to be the source of the oxygen in the acid, for no attempt was made to supply air in quantity to the chambers until Clément and Désormes suggested this improvement in 1793. The same workers in 1806 discovered the central fact of the process, namely, the catalytic action of oxides of nitrogen (derived from the nitre) in converting sulphur dioxide, oxygen and water into sulphuric acid. To quote their words:

> Thus nitric acid is only the instrument of the complete oxygenation of the sulphur: it is its base, nitric oxide, that takes the oxygen from the atmospheric air to offer it to the sulphurous acid in the state which suits it best.

Clément and Désormes mixed the gases sulphur dioxide-air and nitric oxide and observed the formation of ' chamber, crystals ', which on addition of water were converted into sulphuric acid and evolved nitric oxide once more. A vast controversy has raged concerning the true nature of the reactions that take place in the chambers, but Clément and Désormes told the industry all that was required to set the improvements going. It became apparent from their work that the chamber-process needed very little nitre and much air —and nitre was the most expensive material used in it. It must not be thought that this work was at all quickly exploited, for it seems that even in the 1820's English manufacturers were still burning charges of sulphur and nitre in closed lead chambers. Sulphuric acid was difficult to transport and so tended to be made locally; this helped to eliminate keen competition and the need to adopt the latest improvements. However, the size of the chambers increased from some 200 cubic feet in the 1770's to 5,000–100,000 cubic feet in the 1830's.

By 1803 some works were burning the sulphur in furnaces and carrying the gases into the chambers, into which a continuous current of steam was introduced. This process, provided that the draught was suitably regulated, afforded a continuous supply of the three necessary constituents of the acid, namely, air, water and sulphur dioxide. The nitrogen oxides which catalysed the reaction were introduced by means of a nitre-pot containing potassium nitrate and sulphuric acid —an improvement brought into use during the 1830's.

The next great advance was in the discarding of sulphur, as a source of sulphur dioxide, in favour of iron pyrites. The world's sulphur came from the Sicilian deposits, for only small quantities were made elsewhere, e.g. by distilling pyrites; thus until 1838 sulphur was almost the sole source of sulphuric acid. It had long been known that pyrites would burn, evolving sulphur dioxide, and the burning of it for making sulphuric acid was patented as early as 1813 ; nevertheless pyrites was not in practice used for this purpose until the years after 1838. In that year the King of Sicily was so unwise as to grant a monopoly of the export of sulphur to a French firm, who raised its price from £5 to £14 a ton, which made the discovery of another source of sulphur dioxide very necessary. The burning of pyrites was well known, but the objection to it was the evolution of arsenical vapours, some of which found their way into the acid. This did not matter, however, if the acid was to be used in the manufacture of Le Blanc soda, for the arsenic was then carried off with the hydrochloric acid in the form of its volatile chloride. Sicilian sulphur continued to predominate in the U.S.A. at least until the '90's, but the Sicilian sulphur industry never fully recovered, despite improvements in extraction, such as Gill's regenerative furnace (1880). The Chance-Claus process for recovery of sulphur introduced a further competitor in 1894, and finally, in 1902, when Hermann Frasch introduced his wonderful process for melting the sulphur of the Louisiana deposits underground and pumping it to the surface, the United States ceased to import sulphur and even began to export it. The cheapness of Frasch sulphur was such that it could compete with pyrites as material for the making of sulphuric acid.

The final step in the evolution of the lead-chamber process was the working out of means for recovering the nitrogen oxides, which were formerly discharged into the atmosphere together with the waste nitrogen left in the chambers after the reaction. The first step towards the recovery of the nitrogen oxides was taken when in 1827–28 J. L. Gay-Lussac invented the tower that bears his name. The waste gases from the chambers passed up this tower on their way to the stack: some of the acid made in the lead-chambers was allowed to flow down the tower and dissolved the oxides of nitrogen. The difficulty was to liberate these from the acid, so that they could be returned to the chambers. The earlier method was to dilute the ' nitrous vitriol ', as the acid containing nitrous gases was called; this caused the nitric oxide to be evolved as gas. But this process was too expensive for general use, on account of the cost of concentrating the acid that had been diluted. Thus the Gay-Lussac tower did not come into general use until Glover in 1860 introduced, between the pyrites burners and

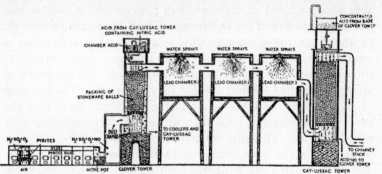

FIG. 37.   Sulphuric acid works.

the chambers, a second tower (Fig. 37) up which the very hot gases flowed while the nitrous vitriol from the Gay-Lussac tower ran down it; at the high temperature that there prevailed the nitrous vitriol liberated its oxides of nitrogen, which passed on into the chambers. Even then the use of these towers was but slowly adopted; thus even in 1890 only about half the American vitriol works employed them.

The acid from the chambers was used without further concentration for many purposes (*e.g.* the Le Blanc process or the manufacture of superphosphates). The concentrated acid was made by distillation in stills of glass or platinum (p. 196). Glass broke, and platinum was even then extremely costly, so much so that the English manufacturers continued for the most part to employ lead. The high-silcon cast-irons, which withstand hot concentrated sulphuric acid, did not become available until about 1882. This difficulty of concentrating chamber acid was one of the reasons for the survival of the ancient Nordhausen process (p. 96) and the rapid progress of the contact process (p. 424) in the twentieth century.

In the early nineteenth century the uses of sulphuric acid were manifold. First and foremost was the making of soda and, directly or indirectly, of chlorine for bleaching or making bleaching-powder. It was also used in the making of nitric and acetic acids, and of sulphates such as alum, copper sulphate and ferrous sulphate. A great number of industries employed the acid for various minor purposes.

The manufacture of the other mineral acids depended on that of sulphuric acid. The production of hydrochloric acid in the course of the manufacture of soda has already been described.

Nitric acid was a comparatively unimportant substance, finding its chief use in the cleansing of metals, the making of oxalic acid, etc.; towards the end of the 1860's, however, appreciable quantities were required for making the lower nitro-celluloses, which were dissolved in alcohol and ether to make collodion, used as a photographic material. The era of nitro-explosives and of nitro-compounds as intermediates in the dyestuffs industry was not yet.

Bleaching

Bleaching was of the first importance in the period of the industrial revolution. Before the rise of industrial chemistry it was a very slow process. Linen used to be bleached in the early eighteenth century by repeated boiling, washing and exposure to sunlight for a period of months. Many acres of land were covered with bleaching textiles; the labour and rent were serious charges on the product. The linen was steeped in lye, washed and boiled and exposed to the sun for two or three weeks; this whole process was repeated as many as five times, and the linen was finally 'soured' in sour buttermilk for several weeks. Linen required, in fact, six months for bleaching, and cotton from six weeks to three months. The first improvement was the substitution of dilute sulphuric acid for the sour milk, which cut the souring period from weeks to a few hours, and this it was which aroused the new demand for sulphuric acid from 1750 onward. Scheele discovered chlorine in 1774 and remarked on its bleaching properties, which were soon utilized. The first method was to make the gas from manganese dioxide (much used in the glass trade), salt and sulphuric acid and to saturate water with the gas. The goods were then heated in the chlorine water. The process was, of course, very dangerous for the workers, but it continued to be used quite considerably until 1830.

This process was soon succeeded by the dissolving of chlorine in alkaline solutions (giving hypochlorites), which were much easier and safer to handle. This was practised both in England and on the Continent. However, Charles Tennant's bleaching liquor (1798), made from lime-water and chlorine, proved to be very cheap and effective; in the year after this discovery he began to convert chlorine and lime into solid bleaching powder, which was later used in much the same way as it is to-day. All chlorine-bleaching demanded the use of sulphuric acid, and this further swelled the demand for that material.

Wool and silk could not be bleached with chlorine without damage, and 'sulphuring' (bleaching with sulphur dioxide) remained the normal practice, as it is still to-day. In fact, the only really new bleaching principle successfully introduced since 1800 is the use of hydrogen peroxide (p. 306).

Chlorine continued to be made by the action of some form of manganese dioxide on hydrochloric acid, or on sulphuric acid and salt. Great quantities of manganous chloride or sulphate were left as waste products, and naturally many attempts were made to recover the manganese dioxide. In 1850 Dunlop patented his method of precipitating the manganese solution with chalk and roasting the resulting manganese carbonate. This was quite successful, though it was displaced by Weldon's process, invented in 1866 and generally adopted in the following decade; this in its turn gave place to the Deacon process, and finally to the electrolytic manufacture of chlorine. These are further discussed on pp. 388, 413. The liquefaction of chlorine and its transport in tanks or cylinders had begun by 1914, and therefore the use of the gas in chemical warfare from 1915 onward involved no new chemical processes.

Bromine and Iodine

Iodine was discovered by Courtois about 1811, and the first accounts of it were published in 1813, while bromine was first recognized as an element in 1824.

PLATE XI

A.—Nasmyth's Steam Hammer (see p. 199).

B.—Coalbrookdale Iron Works (see p. 198).

PLATE XII

Puddling as Practised To-day (see p. 199).

Iodine was identified as early as 1819 as the principle which gave burnt sponge its efficacy in the treatment of goitre, and the notion that deficiency of iodine was the cause of endemic goitre was made by Prévost about 1830. During the 1820's an alcoholic solution was used as a counter-irritant, and later as a treatment for wounds, while Lugol introduced the solution of iodine in potassium iodide about 1831. Thus there was from the first a small demand for the element, a demand which became greater in the 1840's, when iodine began to be used in photography (p. 416).

Iodine was at first obtained only from kelp (p. 129). The soluble part of this was crystallized, yielding potash, while the mother-liquors, containing the very soluble iodides, were heated with manganese dioxide and sulphuric acid, whereupon the iodine volatilized and was condensed in earthenware vessels known as udells. The preparation from kelp gradually gave way to that from the caliche (sodium nitrate deposits) of Chile, from which iodine began to be made in 1874 and which is now much the most important source of the element.

Bromine owed its first industrial importance to photography; after 1837 it was made from the residues left after the crystal-lization of salt from brine by treating them with manganese dioxide and sulphuric or hydrochloric acid. The demand for bromine was increased by the organic chemical industry, and it price was much reduced when it was discovered to be present in the residues from the crystallization of the potash salts at Stassfurt. From the date of this discovery (1865) bromine became a common chemical. To-day bromine is also made from Dead Sea brine, and in very large quantity from sea-water at the Texas plant of the Dow Chemical Corporation.

Non-ferrous Metallurgy (1780—1860)

The metallurgical industries expanded vastly during the industrial revolution, but the change in methods was slight compared with the great advances of the second half of the nineteenth century.

Gold and silver were still made by the old amalgamation processes, somewhat improved and mechanized. The greatest advance was the cyanide process of J. S. MacArthur and the Forrest brothers, patented in 1887, which occasioned an enormous demand for cyanides. The making of these from animal refuse and potash had been displaced by extraction from the spent oxide of the gas-works from 1860, but even this would not suffice and synthetic methods (p. 392) were developed between 1890 and 1902.

The great centre for copper-smelting was South Wales, which had good supplies of coal (permitting rapid smelting) and easy access by sea for ore from Cornwall and further afield. Copper-works were set up at Neath in 1582, and in 1717 at Swansea, which town remained the centre of the industry. The processes used did not differ very greatly in principle from those described by Agricola. The larger scale of the processes entailed the discharge of torrents of sulphur dioxide and arsenical fumes into air, destroying all the vegetation for miles around. The copper finally produced was far from pure: much of it was made into brass by means of calamine, as of old. In 1779 James Emerson set up a works at Henham to make brass from copper and metallic zinc, but the calamine process remained the chief source of supply until the middle of the nineteenth century. The electrical industry was not yet making much demand for pure copper: but later in the century it provided both the demand and the means of satisfying it by electrolytic refining (p. 385). Even to-day the principles of the ancient method survive. The ore is, however, roasted in reverberatory furnaces or water-jacketed blast-furnaces provided with stacks to disperse the sulphur dioxide, which in some places is used industrially. The smelting is commonly performed in water-jacketed blast-furnaces with a limited supply of fuel, and the impure metal or *matte* is refined in a single operation in a Bessemer converter. New sources of copper replaced that of the Cornish mines. These were successively Spain, Michigan and Utah, Bolivia and, to-day, the Belgian Congo.

Lead continued to be made by the traditional processes. Until about 1750 lead ore was smelted in very crude furnaces urged only by the wind, but after that time simple reverberatory and small blast-furnaces came into use. To recover the silver from lead it was formerly necessary to oxidize the whole of the lead to recover the small proportion of silver (p. 42): the oxide had then to be resmelted to give lead. It therefore did not pay to remove the silver from lead unless a fair proportion were present. In 1829, however, Pattinson invented the method of letting molten lead slowly cool, ladling out the solid crystals of metal as they formed. These crystals consisted of nearly pure lead; the residual molten lead retained the silver and, when it had become sufficiently concentrated, it could be cupelled. This discovery put Great Britain (which in 1831 produced 40% of the world's lead) for the first time among the important silver-producing countries.

Between 1850 and 1852 Parkes worked out an even more effective method, depending on the addition of molten zinc, which is not miscible with lead but extracts the silver from it. This process came into use in 1859 but only slowly displaced Pattinson's method.

Mercury was still made by heating cinnabar with iron or lime, as in antiquity; but it was also produced by roasting the ore in air and condensing the mercury from the fumes in the furnace invented by Bustamente in 1650. Little or no effort was made to reduce mercurial poisoning.

Tin was also still made by the traditional methods; as the century advanced the contribution of the Straits Settlements to the world's supply became greater, and in 1865 about half came from Cornwall and half from the Far East. The canning of food-stuffs became an important industry in the 1870's, and this greatly increased the demand for tin.

Several new metallurgical processes, however, came into use during and soon after the industrial revolution. Metallic zinc began to be distilled, usually *per descensum*, *i.e.* with the receiver vertically below the retort; Bristol (where it seems to have been manufactured by the brothers Champion as early as 1740), Birmingham and Sheffield were the chief English centres. In Silesia, the chief producer, the furnaces employed were almost of the modern type. The zinc was rolled hot, as to-day, into sheets. A certain amount of the metal was used for galvanizing, a process which originated in the eighteenth century but became important only from about 1870.

Nickel, discovered by A. F. Cronstedt in 1751, was made from the 'speiss', or mixture of sulphides (p. 87), which separated from cobalt ores in the course of making the pigment cobalt-blue, or smalt.

In 1776, Von Engestrom discovered the presence of nickel in the oriental alloy, paktong, but the first imitation of this was not placed on the market until 1824 by the brothers

Henninger, of Berlin. Geitner at about the same time produced a similar metal (argentan) in Saxony. In 1830 this metallurgist brought a sample to Sheffield and thereby started the manufacture of ' electrum ' in this country. The metal was soon used for making German silver, a white alloy very popular as a basis for electro-plating (copper 40–55%, nickel 15–30%, zinc 20–40%). The production of nickel expanded after the year 1870, when nickel-plating began to be adopted, but no great quantities were produced before the closing years of the nineteenth century. The important event in the production of nickel was the remarkable process developed by Mond, Langer and Quincke in 1890, in which the nickel was converted into the volatile carbonyl, $Ni(CO)_4$, which was then decomposed by heat, depositing pure nickel. In the succeeding years nickel-plating was widely adopted as a means of providing a decorative rust-proof surface for bicycles and the like. New sources of nickel in New Caledonia, Canada, Finland and elsewhere have provided the large quantities required in the twentieth century.

Platinum was recognized as a separate metal in the mideighteenth century. In 1741 Sir W. Watson received some grains of it which had been found with gold in New Granada, now Columbia, and described it as a new semi-metal or metalloid. Its remarkable resistance to chemical reagents and high temperatures aroused interest, but the metal remained useless because it could not be purified and worked into a compact mass. Numerous researches culminated in those of W. H. Wollaston, who revealed in 1804 a process for working it. Regular production from the gold workings of Verkanigisetsk, in the Ural Mountains, began in 1824, and it was thereafter much used for scientific apparatus, and especially for the stills and pans used for concentrating sulphuric acid. At this period it was very much cheaper than gold, the only other acid-resisting metal then available.

Metallurgy of Iron (1780–1860)

The really great metallurgical advances of the period 1780–1860 were in the production of iron and steel. During this period the smelting of iron became fully scientific in some places but remained wholly primitive in others, so that we find, e.g. in 1830, that the ancient processes of the bloomeries and the Catalan forge (pp. 46–8) were in use in less-developed districts, while huge blast-furnaces were being employed in the centres of industry. Primitive methods persisted until recent years in *e.g.* the Sudan and West Africa.

Fig. 38.   Blast furnace with flame and gases escaping.

The feature of this period was the rise of cast-iron .The essentials of making this metal are to charge roasted iron ore, some carbonaceous fuel and, usually, lime into a vertical furnace into which is injected, near the bottom, a blast of air. The charcoal or coke reduces the iron oxide to iron, and the earthy matter forms a slag with the lime; both melt in the heat of the furnace and form separate liquid layers at the bottom of it. The efficiency of a blast-furnace depends on its size, and the size can only be increased if the blast is made proportionately powerful. Thus the development of the blast-furnace depended on that of the blowing-engine. Smeaton made the first steam-driven blowing-engine about 1760, but it was the Watt engines of c. 1785 that began a new era. They enabled mines to be freed of water and shafts could be sunk to greater depths; they were used in many instances for raising the coal, and also operated the blowing-engines at iron-works.

The traditional fuel for the blast-furnaces and their fore-runners was charcoal. In England, owing to the depletion of the forests, felling of wood for making the charcoal required by the iron-makers was forbidden in the reign of Queen Elizabeth. In the first half of the seventeenth century pit-coal was tried without success, but in 1619 Dud Dudley demonstrated that coke could be used in the blast-furnace. Nevertheless it was not until 1735 that Abraham Darby of Coalbrookdale made the use of pit-coal a commercial success, which began an era of rapid progress in the iron industry and a steady change-over from charcoal to coal By 1788 only about a third of the English furnaces employed charcoal, but in most other countries this remained the fuel of choice. The use of powerful blast, with coke as fuel, made English production far more efficient than that of the charcoal-burning countries. In 1824 Neilson patented the hot blast, which saved two-thirds of the fuel formerly needed, and this was the last great advance of the years 1800–60. It was realized that, even so, 80 % of the heat of the coal was wasted in the gases that blazed at the open mouths of the furnaces, and attempts had been made to utilize these gases, but without much success. The regenerative principle of Siemens again showed the way and the use of blast-furnace gas to heat the blast was general by 1880.

England thus led the production of cast-iron, but the charcoal-iron made in France and Sweden and Russia was of far higher purity and was esteemed for many types of work, especially the manufacture of steel. This charcoal-iron was tough and could be forged by the smith as cast-iron could not.

The character of the pig-iron produced by the blast-furnace depended on the degree of purity of the ore and the nature and quantity of the fuel employed. Some of the pig-iron made in this way could be converted into a malleable iron by heating it on a hearth and subjecting it to blast. This hearth was known as a ' finery ' and was a usual adjunct to the small blast-furnace of the seventeenth and eighteenth centuries. Henry Cort's discovery of the process of puddling (1783) may be thought of as a development of the finery process and, like it, depended on the oxidation of the impurities in the cast-iron. The cast-iron was melted and subjected to a strong blast to remove some of the impurities. It was then again melted and exposed to air in a reverberatory furnace till the oxidation of the carbon made its melting point rise, so that it became pasty. The puddler, who was required to be of Herculean strength, formed the iron into masses which were squeezed, hammered and welded till they formed a fibrous mass of wrought-iron. Steam-hammers (Plate XI, A), introduced from 1833 onward, greatly increased production of this type of iron, which remained very important until the 1880's, but thereafter has been steadily replaced by mild steel.

Metallurgy of Steel

Steel is made from pure iron by adding carbon or from cast-iron by removing that element. The standard way of making steel in the eighteenth century was the cementation process, which was in essence to heat bars of soft iron in a mixture of various carbonaceous materials, especially horn or hoof, or simply in a bed of fuel. Their surfaces became impregnated with carbon, and they could then be forged into a homogeneous mass. The process of melting the carburized iron in crucibles instead of forging it was a considerable advance, achieved by Huntsman, a watchmaker, in 1740. Both processes were slow and dealt with but little metal at a time, and steel was therefore expensive. Some of the better cast-irons could be turned into a sort of steel by heating them in a reverberatory furnace so as to oxidize some of their carbon-content, but this was not a very important source of supply. Thus steel remained the material of choice for tools and weapons, but malleable iron and cast-iron were the typical materials of the engineer. During the first half of the nineteenth century the production of iron was enormously greater than ever before. Chemistry had explained the processes of smelting, while analysis had demonstrated the composition of

the ores and of the various types of iron and steel: so the
problem of converting pig-iron into wrought-iron and steel was
theoretically understood but not yet satisfactorily solved in
practice. In the years between 1845 and 1870 improvements
in steel-making were in the air. Numerous patents were taken
out but most of them proved to be impracticable. It was not
so much chemistry as engineering technique that was needed to
solve the problem.

The first successful process for making cheap steel was that
of Sir Henry Bessemer, though he is said to have been anticipated by William Kelly in America. It is to be noted that
neither Bessemer, Siemens nor Thomas, the founders of the
steel industry, were in the first instance manufacturers of
steel, nor in any way professionally concerned therewith.
Bessemer's primary intention was not to manufacture steel but
to make malleable iron without the labour and expense of
puddling. The essential feature of his invention, brought out
in 1856, was the removal of carbon and silicon from pig-iron
by oxidizing them with an air-blast. The principle was not
new, for puddling was commonly assisted in this fashion. What
was new and astounding to the men of the time was the making
of soft iron or steel *without burning any fuel*. Bessemer injected a
powerful blast of air through the molten metal; the silicon and
carbon burned off and at the same time raised the temperature
of the metal. If the process was stopped just at the right time
the iron could be left almost entirely free from carbon and
silicon. If, however, the blowing was too long continued, the
product was a metal which contained iron oxide and was
brittle when hot; but if the process stopped before completion
some carbon remained in the iron and the result was steel.
Bessemer's process attracted interest, but fell short of full
success because, as was soon discovered, the process could not
be applied to the types of pig-iron which contain phosphorus.
That element was not removed by the air-blast and the resulting
metal was so brittle as to be worthless. Bessemer was therefore
confined to the use of Swedish pig-irons, or others made from
hæmatite, which were almost free from phosphorus. The
makers fought shy of his process, so he set up his own steelworks
and made steel for £5 or £6 a ton as against the £50 or £60
which was the current price. In a few years the partners in
his factory had multiplied their capital eighty times and con-

vinced the world of the value of Bessemer steel. The low price
of this material soon opened up a vast number of new uses for
steel—rails, girders, ships' plates and the like.

In 1867, eleven years after Bessemer's invention, Charles
William Siemens, in collaboration with his brother Frederick,
brought out a process which has proved to be even more
effective than the Bessemer.

The work of Siemens on steel arose out of his discovery of
the regenerative gas-furnace, which in its turn arose from his
theoretical studies concerning the economizing of heat. The
principle was to lead the hot gases issuing from a furnace
through a fire-brick chamber and then to use this chamber,
when hot, to preheat the air supplied to the fuel. In order
that the arrangement should be continuous two such chambers

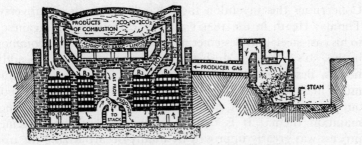

FIG. 39.   Principle of the regenerative furnace.

were needed, of which one at any time was being heated by
the gases from the furnace, while the other was heating the air
to be supplied thereto. When the former was fully hot and the
latter had somewhat cooled, the hot gases were diverted to the
second and the air drawn from the first. Siemens found that,
not only was 70–80% of the fuel saved but that a very high
temperature resulted. The principle of regenerative heating
was applied by Cowper to the blast-furnace in 1857. In 1861
the Siemens brothers patented the use of a gas-producer to
turn solid fuel into gas which should be used in a regenerative
furnace, thus enabling both air and fuel-gas to be preheated.
Regenerative furnaces had the advantage of giving flame free
from ash, etc., and a very high temperature. They were at
once adopted for glass-making by Messrs. Chance, and were
also used for puddling and for melting steel.

The possibility of making steel by melting together the low-

H*

carbon wrought-iron and the high-carbon cast-iron had been suggested as early as 1722 but remained impracticable because the temperature required was so high. P. and B. Martin, in France, were experimenting with this process in the early 1860's, but could not overcome the temperature difficulty. But with the regenerative gas-furnace the required temperatures became readily attainable, and in 1867 Siemens patented the making of steel by melting cast-iron with low-carbon iron, such as wrought-iron or steel, or with iron oxide (iron ore). This process, known as the Siemens-Martin or open-hearth process, has stood the test of time and is still the greatest producer of steel.

A very important adjunct to both the Bessemer and the Siemens processes was the addition of manganese, which removed the tendency of the steel to be brittle at a red-heat. Concerning this invention there has been much controversy. Thomas Heath in the 1840's added ' carburet of manganese ' to his cast-steel, and Bessemer maintained that this was common in the '50's. Robert Mushet, however, claimed that the addition to Bessemer steel of spiegel-eisen, a cast-iron containing much manganese and carbon, was his own invention: he took out patents for this but, not being a man of means, he could not maintain them. It is certain, however, that the Bessemer process was greatly improved by totally decarburizing the iron and then converting it into steel by addition of spiegel-eisen or some other composition of manganese and carbon. A disadvantage of spiegel-eisen was its high carbon content, which meant that if enough manganese were added the proportion of carbon in the steel would be too great; consequently ferro-manganese was introduced in 1868 to replace it.

Neither the Bessemer nor the Siemens process could as yet utilize ores rich in phosphorus, but this problem was soon to be solved by Sidney Gilchrist Thomas (a police-court clerk with a passion for chemistry) in collaboration with his cousin, Percy Gilchrist. In 1875 it struck him that the problem could be solved if the Bessemer converter were lined with a refractory substance that would combine with phosphorus. Success was attained by the use of a lining of magnesian lime, and the process was brought into successful operation in 1879. Soon afterwards the same principle was applied to the open-hearth process. The slag formed in these processes contained a notable proportion of calcium phosphate. It was at first treated as rubbish, but in 1882–83 finely-ground basic slag was tried in Germany as a fertilizer and has remained one of the most important of plant-foods.

The further developments of steel have come about through investigations of the effect of alloying metals or other elements therewith. Between 1859 and 1861 Mushet took out twenty patents for the manufacture of alloys of iron, tungsten and chromium. His experiments with tungsten alloys led to the invention, round about 1870, of the celebrated Mushet ' self-hardening ' steel.

The great development of special steels had, however, to await the production of the more refractory metals by the aluminothermic process (p. 386).

The Phosphorus Industry

Almost the only use for phosphorus in the first three-quarters of the nineteenth century was in making matches. Phosphorus was discovered in the seventeenth century, but its preparation was not in any sense an industry until the demand for matches made it so. The original preparation was from urine, a hogshead of which yielded but an ounce of phosphorus. The essential improvement which made its manufacture possible was Scheele's discovery (1769) that bones contained a considerable quantity of phosphorus. The process practised in the early nineteenth century was to treat crushed bones with sulphuric acid, extract the phosphoric acid with water, evaporate it, mix it with charcoal and distil at a high temperature, condensing the fumes of phosphorus in water.

Matches

Before the introduction of matches in the early nineteenth century the making of fire was comparatively slow and un-certain, and where possible a light was obtained from an existing fire. Fires often remained unextinguished for genera-tions. Wood and charcoal were the usual fuels, so it was almost always possible to find a glowing ember among the ashes or borrow one from a neighbour. It was, however, sometimes necessary to make fire, and the most ancient method was by friction. The many devices employed are outside the scope of a work on the history of chemistry. Suffice it to say that the drill, plough and saw were all efficient means of heating wood to the ignition point. In Græco-Roman times an ivy-wood block was drilled with a stick of laurel turned by a bow and string. Much skill is needed to obtain a light by such means.

Alternatively a light was obtained by striking steel with flint, quartzite or pyrites and receiving the spark on tinder (scorched linen) or other dry combustible material. This requires some practice, for the sparks from steel are by no means so plentiful and hot as those from the cerium-iron alloys now used in cigarette-lighters.

The glowing tinder did not easily give a flame and it was usual to apply to it a sulphur-match, which very easily caught fire. This consisted of a splinter of wood (or some other combustible) tipped with a little sulphur.[1] Sulphur-matches are recorded as early as 1530 and are probably a much more ancient invention. Thus we know that the Romans impregnated candle-wicks with sulphur, and they may well have used sulphur matches. These were employed for obtaining a flame, not only from glowing tinder, but also from the embers of a wood-fire.

Finally burning-mirrors or lenses could be used. There are some indications that the ancients occasionally used them for ritual purposes; they were certainly rarities in the Middle Ages, but in the seventeenth century were a recognized means of obtaining a light.

The use of phosphorus for making fire dates from the closing years of the eighteenth century. The simplest form of phosphorus lighter, dating from before 1790, was a match or wax taper tipped with phosphorus and enclosed in a small close-fitting glass tube. By breaking the tube the phosphorus was made to catch alight. ' Phosphoric or philosophical bottles ', dating from 1786, were small glass bottles, the inner walls of which were coated with partly oxidized yellow phosphorus. The bottles were, of course, kept corked; to obtain a light, a

---

[1] Sulphur matches were often made at home. Swift's Stella once called to her servants " to know what ill Smell was in the kitchen? They answered, they were making matches: Well, said she, I have heard Matches were made in Heaven, but by the Brimstone, one would think they were made in Hell " (*Works of Dean Swift.* Dodsley. 1750. Vol. X. 244).

sulphur-match was pushed into the bottle, turned round and quickly drawn out, whereupon the phosphorus sticking to it caught fire.

The earliest type of self-igniting match contained no phosphorus. The stick was tipped with potassium chlorate and sugar and was dipped into a small phial containing concentrated sulphuric acid, which caused it to ignite. These were made in France shortly after 1805. The invention of matches tipped with a mixture containing white phosphorus is said to date from 1809 and to have been a French invention, but it is clear that neither these nor any of the early phosphorus matches were a practical success.

A new principle was introduced by the ' Temple of Vesta ' (1807), which consisted of a hydrogen generator, the jet of gas from which was to be ignited by a spark from an electrophorus. A more convenient method of ignition was provided by Döbereiner (1823), who designed a hydrogen generator from which, on turning a tap, a jet of hydrogen was directed upon a piece of spongy platinum. This acted as a catalyst for the combination of the hydrogen and air and soon became hot enough to ignite the jet. The Döbereiner lamp had a certain vogue, but the platinum catalyst soon became ' poisoned ' and had to be replaced.

John Walker in 1826 used a mixture of antimony sulphide, potassium chlorate and gum arabic to form the heads of matches, to be ignited by pinching between glass-paper and sharply withdrawing, but these were uncertain in action. The really important step was the use of a mixture of yellow phosphorus, sulphur and potassium chlorate, invented by Dr. Charles Sauria in France in 1830 and brought into use as ' Congreves ' in 1832. Phosphorus matches rapidly became popular in all civilized countries. White phosphorus, the only kind then known, had begun to be made in quantity in France about 1825, and in 1844 Albright introduced the industry into England.

Matches became articles of ordinary use from about 1840 onward. The typical match-head of the early nineteenth century contained about 5 % of white phosphorus together with potassium chlorate and other combustibles, and from the user's point of view was very satisfactory. But continued exposure to the vapour of white phosphorus slowly produced a terrible and agonizing necrosis of the jaw-bone, which was generally prevalent among match-workers, especially in the small dirty workshops where much of the work was done; the large, cleanly and well-ventilated factories were less dangerous but by no means free from the disease. The effects of phosphorus necrosis began to be noticed in 1839: five years later Schrötter discovered red phosphorus, which produces no vapour and does not cause necrosis of the jaw. In 1844–45 Gustave Pasch in Sweden and Professor R. Bottger of Frankfurt-on-Main suggested the principle of the safety match, red phosphorus being incorporated with the striking surface and the match-head being without phosphorus. These matches were not altogether successful, having a tendency to explode. In 1851 the manufacture of red phosphorus in England was improved, and in 1855 J. E. Lundstrom invented methods of making a safety match that was found by its users to be satisfactory. In 1856 they were manufactured in Britain by the firm which is now Messrs. Bryant & May, but they were not at first so popular as white-phosphorus matches, which could readily be struck on any surface. The modern strike-anywhere match was made possible in 1898 by the introduction by Sévene and Cahen of Paris of tetraphosphorus trisulphide (sesquisulphide of phosphorus) as the combustible material. The safety match is, however, the most popular, constituting about 60 % of the matches sold. Protection of the worker by the prohibition of white phosphorus might then, at least, have been expected. Denmark and Switzerland, it is true, prohibited all but safety matches in the 1870's, but the rest of the world permitted the use of white phosphorus matches until after the Berne Conference on the subject in 1905–6. In Great Britain they were prohibited in 1910; in the U.S.A. it was constitutionally impossible to prohibit them, but in 1913 they were made subject to a prohibitive tax. Some few countries permitted the use of white phosphorus matches as lately as 1939. Match-making machinery is perhaps beyond the scope of this volume, but it may be noted that the American makers were pioneers in rendering the process almost automatic.

Illuminants

The only artificial illuminant in use in the years before 1860 was the naked flame; in English towns the field was fairly equally divided between candles, lamps and coal-gas, but in the country candles and lamps were the only competitors.

Candles at the close of the eighteenth century could be made of fats or waxes. The tallow-candle, made of fat, was the cheapest but gave out an objectionable smell, due to the glycerol with which the fatty acids were combined. Bees-wax is not a fat and contains no glycerol; candles made from it did not suffer from this defect and had the further advantage of remaining hard in a heated atmosphere, but they were relatively expensive—in 1819, about 4s. 6d. a pound. Spermaceti, contained in the skull of the sperm-whale, is also a wax: it had all the merits of bees-wax and at the same time was much whiter. The sperm-whale had been hunted by American whalers from 1690, but spermaceti was regarded as a medical or cosmetic material and did not find extensive use for candles in Europe until the years after 1770.

These natural illuminants were supplemented in the early nineteenth century by an artificial product known as stearine, which consisted of the fatty acids made by saponifying fats. The researches of Chevreul (1815) had shown that fats were compounds of glycerol and fatty acids, and J. L. Gay-Lussac patented the making of fatty acids for use in candles by the conversion of fats into soaps, which were then decomposed by mineral acids, setting free the fatty acids. This process was exploited in France as early as 1833, and in England by Messrs. Price in 1835. In 1840 they made white candles at 1s. a pound from equal proportions of stearic acid from tallow and hard fat from coconut oil. Frémy discovered the saponification of fats by acids in 1836, but neither his nor Gay-Lussac's process achieved much success.

Saponification by steam was the important step. Gwynne was experimenting with steam distillation at Battersea in 1843, and by 1847 it was widely used by Messrs. Price. After 1850 the stearine candle became very popular and is still produced to-day. George Wilson in 1854 took out a patent for purification of the glycerine so produced by steam distillation, a process which made it a relatively cheap and common material. The bees-wax candle soon disappeared except for ritual purposes.

In 1840 paraffin wax was first produced by James Young from the oil distilled from shale: this wax (made from Burmese petroleum) was first used for candles about 1857. The

Pennsylvania oil-fields of 1859 provided ample raw material, and this wax rapidly became cheaper and entirely replaced tallow. Stearine and spermaceti, however, held their own against it because of their immunity from softening in a hot room.

The chief competitor of the candle was the lamp. The lamps of the first half of the nineteenth century necessarily burned vegetable oils. These had low capillarity and would not rise far up a wick. For this reason the reservoir either had to be very low and flat, so that the fall of the level of the oil should be minimized, or some kind of forced or gravity feed had to be provided.

The illuminating power of these vegetable oils was inferior to that of the modern paraffin oil. Attempts were made to remedy these defects by burning terpene products, such as ' camphine ' (redistilled oil of turpentine mixed with alcohol), which gave a more brilliant light, though at a higher cost; but the real popularity of the lamp came only with the introduction of mineral oils after 1855 (p. 270).

The third type of illuminant was coal-gas, to be discussed in the succeeding section. The process of setting up gas-works and piping houses for gas was not very rapid and the light given by the naked gas-flame, though brighter than several candles, was not so conveniently placed for illuminating what was to be seen: moreover, the early coal-gas contained appreciable quantities of sulphur compounds which formed sulphur dioxide and trioxide and damaged the textiles with which the Victorian room abounded. It may be said that gas-lighting was at first more favoured for streets and public places than for the private dwelling-house, and that its very general adoption belongs to the second half of the nineteenth century. The introduction of the steatite burner in place of the metal orifice, which oxidized and corroded, was perhaps the decisive factor in the public's acceptance of it.

The Coal-Gas Industry

The gas industry, unlike most of the chemical industries of its time, was something perfectly new and unheard of till the close of the eighteenth century. Its forerunner was the technique of the handling of gases developed, especially by Priestley, in the 1770's. J. J. Becher and Henry Searle were granted a patent for making pitch and tar from coal in furnaces as early as 1681, and the knowledge that an inflammable gas was evolved from it probably dates from this time. Several persons seem to have experimented with coal gas during the century, but it was only from *c.* 1785 that serious attempts were made to put the gas to use. We may first note Lord Dundonald's patent for making coal-tar by distillation. This was worked in 1787, and the gas evolved was noticed and actually used by the workmen to give themselves light to work by. Lebon in France, a couple of years earlier, had the notion of using the gas from distillation of wood for the same purpose; he developed the process, patented it in 1799, and gave a display of it in 1802; the light given by wood-gas was, however, but a poor one. Murdoch carried out experiments on the utilization of coal-gas for lighting, first on his own between 1792 and 1798, and later at the works of Boulton and Watt, where the first public display of gas-lighting was made in 1802. An enterprising German, by name Winsor, exploited Lebon's work and took out an English patent for his own process in 1806, and in the following year Pall Mall was lit by gas-light. The Chartered Gas-light and Coke Company was established in 1812, and within ten years most of the great English cities had gas-works.

The coal when distilled left a residue of coke. The quantity of coke made by the gas industry was for a long time small compared with that required in industry, for coke had been in use at least from the seventeenth century and was much employed in metallurgy. At this period it was commonly made by stacking coal in heaps and setting light to it; sometimes it was covered by earth in much the same fashion as the wood used by charcoal burners. Until quite recent years coal continued to be coked without collecting the by-products.

From the point of view of the chemical industry, great interest attaches to the purification of coal-gas and the separation of the by-products.

The gases evolved were cooled and condensed, forming a watery liquid ('ammoniacal liquor') and gas-tar. The possibility of making ammonium salts and ammonia from the former was very soon demonstrated. Ammonium sulphate was made by treating the liquor with calcium sulphate, and ammonium chloride by treating the sulphate with common salt. Despite this new and convenient source of ammonia, the greatest quantity of it continued to be made by the distillation of bones and from the imported sal-ammoniac made from camel-dung. However, by the 1850's the production of ammonium salts from gas-liquor for use as fertilizers was an important industry.

The great importance of gas-tar dates only from the period of synthetic organic chemistry (Chapter Sixteen). None the less tar was very early separated into an ' essential oil ', known as coal-oil or naphtha, and pitch (a word formerly employed for the residues of the distillation of wood-tar). Thus before 1830 Anderson was distilling ' naphtha ' from coal-tar for Macintosh to use as a solvent for rubber. By 1838 creosote was also being made from tar and used for the protection of wooden railway-sleepers. The pitch was made into an ' arti-ficial asphalt ' used for paving, waterproofing tanks, etc., and was also used for making briquettes with coal-dust, as early as 1838. The volatile products, benzene, toluene, xylenes, etc., were thought of even in the '60's as promising solvents, and perhaps illuminants, rather than as materials for the synthesis of new bodies. Mansfield, who lost his life in the process, worked out the method of obtaining reasonably pure benzene from tar in 1849, but it was only after the beginning of the manufacture of synthetic dyes (pp. 235 *et seq.*) that benzene became an important chemical intermediate.

The purification of the uncondensable part of the gas from hydrogen sulphide and ammonia was very soon worked out. The first method of removing the sulphurous impurities was by means of lime. This was effective, but the ' gas-lime ' which resulted was a very objectionable substance and difficult to dispose of. Purification by means of iron oxide was intro-duced by Frank Clark Hills in 1849. We may say that the gas-works of 1860 differed very little in principle from that of the present day, greatly as the latter exceeds it in size, mechanization and refinement of control.

Use of Gas

After 1880 gas was increasingly used in gas-engines. It was not, however, much used for heating, although Bunsen, about 1855, and others before him, had shown how it could be burned with a smokeless flame. While domestic service was cheap and plentiful there was, indeed, little inducement to burn any fuel other than coal. Gas-lighting was, however, revolutionized by Welsbach's invention of the gas-mantle between 1885 and 1893, in which year he discovered the ideal mantle-composition of 99% thoria and 1% ceria. This enabled a given quantity of gas to give far more light and enabled it to compete with electricity as an illuminant till the end of the first decade of the twentieth century. The inverted mantle, introduced about 1900, much increased the popularity of this means of lighting, while the use of high-pressure burners from about 1908 was, and still is, of much value for street-lighting.

Coke was used in gigantic quantities by the metallurgical industries of the nineteenth century. Some was obtained from gas-works, but most of it was made by burning coal in covered heaps or, later, in beehive ovens. The collection of the by-products of coking-ovens began only about 1900, and was not universally adopted until about 1930 in America and 1935 in Great Britain.

Miscellaneous Inorganic Products

The development of so many new industries in the first half of the nineteenth century called for cheaper and more extensive manufacture of many chemicals. Hydrogen was made on a large scale for filling balloons and for the limelight. Some new medical products were discovered or reintroduced: hypophosphites, bismuth subnitrate and nitrous oxide are examples. Photographic chemicals opened up a new field of chemical manufacture, and one in which high purity was needed. Bromine and iodine and their salts, pure silver nitrate, sodium thiosulphate (hypo), sodium sulphite, potassium cyanide, gallic and pyrogallic acids, were brought into commerce in this manner.

The manufacture of boric acid and borax from the vapours emitted by the fumaroles of Tuscany became an important industry at the beginning of the nineteenth century.

Water-supply

The supply of water, whether for domestic purposes or for industry, is an engineering problem, but the control of its quality and the removal of impurities has long been the province of the chemist. Water for the chemical industries may be derived from public water undertakings, but large works commonly take their supplies from natural sources and themselves apply whatever treatment may be required.

In the prescientific era of applied chemistry water was taken as it was found, but with the development of town-supplies the desirability of sand-filtration for water containing visible impurities was early recognized and was applied at the Chelsea waterworks by James Simpson in 1829. Studies of the ætiology of cholera showed that water so filtered was much less likely to transmit the disease and the process was put on a scientific basis in the 'seventies and 'eighties when the rôle of bacteria in transmitting disease came to be understood.

Chemical treatment of water had been envisaged as early as the mid-eighteenth century. The hardness of certain waters, their failure to lather until much soap had been added, had long been known, as had the fact that this property was removed by the addition of wood-ashes or lye. Francis Home and later Henry Cavendish investigated the property and the latter suggested the use of lime-water for softening water. The distinction between temporary and permanent hardness was soon recognized, and in 1841 Thomas Clark, Professor of Chemistry in Aberdeen, put forward his method of removing temporary hardness on the large scale by adding lime so as to precipitate the dissolved calcium bicarbonate as the insoluble carbonate. This process still has a limited field.

The ion-exchange process was introduced and put on a practical footing by Gans in 1905. That calcium and ammonium salts could exchange radicals in passing through soils had been proved by Thompson and Way in 1848-54 in the course of investigations upon the agricultural use of lime. In 1876 Lemberg worked out the theory of the process. The chief contribution of Gans was to show that natural and synthetic zeolites could act in this way. The calcium ions in hard water passed through a bed of zeolite were taken up by it, liberating sodium ions: when these sodium ions had been fully replaced by calcium, the zeolite could be restored by passing through it a concentrated solution of common salt. This cycle of operations is familiar to those who possess a domestic water-softener.

In 1935 Adams and Holmes discovered the power of some synthetic resins (p. 266) to absorb and exchange ions, and these materials can be used to remove all ions from water and leave it as pure as water several times redistilled.

The purification of water is not only a domestic convenience but an industrial necessity. High duty boilers require water that does not deposit scale; dissolved gases have also to be removed. Dye and foodstuff manufacturers require water freed from certain deleterious substances: on the other hand water for brewing requires to be of a certain degree of hardness. Water treatment has in fact become a characteristic feature of the modern chemical economy.

CHAPTER FIFTEEN

The Rise of Theoretical Organic Chemistry

Theories of Organic Chemistry before 1860

WE have seen in Chapter Thirteen how the simple atomic theory of Dalton and Berzelius came to serve the needs of chemical industry.

The inorganic chemists and analysts were not deeply concerned about the conventions to be adopted in writing formulæ, as long as these met the simple requirements of chemical calculations. But the need was felt by many organic chemists, whose science was rapidly advancing from the 1840's onward, of some more detailed interpretation of their own analytical figures. The attribution of formulæ of greater complexity than those satisfying the inorganic chemist was an obvious path to take. Chemists had analysed hundreds of organic compounds whose molecules were made up of carbon, hydrogen and oxygen atoms, and the relation between these compounds could not begin to be understood until their true formulæ were known. From the analyst's point of view it makes no difference whether we write the formula of benzene as C_2H (carbon $= 6$) or CH (carbon $= 12$), or, as we write it to-day, C_6H_6; but from the point of view of understanding the relation of benzene to other hydrocarbons (the organic chemist's point of view) it makes all the difference. Thus the second formula, CH, shows benzene as closely related to the chemical compounds containing a single carbon atom, *e.g.* methane: but the last shows it as related to compounds containing six atoms of carbon, *e.g.* ' carbolic acid '. Again, there were two well-known compounds, commonly called alcohol and ether, whose formulæ we now know to be C_2H_6O and $C_4H_{10}O$ respectively. From these formulæ it is easy to understand their relation, namely, that ether consists of two molecules of alcohol less one of water:

$$2C_2H_6O = C_4H_{10}O + H_2O.$$

If, however, the formula of alcohol is doubled and written as $C_4H_{12}O_2$ the relationship is at once obscured.

By the middle of the century it had become clear that within the organic molecule there could exist groups of atoms that retained their identity in chemical changes. The work of Wöhler and Liebig in 1831 on oil of bitter almonds showed the existence of a radical ' benzoyl ', a group of atoms which could undergo reaction as a whole and preserve its identity. By 1850 the formulation of bodies as compounds of such radicals as ethyl, acetyl, etc., had become common. This was a great advance and has become a permanent part of our chemical system. Thus we write the formula of acetic acid to-day as $CH_3.CO.OH$ to indicate that these three groups of atoms, CH_3 (methyl), CO (carbonyl) and OH (hydroxyl), retain their identity in many of the chemical changes of acetic acid and imply characteristic properties which other compounds that contain them also show. Throughout the first half of the nineteenth century an enormous amount of work was done on the establishment of these groupings, and this was made very hard by the uncertainty concerning formulæ. A. Kekulé illustrated this fact by giving nineteen different ways of writing the formula of acetic acid!

Until the years round 1860 the formulæ of organic compounds were the subject of controversy and confusion. The favourite theories of the structure of molecules were those known as the type-theories. The formulæ of certain compounds were deduced or assumed, often on insufficient grounds, and other formulæ were derived from these by substituting other atoms and groups for those of the type. Bodies of the same type were supposed to have analogous chemical behaviour. The type theory was put forward by J. B. A. Dumas in 1839 and was both simplified and extended by Gerhardt in the late 1840's.

Thus Dumas wrote:

TYPE	Marsh gas (methane)	C_2	H_8
DERIVATIVES OF TYPE	Methyl chloride	C_2	H_6 Cl_2
	Methylene chloride	C_2	H_4 Cl_4
	Chloroform	C_2	H_2 Cl_6
	Carbon tetrachloride	C_2	Cl_8

a formulation which went far to show the relation between these compounds.

Gerhardt based his formulæ on simple inorganic compounds. Thus as examples of the water type we may write:

$$\text{Water} \qquad \left.\begin{array}{l} H \\ H \end{array}\right\}O$$

$$\text{Ethyl alcohol} \qquad \left.\begin{array}{l} C_2H_5 \\ H \end{array}\right\}O$$

$$\text{Ethyl ether} \qquad \left.\begin{array}{l} C_2H_5 \\ C_2H_5 \end{array}\right\}O$$

$$\text{Acetic acid} \qquad \left.\begin{array}{l} C_2H_3O \\ H \end{array}\right\}O$$

$$\text{Acetic anhydride} \qquad \left.\begin{array}{l} C_2H_3O \\ C_2H_3O \end{array}\right\}O$$

These type-formulæ at least established a true relationship between members of groups of closely related compounds, but they had great defects as compared with the modern formulæ in use after 1860. In the first place there was no agreement even as to the formula of the type-substance: thus, according to the atomic weights adopted, water might be HO or H_2O; methane C_4H_4, C_2H_8 or CH_4. Secondly, they illustrated only one feature of the structure of a compound, out of many equally important. Thirdly, *they did not even intend to indicate a real structure*, or to copy the arrangement of atoms in the molecule, but simply to group the symbols of the atoms so as best to express the reactions of the compound of which the formula was in question.

Cannizzaro's Establishment of True Atomic Weights

The greatest work of the decade 1850–60 was the discovery of a means by which formulæ could be determined with reasonable certainty.

Those who are familiar with elementary chemical theory will realize that, given the percentage composition of a compound, the atomic weights of the elements it contains and its molecular weight, its formula (though not its structure) is settled beyond dispute. The percentages could readily be obtained by combustion analysis: thus acetic acid was known, independently of any theory, to contain 40·0% carbon, 6·7% hydrogen and 53·3% oxygen. But before the formula of acetic acid could be shown to be $C_2H_4O_2$, the atomic weights [1] of carbon, oxygen and hydrogen had to be agreed as 12, 16 and 1, and the molecular weight of acetic acid had to be shown to be 60. Before the year 1860 there existed no such agreement about atomic weights, which were generally taken as equal to what we call equivalents; and the meanings of the terms ' atom ' and ' molecule ' were not always clearly distinguished: thus chemists often spoke of ' an atom of water '.

The first sound method of discovering true atomic and molecular weights stands to the credit of the Italian Stanislao Cannizzaro (1826–1910), who showed that the half-forgotten hypothesis of his countryman Amadeo Avogadro (1811), *that equal volumes of gases and vapours contain equal numbers of molecules*, agreed with all the facts and could be used to discover atomic and molecular weights. The principle had been proposed from time to time but never generally accepted. The chief objection to it was on the ground that it led to the conclusion (quite correct, as we now know) that oxygen, hydrogen, nitrogen and other elementary gases consisted of double molecules, O_2, H_2, N_2, etc. To the chemist of the time, bred up to believe with Davy and Berzelius that chemical combination was due to opposite electrical charges on the combining atoms, it seemed that only unlike atoms could combine, and that the combination of two identical atoms was most improbable.

Cannizzaro was Professor of Chemistry in Genoa from 1855; he was not provided with a laboratory, and this may be the reason why his mind turned to chemical theory! At any rate, in 1858 he published a brief *Sketch of a Course of Chemical Philosophy*, in which the whole scheme of determining atomic and molecular weights was expressed with wonderful clarity. He showed, moreover, that the results of his arguments based upon the weights of volumes of gases and vapours led to the *same* atomic weights as did the generalization of Dulong and Petit, put forward in 1819, that the product of the atomic weight and specific heat of an element is approximately equal to 6·4. Once the atomic weights of the elements composing a compound and its molecular weight were known, its true formula (the number and kind of the atoms in its molecule) necessarily followed. The adoption of Cannizzaro's system

---

[1] For the purpose of these arguments atomic weights rounded off to the nearest whole number are used.

was not very rapid, but by about 1863 all the more enlightened chemists adopted it, though the older formulæ (*e.g.* HO for water) persisted in some chemical textbooks even up to the 1880's. Thus from 1858 chemists had the means of arriving at correct atomic and molecular weights and could ascertain the formulæ of all substances that could be turned into vapour. But, since the only method of obtaining molecular weights was by ascertaining the vapour density of a compound, the true formulæ of non-volatile compounds, such as urea or glucose, remained unknown. Thus the composition of the latter substance showed that the formula was some multiple of CH_2O, but the only arguments which could show whether it was CH_2O, $C_4H_8O_4$, $C_6H_{12}O_6$ or $C_{24}H_{48}O_{24}$ were based on its chemical reactions alone and could not be conclusive. A great advance was therefore made when, about 1882, F. M. Raoult showed that molecular weights of dissolved substances could be ascertained from the freezing point of their solutions. Other methods were developed, but all were dependent on measurements made upon the compounds in the state of vapour or solution: so the molecular weights and true formulæ of bodies neither volatile nor soluble (such as the silicates that form the rocks) could not be discovered until Bragg perfected his methods of X-ray analyses in the period round 1920.

Cannizzaro's discovery was of great value in organic chemistry, for most of the carbon compounds are volatile. But its most valuable contribution was a single universal system of atomic weights founded on experimental evidence and incontrovertible reasoning. This system alone made possible the periodic Law of Mendelejef, which is the foundation of systematic inorganic chemistry: furthermore, it made possible the valency theory and the discovery of structural formulæ, which are the foundation of the science of organic chemistry and the means of development of the organic chemical industry.

Valency and the Structure-Theory

The organic chemists, as we have seen, had for some little time been attempting to break up their formulæ into atom-groupings that indicated the chemical behaviour of the substances they dealt with. These groupings were based on the chemical reactions of the bodies in question and, as is shown by the number of alternative formulæ, there was a notable element of individual judgment in propounding them. What was needed was a method which should lead inescapably to a certain formulation of the arrangement of the atoms in the molecule, and a considerable step towards this was made by the theories of valency and of atomic linkage.

The valency (quantivalence) of an atom is the number of univalent atoms with which it will combine. Thus Frankland in 1852 pointed out that certain elements—nitrogen, phosphorus, antimony, arsenic—generally combined with three or five equivalents of other elements, but, owing to the uncertainty that then prevailed as to atomic weights, the theory could not be further advanced. From about 1854 F. A. Kekulé considered the question, with especial reference to organic chemistry. Kekulé was trained as an architect, and after he adopted chemistry as his life's work he still had an architectural tendency—a consuming interest in molecular structure. At the beginning of his career (1854) Kekulé spent some time in England, where such men as A. W. Williamson and W. Odling were giving attention to these very problems. He has left a remarkable account of the manner in which he arrived at his two great notions, that of the linkage of atoms into a definite structure, and later (1865) of the hexagonal ring-formula for benzene.

One fine summer evening I was returning by the last omnibus, ' outside ' as usual, through the deserted streets of the metropolis, which are at other times so full of life. I fell into a reverie, and lo, the atoms were gambolling before my eyes! Whenever, hitherto these diminutive beings had appeared to me they had always been in motion; but up to that time I had never been able to discern the nature of their motion. Now, however, I saw how, frequently, two smaller atoms united to form a pair, how a larger one embraced two smaller ones, how still larger kept hold of three or even four of the smaller; whilst the whole kept whirling in a giddy dance. I saw how the larger ones formed a chain dragging the smaller ones after them, but only at the ends of the chain. . . . The cry of the conductor: ' Clapham Road', awakened me from my dreaming; but I spent a part of the night putting on paper at least sketches of these dream forms. This was the origin of the *Structure-Theory*.

From 1857 Kekulé introduced the notion that carbon is quadrivalent and that in organic compounds the carbon atoms are linked together by one or more of their four units of combining power, the rest being available for attachment of other atoms and groups. In 1858 the Scotsman A. C. Couper independently came to almost the same conclusion as Kekulé about the structure of organic compounds.

The acceptance of the valency theory made the assignment of a structural formula to an organic compound very much easier. Thus in the case of acetic acid, cited above, the formula, settled by the application of Cannizzaro's rules as $C_2H_4O_2$, could not have any other structure than

$$
\begin{array}{c}
\text{H} \\
| \\
\text{H—C—C—O—H} \\
|\quad\ \| \\
\text{H}\quad\text{O}
\end{array}
$$

(where each line represents the mutual satisfaction of one unit of combining power) if the carbon and oxygen atoms had valencies of four, one and two respectively. Moreover, this formula was confirmed by the fact that acetic acid shared properties with other bodies that could be shown to contain CH_3, CO or OH groupings. In other cases there was the possibility of doubt. Ethyl alcohol and methyl ether both had the formula C_2H_6O. This could be written as CH_3—CH_2—OH or as CH_3—O—CH_3, but the likeness of alcohol to other bodies that certainly contained the —OH group made it clear that its formula was the first-named. From 1858 onward a wonderful activity ensued. Arguments based on valency considerations and the likenesses between compounds soon settled the formulæ of all the simpler compounds; many of these had, of course, already been propounded by earlier chemists, whose formulæ had only to be transposed into the new mode.

One well-known compound presented serious difficulties, namely benzene, C_6H_6, in which there seemed to be too little hydrogen to satisfy the new valency-rules. In 1865 Kekulé, then at Ghent, solved the problem in another of his half-waking dreams.

> I was sitting writing at my textbook, but the work did not progress; my thoughts were elsewhere. I turned my chair to the fire and dozed. Again the atoms were gambolling before my

eyes. This time the smaller groups kept modestly in the background. My mental eye, rendered more acute by repeated visions of this kind, could now distinguish larger structures, of manifold conformation: long rows, sometimes more closely fitted together; all turning and twisting in snakelike motion. But look! what was that? One of the snakes had seized hold of its own tail, and the form whirled mockingly before our eyes. As if by a flash of lightning I awoke; and this time also I spent the rest of the night in working out the consequences of the hypothesis. Let us learn to dream, gentlemen, then perhaps we shall find the truth . . . but let us beware of publishing our dreams before they have been put to the proof by the waking understanding.[1]

So in 1865 Kekulé solved the problem of the formula of benzene, whose derivatives form a large proportion of the known organic compounds, by postulating a hexagonal ring-formula with alternating single and double bonds:

$$
\begin{array}{c}
H \\
| \\
C \\
\end{array}
$$

The ring-formula was never seriously questioned, but the disposition of the valency bonds was a matter of discussion for three-quarters of a century and has only lately been resolved in terms of the theory of resonance (p. 354). This formula of Kekulé opened the way to the scientific study of the aromatic compounds, which had even then begun to be industrially important in the dye industry.

Three-dimensional Formulæ

From 1865 onward it was possible, and usually not difficult, to map out on paper a pattern of atoms and groups which explained the reactions of the organic compound it represented.

---

[1] *Journal of the Chemical Society.* Trans. 1898. p. 100.

Not all chemists believed that these patterns really existed in nature as they wrote them; for they seem to have thought of them rather as a notation than as a picture. Many cases of isomerism, *i.e.* the existence of two or more different substances whose molecules contained the same number and kind of atoms, were easily explained when two or more possible arrangements of these atoms could be shown to be consistent with the valency rules and with the chemical behaviour of the compounds. But investigation showed that in some cases different structural formulæ could not be found for all the isomers unless these formulæ were represented three-dimensionally—as solids and not as mere two-dimensional diagrams on paper. This went further to convince chemists of the reality of

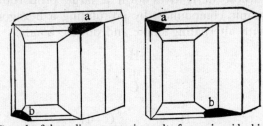

FIG. 40. Crystals of the sodium ammonium salt of racemic acid which are mirror images of each other and yield d-tartaric and l-tartaric acid respectively.

molecules than anything else until the mapping of them by physical means after 1920.

Louis Pasteur realized the problem and indicated the nature of its solution in 1848, long before the structure-theory was formulated. As early as 1815 it was known that certain compounds, in the solid state or in solution, rotated the plane of polarized light, some to the right, some to the left. Two very similar acids, tartaric acid and racemic acid, were known; and in 1844 E. Mitscherlich observed that tartaric acid had this property of 'optical activity', whereas racemic acid had not. Quartz crystals were known to exist in two forms, one of which rotated polarized light to the left and the other to the right; they were also known to have little 'hemihedral' facets, differently placed in each form, so that one crystal was the mirror image of the other, as are a left and a right shoe. Pasteur noticed in 1848 that crystals of tartrates had certain small facets similar to those of quartz crystals, which also are optically active.

Pasteur carefully crystallized a salt of the optically inactive racemic acid and showed that the crystals were of two kinds, each with hemihedral faces but so situated that each kind was the mirror-image of the other (Fig. 40). He dissolved these different crystals separately and found that the solutions were optically active. From them he made two different optically active acids, rotating the plane of polarized light to an equal extent but in different directions, and showed that these, mixed in equal proportions, formed racemic acid. He worked out three general methods of separating optically active forms from the inactive mixtures.

How did these tartaric acids differ in structure? Pasteur suggested in 1860 that the individual molecules, like the crystals, were asymmetric and could therefore exist in two

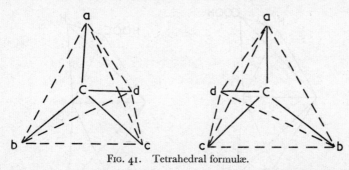

FIG. 41.   Tetrahedral formulæ.

forms, mirror-images of each other. He suggested that the atoms might be arranged in the form of a right-handed and left-handed screw or an irregular tetrahedron. Between 1860 and 1874, in the early days of the structure theory, there was speculation about the possibility that the four atoms or groups with which a carbon atom could combine might be situated at the corners of a tetrahedron (Fig. 41): and in 1874 that great chemical genius van't Hoff and a friend of his, Le Bel, arrived independently at the explanation of optical activity in terms of atomic structure. They showed that asymmetry of the molecule and optical activity occurred *when a carbon atom was attached to four different groups*. They boldly adopted the idea of the tetrahedral atom : furthermore, they did not offer the notion as merely an interesting speculation but developed the full consequences of the theory.

Van't Hoff's theory enabled him to explain another type of

isomerism which had given difficulty. Maleic and fumaric acid both had the formula HOOC—CH=CH—COOH, but were not identical in chemical properties. According to his tetrahedral theory the double bond was interpreted as meaning linkage along the edge of a tetrahedron. The two atoms so linked could evidently not rotate relatively to each other, and so two forms (Fig. 42) would be expected, which explained the existence of the two acids.

The older chemists were shocked at the suggestion that atoms were real bodies that could be arranged spatially, but to the younger chemists it brought a vivid belief in the reality of the molecules they talked about, for it demonstrated that these were solid three-dimensional bodies, like the real things

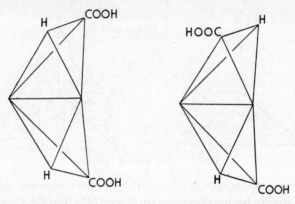

FIG. 42. Geometrical isomerism. *Left:* Maleic acid. *Right:* Fumaric acid.

of which they had experience. The study of these asymmetric molecules has given rise to a department of chemistry known as stereo-chemistry. In the early years of the twentieth century it was shown that optical activity can arise from many different types of asymmetry in the molecule, the carbon atom attached to four different groups being by no means the only source of it. Optically active compounds containing no carbon at all have been prepared.

Even at this stage there was a great deal more to know about the molecule. The nature of the linkage that held the atoms together was not known, nor was anything known about the sizes of molecules, the relative distances of the atoms in the molecule from each other, nor the extent of their independent movement. These matters were not, in fact, demonstrable until the twentieth century. Nevertheless, the structural ideas which we have outlined were worked out with great ingenuity and elaboration and were extremely successful in building up the science of organic chemistry, which by the 1880's had greatly excelled all other departments of chemistry in order and regularity.

The Idea of Organic Synthesis

Perhaps the most important idea of industrial organic chemistry is that of synthesis, the building up of complex molecules by linking together simpler molecules.

The idea of organic synthesis as a programme dates from the discovery by Wöhler in 1828 that, whether or not organic compounds were mysteriously made in animals and plants by a vital force, they could also be prepared by ordinary methods in the laboratory. He had prepared the animal product, urea, from the inorganic ammonium cyanate, and this discovery led Liebig and Wöhler to a magnificent anticipation of organic synthesis. Their words are worth quoting:

> The philosopher of chemistry will from this work draw the conclusion that the production of all organic matters in our laboratories, inasmuch as they do not belong any more to the organism, must be regarded not only as probable but as certain. Sugar, salicin and morphine will be made artificially. It is true we do not know the methods by which this final result will be reached, because the rudiments are unknown from which they are to be developed, but we shall know them in time. We have not to deal with bodies whose composition rests on assumptions, we know that with positive certainty; we know in what proportions they are combined; we know that they are products of forces of which we are cognisant.

Their prediction proved true. To-day, after 120 years, we have synthesized literally hundreds of thousands of compounds. It is true that only two of the three compounds that Liebig and Wöhler cite as subjects for synthesis has in fact been made in that way, but no organic chemist has any doubt that the one outstanding, morphine, will be synthesized before many years have elapsed.

But the enthusiasm of Liebig and Wöhler was not shared by their fellow-chemists. Indeed their triumphant synthesis of urea from ammonium cyanate was criticized because this substance had been prepared from cyanides which had been manufactured from animal materials. So the case for the possibility of synthesis of animal and plant material from inorganic sources remained to be proved. The effective freeing of organic chemistry from the idea of the vital force, and the advocacy of the idea of synthesis, was the work of P. E. M. Berthelot, soon after 1850. He started with the knowledge, derived from the work of Chevreul, that fats were compounds of glycerol with acids. It seemed possible to him then to combine glycerol with acids other than those found in natural fats, so giving *new* fatty bodies and exercising a creative power greater than that realized in nature. He was stimulated to try to build up the products of animals and plants from inorganic materials, and this task had for him a philosophic interest; for Berthelot, a strong rationalist and materialist, realized that the building up of simple compounds like alcohol or formates from the inorganic was the first step towards the identification of the life-process with chemical reactions—the unrealized ideal of the scientific materialist. In 1855–56 he made formic acid from carbon monoxide and other inorganic materials. He then made methane, ethylene and acetylene from such materials; and from ethylene he made alcohol, previously regarded as purely a product of plant material. Later he made benzene from acetylene. This work effectively broke down the barrier between organic and inorganic chemistry and presented synthesis as an attainable goal.

In the 1850's, when Berthelot's early work was being done, organic chemistry was still chaotic. The type-formulæ (p. 215) were not of much value and the idea of molecular structure had to await the work of Kekulé in the early '60's. Some general rules for forming certain classes of compound were known, but the rapid advance of synthesis had to wait for the two great principles already described, namely, the establishment of known molecular formulæ, following on the work of Cannizzaro (p. 217), and the ideas of structure and valency advanced by Kekulé (pp. 218–221). These principles enabled the chemist to know the molecular structure of what he sought to make and so to plan his methods.

Synthesis has had two chief aims: to prepare natural products by chemical methods and to prepare compounds which had never before existed. Both of these aims have been wonderfully realized in the industries which form the subject of the next chapter.

CHAPTER SIXTEEN

Industrial Organic Chemistry

Organic Chemical Industries before 1850

In the years before 1850 the organic chemical industry could scarcely be said to exist. A number of natural products were purified or otherwise treated, and a few newly discovered organic compounds were made on more than the laboratory scale.

In the carbohydrate field we may note that paper was still made almost exclusively from rags: the various textile fibres were not chemically treated except in the process of bleaching. Mercerizing had been invented, but did not come into general use until the 1890's. The only chemical treatments of cellulose were the making of the not fully nitrated nitro-cellulose, pyroxylin (for photographic and medical collodion), and the dry distillation of wood to make charcoal and acetic acid. This was an important industry in the U.S.A. and the Baltic countries and France. In many European countries charcoal remained the principal domestic and an important industrial fuel. The decolorizing and deodorizing powers of charcoal were discovered in 1794, and in 1811 the special efficacy of animal charcoal, made from bones, was discovered by Figuier and very soon applied in the sugar industry. Activated charcoal began to be developed about 1914, and has proved to be of great use not only in the sugar industry but also for absorbing the gasoline vapour contained in natural gas.

Starch-making was an important industry, in which the French were prominent. Most of the starch was used in the textile trade, but by the middle of the century it was being converted into glucose, for use in making beer and alcohol. Much starch was made into dextrin or British gum, which was used for the dressing of textiles and paper and in the preparation of colours for calico-printing.

Cane-sugar, an ancient industry, has already been discussed on pp. 151–152, but we may recall the fact that the decolorization of the syrup by bone-black, the use of the vacuum-pan for evaporation and of the centrifugal dryer all belong to the years 1800–50. Beet-sugar molasses was extensively converted into alcohol.

The distillation of alcohol from various fermented washes has been mentioned in Chapter Twelve. There was at this time great activity in the improvement of stills, but we should single out Coffey's still, invented in 1832, as the principal advance of the period before fractional distillation was seriously studied.

Rubber and gutta-percha came into use in the period we are discussing. Gutta-percha was first brought to Europe from Malaya in 1843. Two years later William Siemens suggested its use for the insulation of telegraph cables, and the first submarine cable, that of 1850 between England and France, owed even its transient success to this tough waterproof electrical insulator. Gutta-percha was one of the first substances to be moulded as a plastic into small ornamental articles, while it also gave the first satisfactory means of making flexible tubing. Much more important was the beginning of the great industry of rubber, but at this early period its treatment presented difficulty, for natural rubber is hard and brittle when cold but soft and sticky when hot. Vulcanization came into use in the 1840's. At this time rubber was chiefly used to make ' elastic ' and waterproofs: the total annual import into Great Britain was in the region of 2,000 tons.

Few organic compounds other than natural products were produced on the large scale. Ether and chloroform were made for use as anæsthetics, and also a few esters for flavouring, but the synthetic drug and dye industry was still in the future. The ancient dyes still held the field, with the addition of a few tropical products. The complex process of dying Turkey-red with madder was introduced from the Near East to France about 1765, and after 1803, when the process was divulged, it became a very important industry in England.

A new departure was made by the introduction of inorganic dyes, made by precipitating metallic compounds on the fibre. Iron buff, Scheele's green, antimony orange, prussian blue, chrome yellow, chrome orange and manganese bronze were the chief of these, but this development was soon to be extinguished by the synthetic-dye industry.

The Industrial Application of Scientific Organic Chemistry

Nothing in the progress of industrial chemistry has been more spectacular than the development of industrial organic chemistry, involving the manufacture of tens of thousands of very complicated substances—dyes, drugs, explosives, plastics and the like.

The processes by which these substances could be made in quantity were decidedly different from those which had been in use in inorganic industrial chemistry. The latter required the services of the chemist as inventor and designer, but once the processes were known they could be carried on for years by intelligent workmen without scientific training, the chemist being called in only in cases of trouble. The range of conditions for success was usually pretty wide; a little higher or lower pressure, a small percentage of impurity, a variation of a few degrees in temperature were generally indifferent in such processes as the Le Blanc soda or the chamber process for sulphuric acid.

Not so with organic chemistry. As the making of more and more complex bodies was essayed, so the need for continual expert supervision became greater: the manufacture of organic chemicals was more of a science and less of a craft than that of inorganic, and, in fact, the countries pre-eminent in industrial inorganic chemistry did not achieve the highest success in the organic field.

In the first half of the nineteenth century France and England were the manufacturers of chemicals, while Germany scarcely had a chemical industry. Before 1843 the Germans made no soda, nor was there in the country a lead chamber for sulphuric acid: the only important chemical industries were metallurgy and the making of cyanides, ferrocyanides and prussian blue. Yet in this period they rapidly became the leaders of theoretical chemistry. We have only to name Gmelin, Liebig, Wöhler and Bunsen to realize that, in Germany of the '40's and '50's, there were not only chemists but the finest schools of chemistry, schools which taught the science to all Europe and most of all to the Germans themselves. These men owed little to their equipment or conditions of work. Some it is true had excellent laboratories, some had none or a dim cellar; and none of them had the laboratory conveniences which we think essential. Coal-gas has been used for lighting since 1805, but it was not every big town that had a gas-supply and heating by charcoal or spirit lamps was the usual practice. Water-supplies were infrequent; there was no rubber tube, no filter-pumps. Quite common chemicals such as aniline or benzene might be unpurchasable. An excellent picture of working conditions in the 1850's is furnished by the experience of Bunsen at Heidelberg as described by his pupil, (Sir) Henry Roscoe:

> Gmelin's old laboratory at Heidelberg, where Bunsen worked after 1852 was situated in the buildings of an ancient monastery . . . the old refectory was the main laboratory, the chapel was divided into two, one half became the lecture room and the other a storehouse and museum. Soon the number of students increased and further extensions were needed, so the cloisters were enclosed by windows and working benches placed below them. Beneath the stone floor at our feet slept the dead monks, and on their tombstones we threw our waste precipitates! There was no gas in Heidelberg in those days, nor any town's water supply. We worked with Berzelius's spirit-lamps, made our combustions with charcoal, boiled down our wash-waters from our silicate analyses in large glass globes over charcoal fires, and went for water to the pump in the yard. Nevertheless, with all these so-called drawbacks we were able to work easily and accurately.

The methods of analysis adopted in these times were slow but accurate. Bunsen was the inventor of gas-analysis (p. 317), but his analyses of coal-gas took a whole week whereas with the methods of to-day it is perhaps a matter of minutes. He was a brilliant manipulator and glass-blower and made all the rather complex apparatus for this gas-analysis; in those days no small feat. Roscoe tells us that ' he had a very salamander-like power of handling hot glass tubes, and often at the blow-pipe I have smelt burnt Bunsen, and seen his fingers smoke.'

In 1855 Heidelberg was lighted with gas. A new laboratory (still in use) was built for Bunsen, and he had to decide what type of burner to use. He rejected the Argand burner, then popular in England, and invented the famous Bunsen burner— the first model of which was constructed for him by the *Universitäts-Mechanikus*. What an invention! Every laboratory burner, gas-ring or gas-fire is its lineal descendant, and after a century its form is scarcely changed.

These German laboratories may have been rough and not always ready, but the teaching was wonderful. Students were not, as a rule, many and they worked under the eye of the master, who commonly took infinite trouble to put them in the right way. Little apparatus could be bought, and so the worker learnt resource in the school of experience. The whole world of chemical discovery opened before him; there was scarcely a research that he could undertake which would not yield substantial discoveries. In England and America, on the other hand, the opportunities for expert chemical teaching were but slight. Thus at Oxford the chemical professor was Daubeny, who, despite his enthusiasm, contrasted very unfavourably with such a man as Bunsen. Daubeny had to build his own laboratory, which he presented to his college; for in 1850 the University laboratory was almost defunct and, it seems, imperfectly separated from the professor's kitchen.

In London the Royal Institution was a great centre of chemical studies, but it did not provide practical classes. It was difficult for an English chemist to acquire a training in his own country; but on the continent science was more esteemed and British chemists were accustomed to work in one of the German laboratories in order to learn their craft, until A. W. von Hofmann was imported and created a centre of research and training at the College of Chemistry, opened in 1845.

Thus it is easy to see that, with such admirable training at hand in the 1840's and 1850's, the German chemists of the next generation were many and excellent; and naturally these men found their outlet in the founding of a chemical industry. The Germans were distinguished in the second half of the nineteenth century by their works research laboratories, which hardly existed elsewhere, directed by first-rate men and staffed with numerous well-qualified assistants. The chemist, moreover, was not a mere expert, but an integral part of the business: German industry was always controlled by a technically trained directorate. This admirable system enabled them to operate with success processes far more complex than could be carried out by the engineers and workmen of the English and French concerns. This was true not only in the field of organic chemistry, but in the application of the principles of physical chemistry to inorganic processes. We find, then, that although much of the early progress in the synthesis of new dyes was made in England and France, which in the '50's were the pre-eminent chemical and textile manufacturers, yet from about 1870 the superior skill, numbers and organization of the German industrial concerns brought nine-tenths of the organic chemical industry into their hands.

The methods of industrial organic chemistry were worked out in the establishment of the synthetic dye industry, between 1856 and 1880. The synthetic drug industry, which did not begin till 1880, was from the first almost entirely in German hands, as was the manufacture of synthetic flavours and perfumes. ' Fine chemicals ' were likewise almost exclusively made in Germany. But the world war of 1914–18 forced other countries to make the materials which could no longer be obtained from German sources, and the consequence was the setting up of organic chemical industries in Great Britain and America, industries which have since become the equals of the German in skill and their superiors in magnitude.

The recent growth of the American organic chemical industry has been phenomenal. In the period following on World War I there was keen world-wide competition in the trade, which led to the formation of great combines and amalgamations. In this period America competed successfully with other countries and excelled them in certain fields where she had exceptional advantages, such as the electro-chemical processes. Up to 1930 the American chemical industry consisted of a collection of individual and largely independent processes, but from this period these have been co-ordinated and concentrated so as to work in with one another and thereby effect economies. In the late 1930's the manufacture of chemicals from petroleum, natural gas, coal and agricultural material led to new types of production. A high proportion of profits (3–4% of sales) was ploughed back into research, and in World War II, and after, the American chemical industry outdistanced every other, whether at home or abroad. Enormous new industries, such as that of synthetic rubber, came into being. In fact, between 1939 and 1950 the American chemical industry increased its production four times.

If the German contribution was scientific direction of

1*

industry, that of the American has been the chemical engineer. The design of chemical plant before the 1930's was often haphazard, based on personal experience and rule of thumb. In the last two decades Chemical Engineering has come forward as a department of technology.

Very important thereto is the notion of unit operations, which dates back at least to the period of World War I but did not come into its own till the 1930's. As its great exponent, A. D. Little, pointed out, any chemical process, on whatever scale, resolves into a co-ordinated series of what may be called ' unit operations ': pulverizing, mixing, heating, roasting, precipitating, crystallizing, etc. In the same way chemical industry can be resolved into unit processes: hydrolysis, hydration, nitration and the like. The intimate and quantitative study of these operations and processes has led to an exact knowledge of the types of plant-unit suitable for the conduct of particular operations. The properties of materials for plant—chemically resistant glasses, silica, rubber cladding, resistant resins such as fluorocarbons, refractories and the like —have been likewise made the subject of exact studies. It has thus become possible to design and build chemical plant with much greater certainty of success and in much shorter time than ever before.

The latest stage in the industry has been the development of instrumentation and automatic control. The typical organic chemical plant of to-day is designed as a continuously operating unit. The various portions of the plant are connected to a central control room, where temperatures, pressures, rates of flow of material, etc., are chronicled and automatically controlled to certain limits presented on the instruments. The effect is that plant annually turning out thousands or tens of thousands of tons of product is controlled perhaps by two men. The condition for such operation is the skill of the chemical engineer, who must design such plant and get it right at the first trial: secondly a supply of reasonably skilled operatives for control, which the recent advances in technical education has gone far to ensure.

The ' Aniline-Dye ' Industry

The aniline-dye industry made much progress before the chemical principles underlying it were understood; yet before

the dyes could even be accidentally discovered, let alone manufactured, the materials had to be made available. Almost all
dyes contain one or more rings of six carbon atoms in their
molecules and are derived ultimately from benzene or some
other coal-tar hydrocarbon. Thus the story begins with the
gas industry. Frederic Accum distilled ' highest rectified
essential oil ' (actually benzene) from tar about 1815, but did
not investigate its composition. In 1825 Faraday characterized
the hydrocarbon benzene, though he did not make it from tar.
In 1841 Fritsche clearly described a base, ' aniline ', made by
distilling indigo with potash: in 1843 Hofmann showed that
the reduction product of the compound made by the action of
nitric acid on benzene was the same as Fritsche's aniline—and
of course very much easier to make, and cheaper too. Hofmann
was indeed the father of the dye industry, for he it was who
trained the English chemists and suggested many of the researches that led to the new dyestuffs and their sources. It
was at his instance that Mansfield investigated coal-tar and in
1849 showed how to distil benzene from it on a large scale.

W. H. Perkin, sen., entered the College of Chemistry at the
age of fifteen and was soon set to work by Hofmann on anthracene, a body whose very composition was still unknown. The
field of the coal-tar hydrocarbons was, indeed, almost un-
explored and Hofmann could truly say to his students:
' Gentlemen, new bodies are floating in the air.' Perkin was
so enthusiastic that he fitted up a rough laboratory in a part
of a room at his home. There he worked with some success on
various coloured compounds.

Hofmann happened to refer to the artificial formation of
quinine (not accomplished till a century had passed) as a
desiderative. The atomic composition of quinine was known
to be $C_{20}H_{24}N_2O_2$: so Perkin thought it might be obtained by
oxidizing allyltoluidine with potassium dichromate:

$$2C_{10}H_{13}N + 3O = C_{20}H_{24}N_2O_2 + H_2O.$$

The process, of course, yielded no quinine, but only a dirty
reddish-brown precipitate. Most men would have tipped it
down the sink, but Perkin looked closer. He tried the effect of
using aniline instead of allyltoluidine; a black precipitate was
obtained, and examination showed it to have the properties of
a dye. A friend thought it might be of practical use and

Perkin approached Messrs. Pullar, the dyers, who were enthusiastic about the success of the dye—if it did not prove to be too costly. Aniline was then made by distilling indigo with potash and was very expensive, but, three years before, Béchamp had discovered that aniline could be made by the action of iron filings and acetic acid on nitrobenzene, which could readily be made from benzene. So Perkin, a boy of eighteen, patented his dye in 1856 and in the next year set up a chemical works. His father and brother put up some capital. There was no pure benzene, no nitric acid concentrated enough to nitrate it; there was no plant suitable for the process, but for all that within six months of starting to build he was turning

FIG. 43.   Perkin's dye-works, 1857.

out ' aniline purple ', later called ' mauve '. Not only had he to discover methods of manufacture but also to work out the practical processes of dyeing fabrics with his product.

The success of the new dye led to a great deal of experimentation. As so little was known about the coal-tar derivatives, the method was mostly trial and error, but it had its successes. In 1859 M. Verquin, in France, manufactured fuchsine (magenta, roseine, rosaniline), discovered by Natanson in 1856, by heating commercial impure aniline with tin tetrachloride. Other ways of making this were soon discovered. The industry was now under way and numerous dyes, which we now know to be triphenylmethane colours, were soon discovered. We may mention Nicholson's blue, Hofmann's violet, methyl violet, iodine green, aurin—all discovered before

1866; and syntheses of important new dyes of this class continued for many years.

Meanwhile another class of dye had been discovered. Peter Griess, a German who spent most of his life in England, working in a brewery at Burton-on-Trent, devoted his spare time to the study of the azo-compounds. In 1859 he discovered aniline yellow (which was manufactured in 1863), while Bismarck brown was discovered by Martius in 1867. These were made by action of nitrous acid on amines. But Griess's really significant discovery was that of the diazonium compounds (1858–64). Solutions of these diazonium compounds 'couple' with the numerous phenols or amines, thus giving a very wide range of dyes. It is curious, however, that these were not practically developed until c. 1877. Two very important discoveries in this field were the benzidine colours, which dye cotton without a mordant, and ' para-red ', which gave the best scarlet hitherto known on cotton.

We may consider then that the year 1870 marks the period when the semi-empirical invention of new dyes gave place to researches planned on scientific principles. At this period efforts were made to discover laws describing the molecular structure of the classes of bodies that had proved to be dye-stuffs. Witt's rule (1876) indicated the need for two different factors, the ' chromophore ' and ' auxochrome ' groups, and H. E. Armstrong in 1888 showed the importance of the quinonoid structure as a cause of colour. These researches went far to guide the efforts of the chemists who were continually and successfully seeking to synthesize dye-stuffs.

A third important class of dyes was the phthaleins discovered by Adolf von Baeyer. Phenolphthalein was the first (1871), though of little use as a dye; but eosin (1873), eosin scarlet (1875), erythrosin (1876), phloxin (1876), rhodamine (1887) gave new and beautiful though fugitive shades. The oxazine dyes were initiated in 1879 with Meldola's blue.

By this time the structure of most of the dye-stuffs was pretty well understood and dye-manufacture was a scientific and well-established industry. Several new classes of dye were introduced in the later years of the nineteenth century; among them may be mentioned the sulphide dyes. The first of these, the dark-brown Cachou de Laval, was made by heating a mixture of sawdust, sodium sulphide and sulphur. It was a useful product, but its composition was unknown. A. G. Green's primuline, made by heating paratoluidine with sulphur, was very important because cotton could be dyed directly with it without the use of a mordant.   The dull-yellow cloth was then treated with nitrous acid and run through solutions of various phenols and amines, which formed new and brilliant dyes in the substance of the cloth.   Many other sulphide dyes of great fastness were developed between 1893 and 1902.

Synthesis of Natural Dye-stuffs

The production of naturally occurring substances proceeded somewhat slowly because their molecules are for the most part very complex.   Their formation is, moreover, the result of unknown processes, quite different from those we employ in the laboratory, so that the apparent ease with which even such a simple compound as glucose is synthesized by the plant is in great contrast to the difficulty with which it is synthesized by the chemist.

Berthelot's work, after 1850, had shown the possibility of such syntheses, but it was many years before any synthetic product could be produced with sufficient ease to enable it to supplement or replace its natural prototype.   Among the early syntheses of natural substances of practical use were the making of coumarin, the sweet-smelling principles of new-mown hay, by Perkin in 1868, and the synthesis of the important natural red dye-stuff alizarin, the active principle of madder, by Graebe and Liebermann in 1869; but the greatest achievement of the century was the synthesis by Baeyer in 1880 of indigotin, the main constituent of the most important of industrial dye-stuffs, indigo.   Both madder and indigo contain more than one colouring matter, but the most important constituent of the former is alizarin, and of the latter indigotin. These have both been synthesized and have almost entirely replaced the natural product.

Madder is the root of the plant *rubia tinctorum*.   It is almost the most ancient of dyes (p. 121) and still retained its full importance in the nineteenth century.   An extract of it would dye textiles in a wide range of colour, depending on the mordant used.   Red, pink, orange, lilac, black, brown, chocolate and the fine, brilliant permanent Turkey-red, were obtained by its use.   It was therefore one of the most widely used and important of dyes. Its active principle was isolated in 1826 and called *alizarin*. It is now known to be an anthraquinone derivative,

$$
\begin{array}{c}
\text{O} \qquad \text{OH} \\
\text{H} \quad \parallel \qquad | \\
\text{C} \qquad \text{C} \qquad \text{C} \\
\text{HC} \qquad \text{C} \qquad \text{C} \qquad \text{C--OH} \\
\text{HC} \qquad \text{C} \qquad \text{C} \qquad \text{CH} \\
\text{C} \qquad \text{C} \qquad \text{C} \\
\text{H} \quad \parallel \quad \text{H} \\
\text{O}
\end{array}
$$

but nothing was then known about its composition.

In 1868 Graebe, following up some earlier work, distilled alizarin with zinc-dust and obtained anthracene: the dye had previously been shown to be a quinone and Graebe rightly concluded that it was a hydroxyanthraquinone. Anthraquinone had been made in 1826 by oxidizing anthracene. Graebe brominated this and fused it with potash, obtaining alizarin. It was great good fortune that this process gave the right dihydroxyanthraquinone, for there are several of these, and only one is alizarin.

Graebe and Liebermann's process proved to be too expensive, and the heating of bromine under pressure was difficult and dangerous with the chemical plant of the time. But Perkin, and several other workers independently, found a cheaper method in the heating of the anthraquinone with sulphuric acid and fusion of the anthraquinone-sulphonic acid with alkali. Perkin was again very active: he taught the tar-distillers how to separate anthracene and he found out how to purify it. No sulphuric acid concentrated enough to sulphonate it was manufactured in England and he had to import the old-fashioned Nordhausen acid. The new alizarin was cheaper than madder and steadily replaced it: to-day the ancient root is scarcely more than a curiosity, and we have forgotten the distress caused to the French cultivators who had for centuries been the main source of supply.

Perkin was the first to make alizarin on the large scale. In 1874 he retired from business, at the age of thirty-five, and devoted the rest of his long life to pure chemistry. The alizarin trade and much of the dye business passed into German hands: however, in 1882 they advanced the price so highly that the British Alizarin Company was formed and was able to sell it for a sixth of the price that the Germans asked. The British dye industry never became extinct, although in the years round 1900–1910 the Germans had 85–90% of the British trade.

The Germans had meanwhile developed a wonderful dye industry, and it is to them we owe the synthesis of indigo. Naturally many attempts were made to investigate so valuable a substance. Since it yielded aniline on distillation, it clearly contained a benzene nucleus. Other hints were available. In 1869 Baeyer obtained indole from it, and in 1870 Emmering and Engler succeeded in synthesizing indigotin by heating *o*-nitroacetophenone with zinc dust. But the yield was very small and the method was industrially useless; the same was true of the other syntheses worked out in these years. Baeyer abandoned the subject for eight years, but took it up again in 1878. In 1880 he succeeded in producing indigotin by a method of possible industrial value, from *o*-nitrocinnamic acid. The Germans were alive to the great possibilities. Every possible process was watched and patented. Baeyer's method did not pay after all, but he continued his researches and in 1883 proved the formula of indigotin to be:

$$
\begin{array}{ccccccc}
 & \overset{H}{C} & & & & \overset{H}{C} & \\
 & /\!\!/ \;\; \backslash & & & & /\;\; \backslash\!\!\backslash & \\
HC & & C\!-\!\!-\!CO & & OC\!-\!\!-\!C & & CH \\
| & & \| & | & | & \| & | \\
HC & & C & C\!\!=\!\!=\!\!C & C & & CH \\
 & \backslash\!\!\backslash \;\; / & & & & \backslash \;\; /\!\!/ & \\
 & \underset{H}{C} & NH & & HN & \underset{H}{C} & \\
\end{array}
$$

He found another synthesis in 1882, but even this did not pay. Finally Heumann, from 1890 onward, solved the problem by showing that yields of indigotin up to 89% of theory could be made from phenylglycine-*o*-carboxylic acid. But how were thousands of tons of this substance to be made? It cost the Badische Anilin und Soda Fabrik a million pounds to find the answer.

Naphthalene, one of the cheapest and most abundant coal-products, was the beginning. This was oxidized to phthalic acid, which was not easy; for, although sulphuric acid was an effective oxidizing agent, it was very slow. But by pure chance a socket containing mercury for the insertion of a thermometer became corroded; and mercury fell into the acid and the oxidation went to completion rapidly and easily. Thus mercuric sulphate was found to be a catalyst for the reaction.

SYNTHESIS OF INDIGO

Vast quantities of sulphur dioxide were evolved in the oxidation, and the contact process (p. 424) was developed in order to turn it back into sulphuric acid. The phthalic acid was treated with ammonia, giving phthalimide, which with sodium hypochlorite gives sodium anthranilate. This had to be treated with chloracetic acid, the making of which required great quantities of chlorine, and the electrolytic process (p. 388) was developed to meet the demand. The product when fused with alkali gave indoxyl, which is readily oxidized by air to indigotin. Other processes were later developed, but it may be said that the above process became a real success from *c.* 1897, after nearly thirty years of research and seventeen of attempts at commercial exploitation. Natural indigo was swept off the market and the growers ruined. Until 1914 the Germans had the monopoly, but after the war of 1914–18 indigo was made in many other countries.

These syntheses of natural products had a further effect, namely, the discovery of a large number of new vat-dyes related to alizarin and indigo. A further result of this work was the synthesis of a series of vat-dyes (notably the indanthrenes) which were very fast to light. There are signs that indigo, indeed, is losing ground because the new synthetic vat-dyes rival it in fastness and beauty.

The Search for Fast Dyes

By 1900 a wonderful range of new colours had been put on the market and allowed of effects in textiles far more brilliant and uniform than ever before. Yet on the whole these dyes were very deficient in fastness to light. In 1902 James Morton, a textile manufacturer, was struck by the way in which some tapestry, dyed by him and exposed in a shop-window, had faded. He at once procured hundreds of samples of dyed fabrics and exposed them to light in a green-house. The result was horrifying to him, for only a small percentage of them survived a few weeks of exposure to light without serious fading. Accordingly he set to work to select such dyes as could be used to dye materials which he could sell as guaranteed not to fade. Among the best of these were the indanthrene colours, made in Germany like 90 % of the world's dye-stuffs. The war of 1914–18 cut off supplies not only of dyes but of most of the chemicals needed to make them. Morton, however, and his assistants worked out a process for the manufacture of indanthrenes, and after the war developed a new dye industry in Scotland to which we owe the best green dye-stuff, Caledon Jade Green.

Similar industries were developed in England and America, nor has the German dye industry ever regained its former pre-eminence.

The perfecting and consequent popularity of the ' artificial silk ' made from cellulose acetate (p. 256) after the war of 1914–18 led to the synthesis of new types of dye capable of colouring these fabrics, such as the ionamines discovered by Green and Sanders in 1922 but now obsolete, and dispersol-dyes introduced by S. R. Ellis in 1924 and still in use. Dye-research, of course, continues; thus the extremely fast and brilliant Monastral Blue, discovered by R. P. Linstead in 1934, has initiated a new class, the phthalocyanines, valuable both as dyes and pigments.

It may be said, then, that in the second half of the nineteenth century the dye industry established the technique of the organic chemical industry. It led to an extensive trade in the substances from which dyes could be synthesized, the so-called intermediates. The plant and intermediates that served for making dyes would serve for making other organic chemi-cals. Thus where synthetic dyes were made synthetic drugs and perfumes could be made likewise.

The Synthetic Drug Industry

The synthetic dye industry began in England and migrated to Germany, but the synthetic drug industry scarcely began before 1880, when the fine-chemical industry was already in German hands. It therefore remained almost entirely a German industry until the war of 1914–18, when the manufac-ture of drugs had to be rapidly developed by the Allies. After that war the manufacture of synthetic drugs continued to flourish in England, France and America, in all of which, as well as in Germany, great triumphs have been achieved.

The use of drugs which were not natural products dates back, as we have seen, to ancient times. In the seventeenth and eighteenth centuries some chemically prepared organic substances, such as ether and ethyl nitrate (sweet spirit of nitre) (p. 161), were in use. In the nineteenth century the systematic preparation of new organic compounds rapidly increased, but very few found their way into medicine before the decade 1880–90. Of these the most important was chloro-form.

The deliberate synthesis of compounds in order to arrive at drugs—materials having a particular physiological effect—began only when the synthesis of dyes was pretty well advanced, and it followed the same lines. We have even now only one guide in such investigations—the principle that compounds of like formulæ generally, but not invariably, produce like effects on living organisms. If, then, we can find out by trial that a certain organic compound has a certain type of effect—that it is an anæsthetic, hypnotic, vasodilator or what you will—then we can attempt to synthesize a number of compounds of similar formulæ in the confidence that at least some of them will have similar effects. Of these, again, some are likely to be more useful or better adapted to certain purposes than was the original drug, so that their synthesis may lead not only to a substitute but to an improvement.

This plan was, of course, not worked out until organic synthesis was well under way. The beginning of it was the search for a means of making a substitute for the drug quinine. Quinine has always been in insufficient supply for the treatment of the hundreds of millions of malaria patients. It occurs naturally in the bark of a tree which is grown in rather limited areas of the world. The bark contains only 2 % or 3 % of the alkaloid and, since its extraction and purification requires a good deal of skill, it has never been cheap or plentiful. Perkin discovered the dye mauve when he was trying to make quinine by oxidizing allyl-toluidine. More than fifty years elapsed before the correct structural formula of quinine was discovered, and it was only a few years ago, more than ninety years after Perkin's attempt, that R. B. Woodward and W. E. Doering succeeded in synthesizing it. In Perkin's day nothing was known about its structure, but later a basic liquid, called quinoline, was made from it. In 1879–80 Skraup discovered an easy way to synthesize quinoline, and O. Fischer made a number of compounds of quinoline in the hope of reproducing something like quinine. Sure enough, one of them had the same effect as quinine in lowering the temperature of a fever patient, though it had no effect on malaria and was rather toxic. This substance, kairine, was perhaps the first deliberately synthesized drug. Organic substances had before this time been synthesized and then found to be of use in medicine, but Fischer's attempt was the result of a planned method. Between

1880 and 1890 one or two other useful synthetic drugs were discovered, *e.g.* antipyrine, pyramidone, phenacetin, all of which have somewhat similar effects.

In 1886–87 the antipyretic character of a very simple synthetic organic compound, acetanilide, was discovered by an odd accident. Kahn and Hepp at Strasburg wished to test the physiological effect of naphthalene, but by a surprising accident they were served not with naphthalene but with acetanilide. The substance proved to have the effect of lowering the body temperature: fortunately its true nature was soon discovered and it became a very popular drug.

It will be noted that there was, and still is, no way of foretelling the effect that a new *type* of molecule will have upon the animal economy. But once the physiological effect of any drug is discovered, whether by accident or design, numerous variants of it can be made, and these can be expected to have a similar effect. This was clearly brought out by Baumann and Kast between 1886 and 1889 in their investigations of the sulphonic hypnotics. The sleep-producing effect of sulphonal was discovered by accident, when it was fed to a dog in the course of experiments designed to discover what happened to the sulphur in organic compounds when they were introduced into the animal system. Baumann and Kast prepared a series of compounds with the essential structure of sulphonal

$$R_1 \quad SO_2-R_3$$
$$\diagdown \diagup$$
$$C$$
$$\diagup \diagdown$$
$$R_2 \quad SO_2-R_4$$

but with different groups in positions R_1, R_2, R_3, and R_4. The products were all hypnotics, but with different degrees of effectiveness and toxicity. The research set the pattern of the drug industry. First, a chance or trial-and-error discovery of the physiological effect of some chemical substance; secondly, preparation of often very numerous substances whose molecules have analogous structures; thirdly, the testing of their effects, first on animals then on human beings; finally, the large-scale preparation of the substances found to be effective drugs. Such work obviously needs the effort of numerous skilled research chemists and the co-operation of physiologists and medical men. All these factors were very much more readily attainable at the turn of the century in Germany than in Great Britain or America.

Between 1890 and 1910 there was a great deal of investigation into this subject. A large number of synthetic drugs were discovered and put on the market, and a few, such as acetylsalicylic acid (aspirin), have been useful enough to win and keep their place in the pharmacopœias. But these drugs did not cure diseases, they merely relieved symptoms and made it easier for the natural curative mechanisms of the body to do their work.

The triumph of the synthetic drug industry has been in the attack upon those diseases which are caused by the multiplication in the body of minute living organisms. There are three main types of organisms that cause disease:

(1) *Virus-particles*, so simple and minute that their classification as living beings has been doubted. These cause many of the common infective fevers, *e.g.* measles, small-pox and the common cold.

(2) *Bacteria*, which are undoubtedly living organisms. These cause a great variety of serious diseases, *e.g.* tuberculosis, typhoid fever, pneumonia, erysipelas, septic conditions of all kinds.

(3) *Protozoa*, which are single-celled organisms decidedly more complex in structure than bacteria. These cause malaria and a variety of tropical diseases. The *treponema* that causes syphilis is sometimes classified with bacteria, sometimes with protozoa.

The body combats these parasites by a number of mechanisms, the chief of which is the synthesizing of complex substances called antitoxins, which destroy the parasites and the poisons they produce. The chemical structure of these is still obscure.

The very nature of infective diseases was unknown until the 1870's, and it was the work of a chemist, Louis Pasteur, and a surgeon, Joseph Lister, to bring it to light. The discovery of the rôle played by ' germs ' in the causation and transference of disease at once showed a road to its prevention. The bacteria must be intercepted and not allowed to enter the body. Bacteria could be killed by heat or by a number of chemical poisons, chief of which was carbolic acid, phenol, a product extracted from coal-tar. After the bacterial theory of disease was generally accepted, *i.e.* about 1880, the chemists synthesized a large number of disinfectants, general poisons to all forms of life, which were effective in destroying bacteria. But these were only useful for prevention; once the bacteria were within the patient's tissues the disinfectants were ineffective, for they poisoned the patient more readily than the bacteria. Attempts to find drugs that should influence bacteria in the tissues remained ineffective for many years, yet the quest for such drugs did not seem an impossible one, because two types of parasites were known to be influenced *in vivo* by drugs. The malaria parasite was controlled by quinine, and that of syphilis by mercury. Why, then, should not other drugs be found to destroy or control other internal parasites?

Paul Ehrlich, about the turn of the century, set himself the goal of finding drugs that, when administered to a patient, should destroy the protozoa or bacteria in his tissues without harming him. He was admirably equipped for the task in that he was a medical man, a bacteriologist and an organic chemist. He had been impressed by the way that dyes attached themselves to certain textile fibres and not to others, and by the way in which some of them will stain bacteria and not the surrounding tissues, and he attempted to find dyes that would attach themselves to these microscopic parasites and destroy them. His earlier studies were on the diseases caused by trypanosomes, protozoa which are carried by biting-flies, such as the tsetse. They cause various types of cattle plague, and also the terrible sleeping-sickness which ravaged East Africa at the beginning of this century. In 1906–7 he did in fact find complex azo-dyes which, when injected into cattle, would eliminate the trypanosomes, but they were too poisonous to be anything but a desperate remedy. Ehrlich then turned his attention to compounds containing arsenic. Atoxyl, $H_2N.C_6H_4.AsO(OH)(ONa)$, was his first success (1907). By its aid many cases of sleeping-sickness were cured, but it proved to be capable of causing blindness, a risk that could scarcely be taken even by victims of so fatal a disease. But the success of the dyes (*e.g.* trypan-red and trypan-blue) and of atoxyl proved that chemotherapy, the elimination of microscopic parasites from the system by drugs, was possible. In 1910 Ehrlich and Hata made one of the greatest of all medical discoveries, namely, that of the drug arsphenamine (salvarsan,

$$HO \cdot C \underset{\displaystyle NH_2}{\overset{\displaystyle H}{C}} \quad C - As = As - C \quad \overset{\displaystyle H}{C} \underset{\displaystyle NH_2}{C} \cdot OH$$

' 606 '), which appeared at first to be a complete and rapid cure for syphilis, eliminating the parasites in some cases within a fortnight. It was later found that they were not completely eliminated and that a long course of treatment with heavy metals (mercury or bismuth) was needed to prevent recurrence of the disease, but arsphenamine or a modification of it became the standard treatment for syphilis and made the disease controllable and in the great majority of cases curable. By 1939 it had diminished the number of persons suffering from active syphilis probably to a tenth of the figure that obtained thirty years before. Penicillin treatment has now, however, superseded it with such effect that in England to-day new cases of syphilis are rarities.

The years between 1910 and 1935 saw a gigantic saving of life through the treatment of tropical disease by various organic chemicals. Bilharziasis, kala-azar, amœbic dysentery, sleeping-sickness, yaws, relapsing fever were all made curable by such means, and perhaps half a million lives were saved by the combined labours of the physician and the chemist.

Protozoal diseases are almost confined to the tropics, for they are chiefly transmitted by biting insects which do not survive a cold winter. The parasitic diseases of temperate climates are chiefly caused by bacteria or virus particles. All the successes of chemotherapy up to 1935 had been against protozoa, and some were inclined to doubt whether the method could be applied to bacteria at all.

But Gerhard Domagk, director of experimental pathology and bacteriology at the laboratories of I.G. Farbenindustrie, continued to work on this problem, following up Ehrlich's ideas concerning the use of dye-stuffs. The organic chemists who were working for him synthesized a number of azo-dyes for test. It turned out that a number of these azo-dyes which had the sulphonamide group, —$SO_2 . NH_2$, in their molecules were effective against streptococci—the bacteria that caused most of the cases of what is commonly called blood-poisoning. Curiously enough, they had very little power of killing these bacteria in the test-tube cultures but killed them readily in the tissues of the test-animals. The best of the drugs they prepared was a red dye, later called prontosil, synthesized by Mietzsch and Klarer in 1932. For some reason that has never been

PRONTOSIL

SULPHANILAMIDE

SULPHAPYRIDINE ('M&B')

THE ACTIVE GROUP IN
THE SULPHONAMIDES

satisfactorily cleared up, three years elapsed before it was made available. At once it attracted great interest, for it worked almost magically in the cure of most of the ailments caused by streptococci. Puerperal fever—*i.e.* sepsis following on child-birth—septicæmia and streptococcal meningitis became rapidly curable instead of extremely dangerous diseases. Erysipelas was curable in hours instead of weeks.

Now, prontosil had been tried and found successful just

because it was a dye, but it soon turned out that its being a dye had nothing to do with its success. It was shown that it broke up in the body and formed paraminobenzenesulphonamide, later called sulphanilamide. This had been known for twenty-five years and was not covered by any patents; consequently it could be used cheaply and in quantity, and it was found to be just as effective as prontosil. It was far more effective than anything previously known against streptococci, and also against the bacteria which cause cerebrospinal meningitis and against those which cause gonorrhœa. It was not, however, effective against the bacteria which caused pneumonia, nor against the staphylococci which cause many skin and eye affections. Something still better was wanted. So the chemists set to work to put other groups in place of the hydrogen atoms in the $-NH_2$ groups. They obtained a number of extremely valuable drugs. Sulphapyridine (M & B 693) revolutionized the treatment of pneumonia, and sulphathiazole, sulphadiazine, sulphamezathine and others have various advantages. The result is that the majority of bacterial diseases are now readily curable in a matter of hours and days. Penicillin, of which more on page 291, is exceedingly effective against staphylococci. It seems that the only major bacterial diseases against which we have no effective chemotherapy are diphtheria, whooping-cough and—the worst of all—tuberculosis. The development of streptomycin has led to some successes against tubercle bacteria, but does not appear to be effective against the more chronic forms of tuberculosis.

The result, then, of the synthesis of drugs has been the greatest medical revolution since the bacterial theory of diseases. There is no reason why it should not go further. It is almost certain that many classes of effective drugs are still unknown, and these can at present unfortunately be found only by trial. We could not have guessed from its formula that sulphanilamide would be effective: but once we found that it was we could make variants of it in the confident hope of obtaining something still better. We are beginning now to understand how the sulphonamide drugs affect bacteria. They do not poison the bacteria, as was formerly believed. It appears that they are akin to but not identical with certain substances that bacteria require in order to grow. The bacteria take up the sulphonamides instead of the growth substances: they therefore cannot multiply and the body's normal defences finish them off. Further knowledge of the substances needed by bacteria may enable us to discover new classes of compounds with similar and even more effective powers.

The Synthetic Perfume Industry

The synthetic perfume industry dates from the years round 1880. The natural perfumes are of many different classes, chiefly terpenes, though some are of other classes. In the '70's, when organic chemistry became systematic, Tilden and Shenstone showed how the terpenes, of which a bewildering variety exists in plants, could be distinguished and separated. A succession of great chemists, Tiemann, Wallach, Baeyer and Perkin, investigated this group and so laid the foundation of the industry. Before 1875 synthetic perfumes were almost unknown; to-day the vast quantities of perfume required by the cosmetic industry are either wholly synthetic or blends of natural and synthetic perfumes. Once the composition of the compounds that constitute natural perfumes was known, they could in most cases be synthesized. But the nose is a highly sensitive organ, so that the substances which were needed to make synthetic perfumes had to be of extreme purity if they were to be acceptable. The first synthetic perfumes, which date from 1879, were coumarin and heliotropin, having the scent of tonka-beans and of heliotrope respectively. Since then most of the natural perfumes have either been synthesized or imitated with some success. The preparation of ionone (1903), with the odour of violets, and of trinitro-*tert*-butyl-toluene, with that of musk, are examples of the imitation of perfumes, for the natural substances do not contain these compounds. There are, however, some natural perfumes that cannot be convincingly imitated. Thus no synthetic rose-perfume approaches the true attar, nor is ionone by any means the equal of the natural violets.

The chemist has given less attention to the sense of taste than to that of smell. The conversion of eugenol, a constituent of oil of cloves, into vanillin in 1879 enabled us to dispense with the pods of the vanilla orchid. More important was the discovery of saccharin in the same year. It was manufactured after 1885 and employed for sweetening mineral waters and as a sugar substitute for the diabetic or the corpulent. Several

other intensely sweet compounds have since been discovered,
and improvements in manufacture have removed much of their
former disagreeable taste.

Large-scale Production of Organic Compounds

The organic chemical industry achieved its first successes in
the making of comparatively costly materials, dyes, drugs and
perfumes, by the hundredweight or ton. Its atmosphere was
rather that of the enlarged laboratory. Thus Perkin's workmen nitrated benzene in numerous large glass flasks, and only
slowly was the industry developed to a large scale.

The work of the Germans, notably in the synthesis of the
extensively used indigo, led to new techniques capable of
handling many tons of material together, but this has been
totally overshadowed by the enormous production of explosives,
plastic materials, solvents, elastomers which characterize the
years 1920–50, and have achieved their principal triumphs in
America.

Very influential in this respect was the explosives industry,
which in the years 1914–18 compelled the large-scale development of some part of the chemical industry and paved the way
for the new era.

Modern Explosives

By the middle of the nineteenth century we see clearly a
differentiation of function of explosives. There are three main
jobs to be done by explosives: the initiation of an explosive act
by *initiators* and *detonators;* the thrusting of a projectile from a
gun by *propellants;* destruction by *high explosives* or *bursting
charges.* The function of explosives of the first type, which are
wanted in only quite small quantities as cap compositions and
the like, is to react reliably to a blow, or friction, or electric
heating, so as to produce a flame or a small detonation wave.
Propellants must burn steadily and at a rate which is both
known and controllable at the time of manufacture, so as to
produce a thrust rather than a blow. The degree of reproducibility of the burning-rate must match the accuracy of
other factors used in ballistic calculation in the field. High
explosives used for filling shells must be capable of complete
explosion in the shortest possible time. Their explosion rate
is so much higher than that of propellants that it is referred to

by a separate term, detonation. The whole of their energy is released at once. The high explosive must, however, be very safe to handle and it is therefore required to be relatively inert to normal disturbances but efficiently to accept a detonation wave provided by an intermediate. For civil use (blasting, etc.) explosives with other characteristics are required.

In the first half of the nineteenth century gunpowder had to meet all needs. Its chemical composition was susceptible of only small variation and so recourse was had to variations in the size and shape of its grains. The American invention of the perforated grain was the last stage in the improvement of gunpowder before the development of the ' smokeless powders ' of synthetic chemical origin. The improvement in gunpowder had been aided by the opening up of the sodium nitrate beds in Chile. The Germans began the manufacture of saltpetre from sodium nitrate and potash in order to supply the Russians during the Crimean War. After the Stassfurt potash deposits had come into production this became the standard method of making saltpetre, and by 1880 Indian saltpetre had disappeared from the European market. Nitre-beds fell into disuse during the first half of the century but were temporarily revived on occasion, *e.g.* in the southern states of America during the Civil War.

Various nitro-compounds and organic nitrates were obtained by the treatment of different substances with nitric acid in the early part of the nineteenth century, but the first consciousness of having produced a new explosive must be attributed to C. F. Schönbein, who in 1845 announced the discovery of guncotton (nitro-cellulose or, more correctly, a mixture of cellulose nitrates), made by treating cotton with nitric and sulphuric acids. It was brought into production after 1849, but it was far from safe and the fatal explosions that occurred caused its manufacture to be virtually abandoned until Sir F. A. Abel, in the years round 1865, showed that it could be made stable by pulping it as rags are pulped to make paper.

Nitroglycerine was discovered in 1847, two years after guncotton, by Sobrero, Professor of Chemistry at Turin, but no attempts were made to use so dangerous a substance until Alfred Nobel began to produce and study it after 1859. Despite a terrible explosion in 1864, which killed his younger brother, he put the explosive on the market as ' blasting oil '.

In 1867, however, he made two important discoveries which rendered the use of nitroglycerine and guncotton practicable, namely, the mercury fulminate detonator and the solidification of the liquid nitroglycerine to form dynamite, a putty-like mixture of nitroglycerine with a porous earth, kieselguhr. From this time the new explosives rapidly progressed. In 1875 Nobel patented a jelly-like mixture of guncotton and nitroglycerine which was even more powerful. He now set to work to make explosives less shattering and more suitable as propellants, and finally arrived at ballistite, consisting of 40% nitroglycerine and 60% of nitrocellulose. In 1889 Abel and Dewar patented cordite, a very similar material, which has remained in use as a propellant ever since.

The use of ammonium nitrate began with its incorporation into smokeless powders; later it was mixed with nitroglycerine to make safety explosives for mines. The proportion of ammonium nitrate was then steadily increased until ammonal, consisting of ammonium nitrate, aluminium powder and charcoal, was introduced in 1900 : mixtures of ammonium nitrate with nitro-compounds (amatols) have been much used as shell fillings.

The above explosives are all nitrates, but a very important step was taken when aromatic nitro-compounds were brought into use. The first of these was picric acid (trinitrophenol), which has been known since 1771. Its effective use dated from 1885, when Turpin patented its use as a bursting charge for shells. In the Boer War the British used cordite as a propellant and, in its later phases, picric acid as a shell-filling, under the name of lyddite. The French and Japanese also adopted this explosive for military use. The Germans, on the other hand, adopted trinitrotoluene (later known as TNT), which was superior in many respects.

The war of 1914–18 set the chemical industries enormous problems in providing the materials for an unexampled production of explosives. All nitro-explosives required nitric and sulphuric acid in quantities which both sides had difficulty in supplying. The solutions of these problems are discussed on pp. 424–430. They also required huge quantities of the substances which were to be nitrated. For picric acid, used at first by the British and French, phenol was required, and for TNT toluene. Furthermore, the propellant explosives, such as cordite, required acetone for the gelatinizing process. Phenol was fairly easily extracted from tar in large quantity, but the demand for it was such that the large-scale conversion of benzene into phenol was undertaken, which made further demands for pure concentrated sulphuric acid. The Germans had in peace-time a great coal-tar industry and had all the necessary plant for making toluene. As the war proceeded the British and Americans also set up toluene plants and made trinitrotoluene in quantity.

The result was that both Great Britain and the United States were compelled by the exigencies of war to create extensive plants for the production of nitric acid (which also involved production of ammonia), concentrated sulphuric acid and oleum, benzene, phenol and toluene. They were thus forcibly taught the groundwork of industrial organic chemistry, and after the decline of Germany's industrial potential following her defeat both Powers—and especially the United States—went ahead to create organic chemical industries of hitherto unheard-of magnitude. The demand for explosives, of course, was soon diminished, but new fields for the organic chemist were opened in the development of rayon, plastics and elastomers.

The discovery of explosives has continued. New detonating materials, e.g. DDNP, i.e. diazodinitrophenol (1922), tetracene, i.e. 4-guanyl-1-(nitrosoaminoguanyl)-tetrazene, and perhaps a dozen others have advantages over the older types.

The problem of finding aromatic chemicals for conversion into explosive in war-time conflicts with the need for benzene, toluene and petroleum hydrocarbons as motor fuels. Hence the discovery in World War II of explosives that could be made from coke, water, air and electricity was significant. These included PETN (pentaerythritol tetranitrate) and cyclonite (hexahydro-1-3-5-trinitro-s-triazine).

Rayon

The great artificial silk or rayon industry was initiated in 1889 when Chardonnet invented the spinning of a thick solution of nitrocellulose into fibres by forcing it through fine holes in a metal plate. The process was successful and the silk had an excellent appearance. It was, however, a sort of guncotton and extremely inflammable; indeed, the workmen in his

factory called it 'mother-in-law silk', since the present of a
dress made of it was an effective means of disposing of a
troublesome relative. Sir Joseph Swan had also been experimenting with nitrocellulose fibres for the making of carbon
filaments for electric lamps, reconverting them to cellulose by
removing the nitrate-groups by treatment with ammonium
sulphide. This plan was later adopted for Chardonnet silk,
but although the process decreased its inflammability it also
decreased its strength. In 1900, 80% of the artificial silk produced was of the Chardonnet variety, and this type of silk was
greatly esteemed; indeed, the fibre was so fine and brilliant
that its price is said at one time to have risen above that of
real silk.

Chardonnet's process showed the possibility of making artificial silk, and many inventors sought other methods of doing
the same thing—*e.g.* of dissolving cellulose or some similar
substance to a viscous liquid and spinning this into fibre. From
1857 it had been known that a solution of copper hydroxide
in ammonia would dissolve cellulose, and this solution was
used from *c.* 1897 for making artificial silk by forcing it through
fine jets into dilute sulphuric acid. The product, cuprammonium silk, was strong and brilliant but not very easy to
dye. Though this process reached popularity at an earlier
date, the most important of processes for making artificial silk
was the viscose process, invented by Charles Cross and E. J.
Bevan in 1892; but the process of preparing the solution
presented many problems, and in fact viscose silk was not a
great success until about 1906. The process was very cheap to
operate; it used cotton linters, and later wood-pulp, as its raw
material and dissolved it by the aid of caustic soda and carbon
disulphide: the solution was forced through fine orifices into a
solution of dilute sulphuric acid, followed by sodium bisulphide,
to remove the free sulphur. By 1914 viscose silk had secured
80% of the market.

It had long been known that cellulose could be converted
into an acetate which could be dissolved in certain solvents,
but only in 1906 was a method discovered by which it could
be satisfactorily dispersed in acetone. Earlier attempts to
use it had been unsuccessful. Thus in 1894 Cross and Bevan
had experimented with this, and its manufacture was attempted
in 1902 by the Germans. In the war of 1914–18 great quantities

of the solution of cellulose acetate in acetone were used as ' dope ' for aeroplanes. Extensive plant for producing acetic acid and acetone had been set up and, partly in order to make use of this, the manufacture of acetate silk was begun in England and America. The cellulose acetate was dissolved in acetone, which is very volatile. To spin the solution it was forced through fine jets in the usual manner, but no setting solution was needed, for the acetone evaporated, leaving the dry fibre. The recovery of the acetone presented some problems which have since been overcome. In the U.S.A. no rayon was made until 1911, when the production of viscose began: in 1921 production of acetate silk followed on the cellulose acetate industry set up in war-time.

Both industries prospered enormously in all industrialized countries. Artificial silk became very popular after 1920, and in 1924 it was given the title of rayon, a word which, however, has never attained much popularity with the British public. At this period all four processes were competing. The manufacture of Chardonnet silk was finally given up in 1933, and in 1938 viscose-silk constituted about 82% of the world production, acetate 13% and cuprammonium 3-4%.

From 1927 there had been attempts to make synthetic fibres, but only in 1939 could production begin. The Germans produced samples of silk made from a chlorinated polyvinyl chloride (p. 264), while America began production of nylon (p. 265), a plastic made from amino-acids; these were the first truly synthetic textiles, for the earlier ones all started from cellulose, derived from plants. These more recent materials for textile fibres are considered in the succeeding section.

Mention should here be made of the transparent wrapping material cellophane, derived from viscose. The industry was founded by the Swiss J. E. Brandenburger between 1908 and 1912; the product came into popularity when it was produced in America in the years after 1923.

Plastics

The word ' plastic ' is used as a noun to signify an organic substance which, when heated, can be moulded into coherent solid articles that after cooling retain their shape indefinitely at room temperature. Some of these can again be softened by heat, and these are said to be made of *thermoplastic* material;

some, while being formed in a heated mould, undergo a chemical alteration which renders them incapable of being again softened by heat: these are said to be *thermo-setting*. All plastics are polymers of high molecular weight, some occurring naturally and some made by synthesis.

Thermoplastic organic materials have been in use for about a century; gutta-percha, ebonite (hard rubber), and celluloid being the best-known examples. To these were added in 1897 the casein-plastics, made from milk. Galalith and erinoid, used as ivory substitutes, were of this type and came into very general use.

A complete revolution in the plastic industry began in 1907, when Leo Baekeland patented the first thermo-setting plastic—Bakelite. Baekeland was investigating the possibilities of making synthetic resins for use in varnishes. Several workers had studied the reaction between those common substances phenol and formaldehyde, and indeed had obtained from them passable substitutes for shellac. Baekeland showed that these substances could give products of two types. In presence of acids they gave readily fusible resinous substances which were rather inferior substitutes for the natural resins used in varnishes; but in presence of alkali resinous substances were formed which, when heated, became hard, insoluble and no longer fusible. They proved to be first-class electrical insulators, and Bakelite, as Baekeland called his product, was at first turned out in blocks and sold as insulating material, but soon it was also sold in the form of a powder which could be filled into moulds and hardened therein by heating. The early career of the Bakelite industry was marked by difficulties. The General Bakelite Company was launched in 1910, but engaged in litigation with other firms who had employed phenol-formaldehyde products as synthetic resins. The results were indecisive, and later the parties got together to form the Bakelite Corporation, and the new material thereafter made rapid progress. So great was the simplicity of making strong, hard articles of complex and irregular shapes by moulding that, once its possibilities were realized, a tremendous volume of research was concentrated upon making new plastic materials, both thermo-setting and thermoplastic.

Not much was known in these early days about the molecular structure of plastics, but it was soon established that they were all mixtures of giant molecules, known as high polymers. The researches of Staudinger in 1926 showed that the characteristic of thermoplastics was that they consisted of *linear* molecules of great length—of the order of a thousand or more Angstroms in length (as against about 6 Angstroms for the benzene molecule). Since that time an ever-increasing volume of research has been directed to investigating the details of polymer chemistry, the

sizes and shapes of these molecules as well as their properties in the massive form. The thermo-setting plastics have, in the initial stages of their manufacture, a structure like that of the thermoplastics, but in the final stage of formation of the plastic article the long thread-like molecules join up with one another by numerous cross-linkages (usually under the influence of heat) so that in the limit the whole article becomes but one molecule. Thus in order to make thermoplastic or thermo-setting substances we must first link up small molecules into long chains. The first and still very important thermo-hardening plastics were mostly compounds of phenol and formaldehyde (Bakelite), or of urea and thio-urea with formaldehyde (Beetle), but to-day they embrace a much wider range of composition: modern types include melamine-formaldehyde, furfuraldehyde condensation products, polyester resins (such as the low-pressure laminates) and the vitreous transparent alkyd resins.

The structures of these substances are not easy to ascertain with certainty. It is thought that in the Bakelite moulding powder phenol molecules are linked by the —CH_2— groups of formaldehyde molecules into long chains, and that in the Bakelite after moulding these are further linked into three-dimensional networks. This can happen in a great many different ways and it is doubtful whether formulæ can be usefully written. The formula on p. 259 given by Zinke and Ziegler at least illustrates the types of linkages to be expected therein.

The group of thermoplastics may be defined in general terms as including all substances with very long linear molecules built up on a single 'repeat unit'. Structurally, but not chronologically, polythene may be considered as the archetype; it is made by the polymerization of ethylene, $H_2C{=}CH_2$ (p. 264), resulting in chains of the type

$$\ldots\text{—}CH_2\text{—}CH_2\text{—}CH_2\text{—}CH_2\text{—}CH_2\text{—}CH_2\text{—}CH_2\text{—}\ldots$$

consisting of many thousands of —CH_2— groups. In this case the repeat unit is very simple, namely, the —CH_2— group. In other thermoplastics the repeat unit may be much larger and more complex, as we shall see, and include many other elements, such as sulphur, nitrogen, phosphorus, silicon and oxygen. The properties of thermoplastics vary widely accord-ing to the constitution of the repeat unit, but the variations are systematic; so these materials can be subdivided into three general categories: those which are transparent, vitreous and amorphous; the semi-crystalline materials, which include all the new synthetic fibres; and the rubber-like materials, which include natural rubber and the synthetic rubbers.

Thermosetting Plastics

The phenol-formaldehyde type of plastic (Bakelite) has

maintained and increased its first importance. The material is a good insulator for domestic purposes, where high frequencies and high voltages are excluded: it is very strong and light, particularly when fibrous materials such as wood-flour, wood-pulp or cotton linters are mixed with it. Laminated materials, which consist of piles of sheets of paper, cloth, wood, etc., saturated and bound together with Bakelite, are extremely strong, and their uses in industry are so many and varied that they are impossible to chronicle: in making such articles, the United States in 1943 managed to consume phenol-formalde-hyde resin, not including fillers, to the extent of 30,000 tons. These laminated products are used for panelling, switch-boards, table-tops, counters and, very remarkably, as silent gear-wheels. Bakelite-bonded ply-wood was used in quantity in the war of 1939–45 for ship construction, aeroplane parts, chests, pontoons and for all manner of articles required to be strong, light and resistant to moisture.

The original method of forming articles was by heating the phenol-formaldehyde or other resins under pressure, but about 1927 a quite different and much more ornamental material began to be made by ' casting '. The phenol-formaldehyde and a little alkali are gently heated for some time and then acidified with lactic acid; a plasticizer may be added. The syrup thus produced can be run into moulds of the desired shape and hardened by long heating to 60°–80° C. The resulting cast resins are transparent and nearly colourless. Dyes of various colours can be added, and a very ornamental material is thus produced. Most of it is used for minor decorative purposes, knife-handles, buckles, beads and the like.

Attempts to use urea instead of phenol date from 1920, and the process was almost entirely developed by Fritz Pollak in Vienna. The urea-formaldehyde resins are light, strong and can be made in bright colours: being odourless and tasteless they have been found very useful for table-ware. An example is Beetle, first produced in 1926 and widely popularized after 1929: urea resins, however, are not as strong as Bakelite. At the present date the low-pressure laminating resins with fibre-glass reinforcements are becoming important for the construc-tion of light-weight structural parts in aeroplanes.

These industries are of such magnitude as to make consider-able demands on raw material. Phenol is contained in coal-tar and can be extracted from it, and can be chemically made from the benzene also contained therein. The supplies of coal-tar are very considerable, but it is clear that the rapidly-developing plastics industry is another competitor for its products, also required for the motor-spirit and the organic-chemical industry. Formaldehyde seemed at first to present a more difficult problem, for it is made by oxidizing methyl alcohol with air, and methyl alcohol was found only in very small proportion as a by-product in the distillation of wood, carried out for the making of acetic acid. The synthesis of methyl alcohol from water-gas, *i.e.* from coal (p. 433), or from the methane of natural gas has prevented any problem of supply from arising. Urea is readily obtained by the action of carbon dioxide on ammonia at very high pressures, and requires as raw material only coal and air.

Thermoplastics

The most recent developments in the plastic industry have been in the discovery and production of thermoplastic materials, desirable for their remarkable transparency or for their flexibility and insulating qualities, but relatively expensive as compared to the thermosetting plastics. The simplest types are those formed by polymerization of bodies having the general formula $XHC=CH_2$, where X is some grouping of atoms. There are a great many of their substances, and we can here mention only a few. The first of these to be developed (*c.* 1935) were the acrylic resins, one of which is very well known as Perspex, the trade name of the methyl-methacrylate polymer made by I.C.I.; this is also sold as Lucite by du Pont de Nemours and as Plexiglas by Rohm & Haas.

Acrylic acid has the formula $H_2C=CH$

$$\overset{|}{CO.OH}$$

$$\overset{CH_3}{\underset{|}{|}}$$

and methyl methylacrylate is $H_2C=C$

$$\overset{|}{CO.OCH_3}$$

It is easy to see that these acrylic compounds can polymerize to long chains; in the case of methyl methylacrylate the formula of the polymer is

$$\ldots\ldots-CH_2-\overset{\displaystyle CH_3}{\underset{\displaystyle CO.OCH_3}{\vert\vert}}-CH_2-\overset{\displaystyle CH_3}{\underset{\displaystyle CO.OCH_3}{\vert\vert}}-CH_2-\overset{\displaystyle CH_3}{\underset{\displaystyle CO.OCH_3}{\vert\vert}}-\ldots\ldots$$

indefinitely extended, its molecular weight running into millions. These polymers were observed some eighty-five years ago, in 1872: in 1888 a Swiss chemist, G. W. A. Kahlbaum, studied them and actually made a flexible unbreakable beer-glass from methylacrylate polymer. The first patent, however, dated from 1912, and production in Germany began as early as 1927. In the mid-1930's these materials were developed in England and in the U.S.A., and during the war of 1939–45 enormous quantities, amounting to some 12,000 tons a year, were produced, chiefly for transparent aeroplane domes and windows. Their transparency is quite remarkable and finds them many uses, and the implications of an optically transparent body that can be moulded have not yet been fully realized. Lenses, reflectors, watch-crystals, lamp-housings, dentures, and a wide variety of decorative objects are made from them.

These methyl-methylacrylate polymers are usually made from acetone by a process of several stages, and their manufacture was yet another call on the supply of acetone, which is now largely made from propylene, a constituent of oil-refinery cracking gas: other methods have been developed, but this is the most widely adopted.

Another important acrylic polymer is polyacrylonitrile made by Du Pont under the name of Orlon, and derived from cyanamide or acetylene. Its value is as a fibre-forming material which has some of the qualities of wool.

The vinyl polymers are much more recent. Though patented in 1912, and the subject of extensive research by the B. F. Goodrich Company from 1926, they came into production on a really large scale only in 1939. They start as a rule from acetylene (p. 392). With hydrogen chloride, in presence of mercury salts as catalysts, it gives vinyl chloride,

$$HC\equiv CH + HCl \rightarrow H_2C=CHCl;$$

with acetic acid under similar conditions vinyl acetate is obtained,

$$HC{\equiv}CH + HO.OC.CH_3 \rightarrow H_2C{=}CH.O.CO.CH_3.$$

These vinyl compounds will polymerize in much the same way as does methyl-methacrylate to form long-chain molecules. Variations in properties can be obtained by polymerizing simultaneously two such compounds to produce a 'co-polymer', the molecules of which contain repeat units of both types. Commercially the vinyl-chloride polymers are far and away the most important of the two, and their production is now at the rate of many thousands of tons per year and still expanding. They are largely used in their plasticized forms for making flexible tubing and sheet, and for covering wires and cables. They have good electrical insulating properties and stand up to hard wear. They may be considered as typical flexible plastics.

Styrene, $C_6H_5.CH{=}CH_2$, also polymerizes to a long-chain plastic. It can be made from benzene synthetically or from crude oil. The polymer, styron, which was put on the market in 1937, has outstanding qualities of water resistance and is also a remarkably good insulator, especially for high frequencies, and is almost as transparent as the methylacrylate resins. Great quantities are used as a moulding powder. The product is used for battery cases, refrigerator parts exposed to wet, and purposes where resistance to chemicals is important.

It was long thought that the simplest of the vinyl compounds, namely, ethylene itself, $CH_2{=}CH_2$, would not polymerize. However, in the '30's research workers in England did contrive to make a white waxy solid by heating ethylene gas under the enormous pressures of 1,000–2,000 atmospheres. These polythenes or polyethylene polymers, known in America under the trade name of Alkathene, first went into production in 1939 at a most opportune moment. They combine excellent mechanical properties with outstandingly good high-frequency insulating properties, and their availability was of the greatest assistance in the development of radar in Great Britain and subsequently in America.

Fluorinated ethylenes can also be polymerized, and polymers prepared from tetrafluorethylene (e.g. Teflon) and chlorotrifluoroethylene are distinguished by great stability to heat, chemical inertness, insolubility and low friction. Their price is still high, but they are already solving many difficulties of the chemical engineer, especially in the handling of fluorine and other corrosive materials.

It would be impossible even to mention here the enormous number of substances that have been polymerized to form plastics, but two very important types must be mentioned, the polyamides (typified by nylon) and the various forms of ' synthetic rubber ' (p. 267).

Nylon marks an epoch in the history of applied chemistry because it is the first truly synthetic fibre-forming substance. All the artificial silks which went before possessed their macro-molecular constitution because they were made from cellulose which had been made by living matter. The du Pont de Nemours Company set out on a deliberate search for a syn-thetic fibre which should not depend on living matter for its origin and engaged Wallace Hume Carothers, then a lecturer at Harvard, to lead a sumptuously endowed research team. Carothers was given a completely free hand to pursue his natural academic bent, and his work on high polymers notably advanced the frontiers of the subject. He did, however, also keep the formation of fibres in view and after many setbacks finally succeeded in preparing a super-polyamide of the requi-site physical character. He died before even the name of nylon was coined, but he had made possible the work which put nylon on the market in 1940. The production of nylon in bulk entailed the rapid development of methods of manufacture on a large scale of substances hitherto known only as labora-tory samples. The substances now known as nylon are poly-amides, and the one almost invariably used is made from hexa-methylene-diamine and adipic acid. The latter compound is made by oxidation of cyclohexanol (p. 433), which is hydro-genated phenol. Hexamethylene diamine can also be made from adipic acid and ammonia, so phenol and ammonia were the first starting points of nylon, though it has also been manu-factured from petroleum gases and from furfural, made by treating corn-cobs with dilute sulphuric acid. Its structure is a long chain repeating this grouping of atoms,

$$...-NH-CH_2-CH_2-CH_2-CH_2-CH_2-CH_2-$$
$$-NH.OC-CH_2-CH_2-CH_2-CH_2-CO-...$$

K*

and it therein somewhat approximates to the structure of real silk. Its special advantage is its elasticity and strength, whether wet or dry. Its uses are chiefly for textiles and bristles, but if it could be made more cheaply it would find many more uses. A rapidly developing fibre, made from the condensation product of dimethylterephthalate and ethylene glycol, is known as Terylene in Great Britain, and Dacron in America. The source of both its constituents is the olefinic gases made by cracking petroleum products.

We may expect rapid developments in these fields. The number of possible polymers and co-polymers is very great, and at least one need, the replacement of wool by a synthetic fibre, is unsatisfied and affords a powerful stimulus to research.

Synthetic resins have been developed which possess the property of ion-exchange, long familiar among the zeolite type of mineral and developed via sulphonated coals to provide the basis for an efficient method of water softening (Base Exchange). The new resins, like the older materials, can remove certain ions from water and replace them with others. Their action is not limited to water softening (by removal of calcium ions and replacement with sodium), for they can now be used to remove all the ions from water, so providing, by simple passage through a bed of granular resins, a water as pure as that obtainable by efficient distillation. Alternatively, where the dissolved material in a solution is itself of value, they afford a useful means of extracting it.

Emergency kits for rendering sea-water drinkable, based on roughly similar principles, made a timely appearance during World War II and are still in use.

Synthetic Varnishes and Lacquers

Collodion, the solution of pyroxylin in alcohol and ether (p. 417), may be thought of as the origin of synthetic varnishes.

In 1882 a solution of nitrocellulose and camphor in amyl acetate was brought into use in the United States but did not compete seriously with the traditional varnishes made of gums dissolved in oil. The turning point in the industry was once more the war of 1914–18. Vast quantities of aeroplane dope, consisting of nitrocellulose dissolved in acetone together with a plasticizer such as castor oil, were manufactured, and the end of the war left large stocks of material. In the early '20's synthetic plasticizers such as the esters triphenyl phosphate, dibutyl phthalate, etc., displaced both camphor and castor oil. Amyl acetate, a product of the whisky distillers, soon ran into short supply, and butanol, a by-product of the fermentation process of acetone, took its place: this process has now receded in favour of synthesis of higher alcohols from the cracking-gas of the oil refineries. Leo Baekeland had made synthetic resins from phenols and formaldehyde as early as 1910, but their practical use for varnishes dates from the early '20's, when it was found possible to make them soluble in oil. From about 1920 the coumarone-indene polymers and the maleic resins began to be used. Thus a variety of excellent synthetic varnishes and lacquers came on the market. All the American automobile manufacturers changed over from natural to synthetic varnish between 1923 and 1927. At this time resins were synthesized and then dissolved in natural oils to make a varnish, but in the early '30's the glyceryl-phthalate (glyptal) resins, invented in 1912, were brought into use. These, in conjunction with a fatty acid, yielded an excellent varnish that required no oil. More recently the vinyl polymers and co-polymers have given a series of lacquers of pleasant feel and resistance to wear. The result has been to displace natural varnish and lacquer from most of its field and to provide new and ornamental surfaces resistant to wear for a variety of objects of domestic use.

Rubber-like Materials

The quest for artificial rubber has long been an attraction. Natural rubber is a polymer of isoprene, C_5H_8, and consists of long-chain molecules in tangled and kinked forms which straighten out and therefore lengthen under tension, and return to their original form when the tension is relaxed. These facts were discovered by X-ray studies (p. 377) about the year 1930.

The modern investigator of 'synthetic rubbers' does not seek to reproduce natural rubber but to discover substances of similar or superior properties, which may be of quite different composition. Their success and the importance of it is shown by the fact that towards the end of the war of 1939–45 the U.S.A. were producing 700,000 tons of synthetic rubbers yearly, while the pre-war world production of natural rubber was only just over a million tons.

There is a good deal of controversy about the history of synthetic rubber. The polymerization of isoprene (itself made from rubber) back to a rubber-like body was demonstrated in 1875, and in 1882 Tilden made isoprene from turpentine and synthesized a rubber-like polymer from it. In 1892 he showed that this could be vulcanized. Between 1901 and 1914 rubber fetched very high prices and it seemed that synthesis might be profitable; so Russian, English and German workers tackled the problem, and at this period the use of the more readily synthesized butadiene in place of isoprene was suggested. In the war of 1914–18, blockaded Germany had to have rubber for motor tyres, battery cases, etc., and to synthesize it at whatever cost. It was made from 2,3-dimethyl-butadiene and its quality was so poor that its manufacture was abandoned

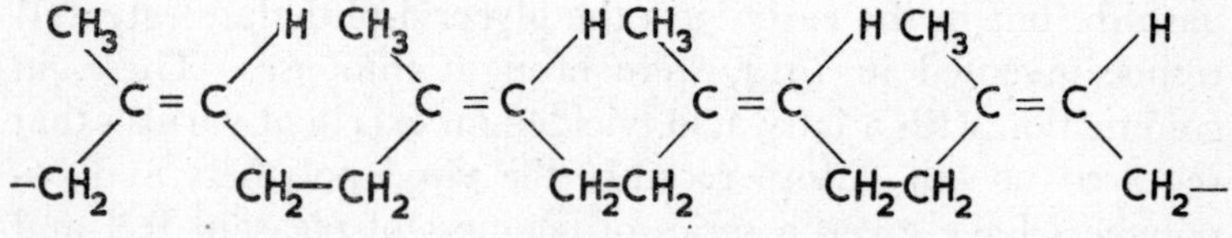

FIG. 44.   Structure characteristic of rubber.

after the war. In 1922 Patrick discovered the first synthetic rubber-like substance that was superior in some respects to natural rubber, namely, Thiokol. This material was made by mixing the very cheap substances ethylene dichloride and sodium polysulphide: it came into general use after 1930. Thiokol has remarkable oil-resistance, but its very unpleasant smell hampered its success.

Soon after, the I.G. Farben Company in Germany developed the Buna rubbers, made by co-polymerizing butadiene with amylonitrile or styrene by the aid of a sodium catalyst: the du Pont Company in America began research on the subject in 1925, and in 1932 marketed a rubber (neoprene) which was a polymer of 2-chlorobutadiene.

The most important of synthetic rubbers is the American GR/S, a co-polymer of butadiene and styrene. Its properties are similar to that of natural rubber and have the advantage of reproducibility. Butyl rubber, developed by Standard Oil of New Jersey, is also produced on a very large scale, especially as a material for inner tubes, being impervious to air.

Processes for the manufacture of elastomers were of enormous importance in the war of 1939–45. They involved the manufacture of the gas butadiene,

$$H_2C=CH-HC=CH_2$$

which was made on a very large scale from alcohol, acetylene, petroleum or natural gas by methods which have not in all cases been disclosed. One method which was used for making it from acetylene is given in the following scheme of reactions:

$$2HC\equiv CH + 2H_2O \rightarrow 2CH_3-CHO \xrightarrow{\text{alkali}}$$

Acetylene   acetaldehyde

$$CH_3-CH(OH)-CH_2-CHO$$

$$\xleftarrow{\text{hydrogen}} \qquad\qquad\qquad \text{aldol}$$

$$CH_3-CH(OH)-CH_2-CH_2OH \xrightarrow[\text{dehydrogenation}]{\text{catalytic}}$$

$$CH_2=CH-HC=CH_2$$

Butadiene

It is difficult to compare the merits of synthetic and natural rubber: there are, as we have seen, many synthetic rubbers of very different cost, excelling natural rubber in some respects and inferior to it in others. Moreover, new synthetic materials of the rubber type are always coming forward: thus a recent product is extremely similar to leather and much harder wearing. The prices of synthetic and natural rubber are influenced by so many different factors, industrial and political, that it is hard to say whether the product of the rubber tree will survive or become as obsolete as natural indigo.

Silicones

The fundamental work on the silicones was that of F. S. Kipping, who spent the forty years from 1899 to 1939 in investigating the organic compounds of silicon without any intention of putting them to practical use. In 1941 Rochow and Gilliam prepared the first silicone polymers by hydrolysing alkyl chloro-silanes; the rubbery product attracted attention as a possibly useful plastic and the process was patented by General Electric in the same year. The Dow Corning Corporation is now, however, their chief producer.

The fundamental reaction is the treatment of silicon tetrachloride with a Grignard reagent. The resulting alkyl chloro-silanes (*e.g.* CH_3SiCl_3, $(CH_3)_2Si_2Cl_2$, $(CH_3)_3SiCl$, etc.) are hydrolysed to silanols such as $CH_3Si(OH)_3$, $(CH_3)_2Si(OH)_2$, $(CH_3)_3SiOH$, etc., and these link up to chains or networks of the typical structure:

$$HO-\underset{\underset{R}{|}}{\overset{\overset{R}{|}}{Si}}-O-\underset{\underset{R}{|}}{\overset{\overset{R}{|}}{Si}}-O-\underset{\underset{R}{|}}{\overset{\overset{R}{|}}{Si}}-\ldots\ldots O-\underset{\underset{R}{|}}{\overset{\overset{R}{|}}{Si}}-OH$$

Naturally the radicals R can be varied and the proportion of cross-linkages can be changed, leading to a great variety of plastic materials, whose characteristic is great resistance to water, chemicals and heat.

Silicone greases are particularly valuable for greasing taps in chemical work. Silicone varnishes and resins are remarkably resistant to heat and are excellent electrical insulators, while ' Silastic '—silicone rubber—though inferior to normal rubber in elastic and wear-resisting properties, has remarkable resistance to temperature, retaining its properties between —70 F. and 500 F. Solutions of the less polymerized silicones can be used to form very resistant films on many types of material, and find a place in the newest types of domestic polishes. The silicone industry is still young but is of the greatest interest as utilizing a wholly new basic material and yielding products with quite new properties.

Petroleum Products

Petroleum has been known since antiquity, but until the latter half of the nineteenth century the Western world regarded it mainly as a medicament. It has, however, long been used in the East as an illuminant and fuel. Young's distillation of shale and torbanite to obtain illuminating oil and paraffin wax (p. 208) dates from 1840. The beginning of the modern petroleum industry dates from 1859, with the opening up of the Pennsylvania oil-field. Russian petroleum at Baku began to be exploited in 1873. The crude oil was distilled, and the products then specially valued were kerosene, lubricating oil, and paraffin wax : the light spirit, benzine or gasolene, was at first of little value, being too dangerous for an illuminant;

indeed it was often disposed of by burning it or running it into rivers.

The whole aspect of the industry was changed by the advent of the automobile in the decade 1900–10. From this time the light fraction—gasolene—became the important product. The demand vastly increased and oil-fields were opened up all over the world. Now it was the heavier oils that were produced in excess of requirement, and they were converted into lighter oils by the process of ' cracking ', *i.e.* decomposition at high temperatures. The idea that heavier hydrocarbons could be broken up into lighter in this way was an old one; it seems first to have been industrially exploited in 1913 in America, but the process became normal practice only in the decade 1926–36. The heavy oils were distilled at high pressures, and therefore at high temperature also; the result was a yield of 50–60% of motor spirit. In modern practice the vapours are led through a bed of finely divided catalyst granules, kept in suspension by the current of gas, thereby obtaining a fuel of greater volatility. The opposite process is now practised on the lightest (gaseous) fraction, which can by polymerized by means of sulphuric acid or phosphoric acid to hydrocarbons heavy enough to be incorporated into petrol. A recent process of high importance is platinum reforming (platforming), which converts naphthas into high-octane gasolenes by means of a platinum catalyst. In fact a wide variety of treatments are employed in order to change the hydrocarbons in crude petroleum and natural gas to the types most suitable for high-grade motor fuel.

Petroleum products have generally to be ' treated ' in order to remove sulphur, oxygen and nitrogen compounds of offensive odour or corrosive character. The oldest process is treatment with sulphuric acid, which has been used since the early days of kerosene-refining. The resulting sludges are now utilized for the production of detergents. Filtration through absorbent clays, such as bauxite or bentonite, is the method of treatment commonly used to-day. Some of the modern cracking processes convert the sulphur compounds in petroleum into hydrogen sulphide, from which elementary sulphur can be recovered.

Detergents and Wetting Agents

Success has been reached in the effort to find bodies with the

detergent powers of soap and without its fault of being put out
of action by acids or the salts of most metals. The earliest of
these was Turkey-red oil, a sulphonated oil long used in dyeing
with madder, but only about 1920 were synthetic detergents
brought into use. In the period 1920–23 alkyl aryl-sulphon-
ates, the first of which was the German Nekal, were developed,
and after 1933 a variety of other types. A cheap source of
these was the sludges from the refining of petrol with sulphuric
acid. Detergents, as put on the market, commonly contain
buffers (*e.g.* trisodium phosphate) to keep the solution alkaline,
and polyphosphates to 'sequester' the lime in hard water.
These materials were popularized during World War II, when
soap was scarce, and have now almost displaced it except for
washing the skin.

Another constituent has become customary in washing
powders. During World War II some 'dyes' were developed
in Germany which were colourless but fluoresced blue in
ultra-violet light. It has long been the custom to 'blue'
linen so as to correct the yellow tinge imparted by washing.
This process whitens but dulls the fabric, because it corrects the
colour only by absorbing light. The new 'optical bleaches'
correct the yellow by adding emitted blue light so giving a
brilliance never hitherto attainable. These optical bleaches have
also found their way into paper manufacture and other processes.

Chemicals from Petroleum

Natural gas and petroleum have become a major source of
organic chemicals and, indeed, furnish material for about half
the total American production of these.

Natural gas is evolved in enormous quantities from oil-wells.
Some of it is burned to make carbon-black, production of
which began about 1920 and has gigantically increased in the
last decade. Nearly a million tons a year are produced,
almost all for incorporation into motor tyres. Natural gas
contains methane, ethane, ethylene, propane, propylene,
butane and butenes. By 'scrubbing' it with gas-oil the C_3
and C_4 hydrocarbons are removed: they are then distilled out
of the gas-oil and sold in cylinders as bottled-gas, for heating
and sometimes for motor fuel. Similar products have been
obtained as a by-product from the Bergius process in Great
Britain and from the cracking-plant of oil refineries. Natural

gas can be converted into carbon monoxide and hydrogen and thus form an important source of many other chemicals (p. 433). The natural gas not used for chemical purposes is pumped far and wide over the United States and used as an industrial and domestic fuel.

Petroleum and natural gas contain a vast number of chemical individuals and constitute a source of organic products which ranks in importance with coal-tar. As early as 1920 the Standard Oil Company of New Jersey began to produce iso-propyl alcohol from the light fraction of petroleum, and by 1927 many of the higher alcohols were being produced from this source. In 1926 Sharples began to separate pentane from casing-head gas and turn it into amyl alcohol and amyl acetate, needed for the lacquer industry.

In 1927 ethylene glycol was produced from ethylene, derived from cracking-plant, and brought into use as an anti-freeze for cars. Ethanolamines, a new and better medium for dyes in textile-printing, followed in the years round 1930. During these years the exploitation of the lightest hydrocarbon, methane, was much developed; thus it was oxidized to formaldehyde and converted into methyl alcohol and the refrigerant Freon.

This early work has been totally eclipsed by the enormous developments of the war-time and post-war period. The essential feature has been the growth of the treatment of petroleum and its distillates so as to produce gasolene of the highest quality for internal-combustion engines. The principal object of the treatment of petroleum is to produce good motor-spirit; but in this process by-products of the greatest value to the chemical industry are produced. The oils may be heated by distillation under pressure; their vapours may be passed through a bed of heated catalyst; they may be mixed with steam or hydrogen at a high temperature or treated with a platinum catalyst at high pressure and temperature. All these processes alter the constitution of the hydrocarbons in one way or another and, in addition to motor-spirit, produce a propor-tion of low-boiling hydrocarbons, of which the most important are olefines—ethylene, propylenes and butylenes, etc. The individual hydrocarbons have to be separated from the mixture of gases, often by fractional distillation of the liquefied gases at temperatures down to — 100° C. or lower. The purified hydrocarbons can then be transformed into a great variety of chemicals. The great source of nineteenth-century organic chemicals was coal-tar, leading to the aromatic hydrocarbons and their derivatives; petroleum supplements this by providing a source of aliphatic chemicals. Petroleum products are not, however, limited to aliphatics, for they can also readily be transformed into aromatic hydrocarbons.

At present about 10% of natural gas and about 0·5% of petroleum in America are transformed into chemicals, the rest being used for fuel. It is impossible to keep pace with the progress of this industry, but some of its chief developments are here summarized.

In the nineteenth and early twentieth centuries ethyl alcohol was the prime source of aliphatic chemicals, but to-day 70% of American ethyl and methyl alcohol are made from petroleum. Ethylene from cracking-gas is polymerized to plastics: it also is made into ethylene-glycol, used as an anti-freeze and as a source of Dacron (p. 266). Propylene is converted into isopropanol and thence to acetone: it is also converted into glycerol and allyl compounds: it can also be polymerized so as to produce xylenes and phthalic acids: benzene is also obtainable in the same fashion. Up to half a million tons of butadiene, mainly from the same source, have been used in a year for synthetic rubber. The petroleum chemicals industry is, in fact, the most flexible and modern of all the fields of industrial chemistry.

It will be seen, then, that the exploitation of the lighter fractions of natural gas and products of cracking has opened up sources of aliphatic chemicals which were previously obtainable only through comparatively expensive biological sources, such as sugars, starch or oil. These processes are only at their beginning, and even the bewildering variety of solvents, refrigerants and intermediates that they have produced on an enormous scale are but precursors of new developments.

CHAPTER SEVENTEEN

Biochemistry

Origins of Biochemistry

THE chemistry of living matter is commonly treated as a separate department of chemistry and termed biochemistry. Since the characteristic constituents of living matter consist of compounds of carbon, biochemistry is mainly the application of organic chemistry to the constituents of the living organism.

The biochemist endeavours to isolate the chemical compounds in living organisms and to discover the chemical reactions that they undergo in the course of the life-process. The difficulties are great, because the compounds of which living matter consists are mostly complex and labile, and necessarily so, for only such compounds could allow of the wonderful variability and adaptation of living beings.

The term *biochemistry* has been in general use only since about 1910, but the science is as old as organic chemistry, which was originally, as its name implies, the chemistry of the products of organisms. The history of biochemistry falls into two chief sections: first, the investigation of what may be called plant and animal chemistry, that is to say, the investigation of the chemical nature of the substances contained in organisms; secondly, attempts to discover the sequences of chemical processes that take place in living organisms. The former began almost as early as chemistry itself and still continues, but the latter is a product of the twentieth century. Biochemistry has contributed extensively to industrial chemistry, especially in respect of the utilization of biological processes, such as fermentation, for the production of chemical individuals, especially the modern antibiotics, such as penicillin, streptomycin, aureomycin, etc.

Plant and Animal Chemistry

It is clearly impossible to discover the reactions that take place in living organisms until we know what chemical compounds are contained in them.

Even in the eighteenth century it was possible to separate pure compounds from plant and animal matter; urea, tartaric acid, oxalic acid, uric acid, lactic acid, gallic acid and glucose were among the pure compounds separated before 1800. In the years 1800–50 the list was greatly augmented. Several of the amino-acids, numerous alkaloids, animal bases such as the ptomaines, and some of the purine bases may afford examples. The preparative part of biochemistry far outran the knowledge of the structure of these compounds, and until this was discovered little light was thrown on the working of the living organisms. Three very important early steps were the discovery of the chemical nature of fats, of carbohydrates and of proteins, three essential materials of life. The composition of fats as compounds of certain acids with glycerol was worked out by Chevreul before 1826. The carbohydrates presented a much more difficult problem and were only satisfactorily cleared up by Emil Fischer in the years 1884–1900, while the general structure of the proteins, the typical and essential materials of life, was demonstrated by the same great organic chemist between 1900 and 1906. Fischer also worked out the constitution of uric acid and allied substances; his work, in fact, is the basis on which the biochemistry of the twentieth century was built.

Many other less important groups of organic compounds derived from animals and plants, e.g. resins, alkaloids, terpenes, ptomaines, amino-acids had been investigated during the later nineteenth century, and it may be said that the composition of the main groups of compounds important in biochemistry was known, in outline at least, by the beginning of the twentieth. In the last half-century this work has been greatly extended and brought to practical use.

Thus Emil Fischer supposed the sugars to be straight-chain compounds, while N. Haworth and his school have shown that the chains return on themselves to form rings. Fischer's general scheme of relationships of the sugars remains true, but we now have far more detailed and exact knowledge of them.

So also with the proteins. Fischer's general idea that they consist of amino-acids linked into extensive chains through —NH—CO— linkages is known to be true, but in a few cases,

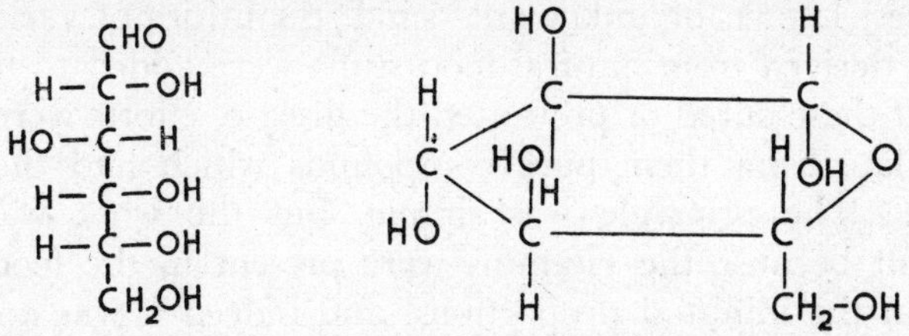

FIG. 45. Structure of glucose, *left* after Fischer; *right* after Haworth.

such as the silk protein, we now have X-ray evidence of the mode of that linkage. Very recently the structure of one simple protein has been worked out with fair certainty. In recent years chemists have studied many groups of plant and

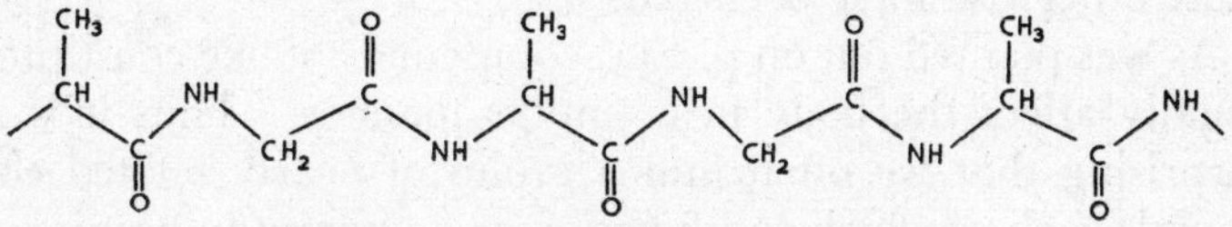

FIG. 46. Amino-acid linkages in proteins.

animal substances of which the nineteenth century knew nothing—for example, the vitamins and the plant and animal hormones.

The Vitamins

A vitamin is an organic compound which is an essential part of the diet of an animal, but only in amounts too small to afford any significant amount of energy. There are quite a large number of these; indeed some forty are known to be necessary in the diets of various mammals and birds, and there is no reason to suppose that our knowledge of them is yet complete.

The discovery of vitamins, and the name itself, dates from 1911–12, with the work of Casimir Funk and Gowland Hopkins, though hints of the idea are found in earlier work. Once biochemists had arrived at the fundamental notion that the absence of a minute quantity of an organic compound from the animal diet could bring about certain diseases, the way of procedure was fairly clear. Animals were fed on diets made up of pure chemical compounds and developed deficiency-diseases, known or unknown: small quantities of various extracts derived from natural food-stuffs were added to the diet and, if these cured or prevented the disease, efforts were made to isolate from them pure compounds which had the same effect. The principle was simple, but the work was very difficult because the vitamins were present in the food-stuffs only in the minutest proportions, and indeed it was not until the period 1925–30 that even the most abundant vitamins were isolated as pure compounds. The obvious step was then to synthesize them, and this has been accomplished in many instances. The importance of this work has proved to be enormous, for synthetic vitamins were added to the deficient dietaries which were the best available in the recent war, and thus prevented the enormous mass of deficiency diseases which must otherwise have occurred.

As was pointed out on p. 244, compounds of like constitution usually affect the body in a similar manner. Thus it is not surprising that we often find a group of nearly related compounds each of which can function as a vitamin in keeping the body in health: thus to one group of similar compounds we give the name of vitamins A, and to another group that of the vitamins D. The nomenclature of these vitamins is rather unsystematic. Before the chemical nature of these compounds was known they were distinguished by their physiological effect on the organism and were denominated by letters of the alphabet, e.g. vitamin A, B, C, etc. Some of these vitamins were, however, found to be complex mixtures, and their individual constituents were marked by the addition of subscript numbers, e.g. vitamin B_1, B_2, B_3, etc. Then, when their chemical nature was known they acquired a systematic chemical name which, being commonly a lengthy and unpronounceable one, is supplemented by another of more convenient dimensions. Thus from vitamin B, discovered in 1913, vitamin B_2 was separated in 1932, and the lack of it was shown to result in certain kinds of dermatitis. It was synthesized in 1935 and shown to be 6,7,-dimethyl-9-(d-ribityl)-isoalloxine, and, this name being somewhat unwieldy, it has been called *riboflavin*. Both the alphabetical and chemical systems are in common use to-day. We cannot here discuss the history of the whole of these compounds but will confine ourselves to the six vitamins which are sometimes deficient in human diets and cause serious conditions.

These include:

Vitamin		Conditions resulting from their deficiency
Vitamin A	Activated Carotenoids	Xerophthalmia
Vitamin B_1	Thiamine	Beri-beri
Vitamin B_2	Riboflavine	Ariboflavinosis
Vitamin C	Ascorbic Acid	Scurvy
Vitamin D	Calciferol, etc.	Rickets
	Nicotinic Acid	Pellagra

The story of the vitamins A begins with the discovery in 1913 by McCollum and Davis, and also by Mendel and Osborne, that besides the water-soluble food-factors there was also a fat-soluble factor, which was called the A factor. Foods which were very deficient in fats were found to result in what

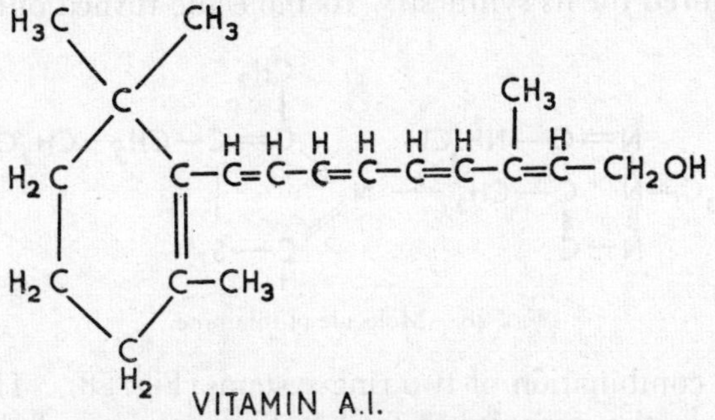

VITAMIN A.I.

FIG. 47.   Structure of Vitamin A1.

is called xerophthalmia, or 'dry-eye disease'. In 1919–20 it was recognized that the yellow pigments called carotenoids, which give colour to many organic substances, had some vitamin-A activity. About 1930 it was shown that carotene, the reddish-yellow pigment found in carrots and elsewhere, could replace vitamin A, but it was not until 1937 that vitamin A was synthesized. It is not identical with carotene, but carotene and some related substances can be converted into it in the body. The formulæ of vitamin A_1 is shown in Fig. 47. There is no accepted theory of the way in which vitamin A operates: its general effect is to prevent the degeneration of various forms of specialized skin structures. Thus the lack of this vitamin causes night-blindness, which is the failure of the rods of the retina to function. These rods are sensitive to dim light: they contain a light-sensitive pigment, *rhodopsin*, or visual purple, which seems to be made from vitamin A and some protein material. The best sources of vitamin A are fish oils and the liver of mammals, but many green vegetables, butter and cheese are useful.

The vitamin B group dates from 1913, when McCollum and Davis found that a young rat required for normal growth something they called ' water-soluble B '. It was contained in a variety of foods and it was effective in curing the disabling and fatal disease of beri-beri. This ' water-soluble B ' proved to contain at least ten different vitamins having different functions. The sorting out of this mixture was a long business, and it was only in 1926 that vitamin B_1, the compound effective in preventing and curing beri-beri, was prepared in a pure crystalline condition and termed thiamine. Another ten years was required for its synthesis. Its molecule turned out to be a

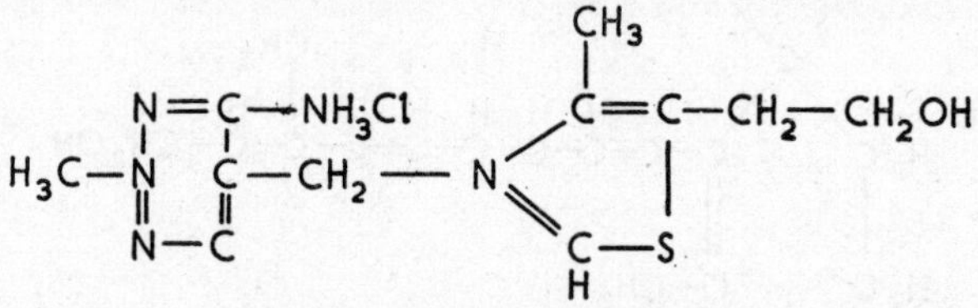

FIG. 48.   Molecule of thiamine.

peculiar combination of two ring-systems (Fig. 48). Thiamine is found in the majority of food-stuffs, but none of them are very rich in it. Rice from which the cortex and germ has been removed is almost free from it, and this is the diet that develops human beri-beri. Thiamine cures this condition very rapidly. Its function in the body seems to be to enable an enzyme to be made which oxidizes and so releases the energy from carbohydrates.

Vitamin C is the substance in the absence of which the disease of scurvy develops. It has been known for centuries that fresh fruit and vegetables cured the disease rapidly, but it proved difficult to investigate because animals were not known to suffer from it and cases of human scurvy were uncommon in civilized conditions. It was, however, shown in 1912 that guinea-pigs could acquire the disease, and this allowed of further experiments. In 1928 Szent-Gyorgyi prepared from cabbage, from lemon-juice, and from adrenal glands a pure compound which had the effect of preventing and curing scurvy. In 1933 this was synthesized and has been termed ascorbic acid. The function of this compound in the economy of the body is still unknown. The great majority of animals can synthesize it for themselves, but man and the guinea-pig must obtain it from outside sources. Lemons, oranges, limes, tomatoes (though not all fruits), cabbage, lettuce and spinach are good sources. It is easily destroyed by the action of oxygen at higher temperatures, and it is therefore gradually destroyed by cooking and storage.

The vitamins D are necessary for the formation of bones. The mineral constituents of bone are calcium compounds, chiefly the phosphate, and these vitamins are necessary in order that calcium shall be deposited where it is required. The

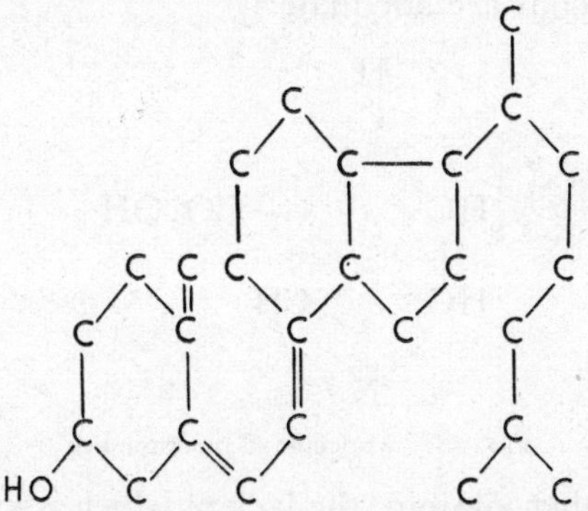

FIG. 49.   Carbon skeleton common to the Vitamin D's.

absence of these vitamins causes rickets. That cases of rickets were cured or improved by cod-liver oil and by sunshine was known as early as 1890. In 1906 Gowland Hopkins suspected it might be a deficiency disease, but it was only in 1919 that Mellanby proved that animal fats could cure rickets. Then in 1924 the remarkable discovery was made that ultraviolet light could impart to foods of many kinds the power of curing rickets, and in the next year the name vitamin D was proposed for the active substance produced therein. In 1927 it became apparent that it could be made by irradiating ergosterol, a substance found in vegetable oils and a member of the family of Sterid substances referred to on p. 285, and between 1930 and 1938 the very difficult task of establishing its structure was worked out. It proved that there were quite a number of very similar compounds having the power of preventing rickets, some being more effective for one species and some for another. The activity is associated with the groups of atoms shown in Fig. 49. The manner in which these substances operate on the organism remains quite obscure.

The ' water-soluble B ' (p. 280) was capable of curing not only beri-beri but also pellagra, a serious and often fatal disease resulting from diets made up of little but maize. Further analyses of the mixture showed in 1937 that the chief factor in curing pellagra was quite a simple compound derived from pyridine—nicotinic acid or nicotinamide. These are required, we now know, in the making of the enzymes (p. 287) that bring about oxidations in the tissues. The best sources of these compounds are meat, especially liver, and yeast, but a number of vegetable foods are adequate.

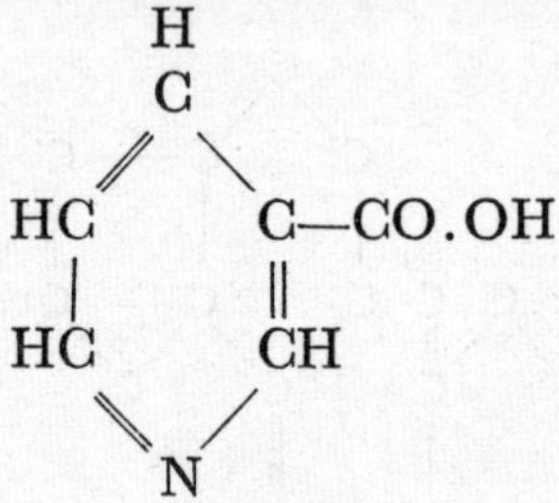

FIG. 50.   Molecule of nicotinic acid.

The only other vitamin, the lack of which is known to cause human deficiency diseases, is riboflavin, already mentioned on p. 278. There are a number of yellow pigments with a greenish fluorescence found in various animal materials, such as milk. From such sources an active compound was extracted, and in 1935 it was synthesized, its formula being shown in Fig. 51.

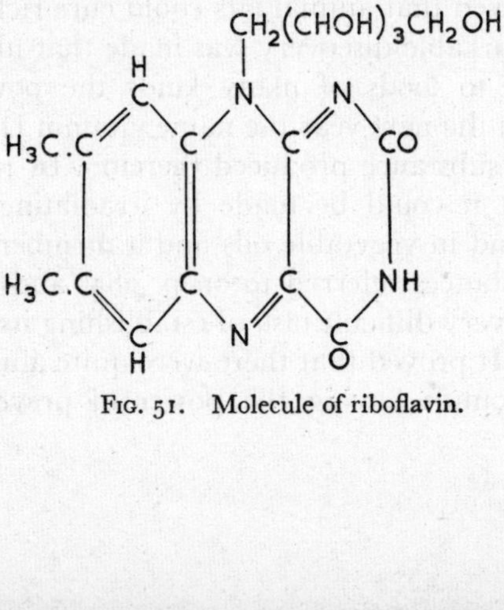

FIG. 51.   Molecule of riboflavin.

The lack of it causes various kinds of skin disease, and after prolonged deprival sudden collapse and death. Its function is to form part of an enzyme required to carry on oxidation in the cell. The best sources are liver, wheat-germ, yeast and green leaves, but it is pretty widely distributed.

There remains, then, some uncertainty about the rôle of the vitamins in the working of the body. The action of some, such as A and D, we do not understand; but, as we have seen, several are required in order that the enzymes which operate the ultimate chemical processes in the cell may be able to function.

The Hormones

A group of substances which, like the vitamins, cause profound physiological effects when present in minute quantity, are the hormones, the product of the endocrine glands. There is no other likeness, for the vitamins are factors operating in the normal processes of the cells, whereas hormones are messengers for control. A hormone is a substance secreted in one tissue and carried by the blood to another tissue which responds to its presence in some definite way. Thus the adrenal medulla can release epinephrin (adrenalin), which travels through the blood stream to the heart, steadying its beat; to the arteries, causing them to contract, so raising the blood-pressure, etc.

The physiology of the hormones is somewhat beyond the scope of this book, which is concerned rather with their chemistry and application.

The first hormone was isolated in 1901 by several investigators. It was epinephrin, the hormone of the adrenal medulla. It is a comparatively simple substance and was easily synthesized. The synthetic material has proved very useful for constricting the arterioles to prevent bleeding.

The isolation of the other hormones was a much more difficult task. The next one to be isolated was thyroxine, the substance secreted by the thyroid gland, the effect of which is to increase the metabolism of the body, *i.e.* to speed up utilization of carbohydrate fat and protein. The first step was to separate from the glands a pure compound or compounds which possessed its physiological activity or some part of it. Kendall worked on this problem between 1913 and 1919, in which year he separated a pure, crystalline and highly active product. Even so, the quantity contained from 3 tons of thyroid gland was little more than an ounce, a quantity insufficient for a complete study. Its formula was found to be $C_{11}H_{10}O_3NI_3$, but it is not easy to determine the formula of a compound containing 65% of iodine when only very small quantities are available. In 1926 Harington found a way of obtaining from the glands a much better yield of the compound. He also discovered a way of removing the iodine from the compound and analysing the residue, whereby he showed the formula to be $C_{15}H_{11}O_4NI_4$. The next problem was to find out the grouping of these atoms. Two different benzene compounds were obtained from it, and so the formula was expected to contain two benzene rings. A compound was made from it which was identical with a known compound

$$HO\langle\ \rangle—O—\langle\ \rangle CH_3.$$

It was concluded by a great many reasonings, based on experiments, that thyroxine, the active principle, had the formula

$$HO\langle\ \rangle—O—\langle\ \rangle CH_2.CH(NH_2).CO.OH.$$

Now the evidence for this formula, though strong, was not unimpeachable, but it was rendered almost certain by a successful synthesis. Thus Harington started with two well-known compounds, p-methoxy-phenol and 3 : 4 : 5-tri-iodo-nitrobenzene, whose formulæ are known with certainty; these reacted to form a compound, which was converted into a second, this into a third, and so on through eight stages, finally giving thyroxine. There was no doubt about what happened at each stage, and thus the correctness of the formula was confirmed.

The most remarkable source of hormones is the pituitary gland at the base of the brain, which produces a great number of hormones, most of which are proteins. Some of these modify the bodily function directly, others act upon other glands and cause the production of another hormone. The pituitary is therefore in some sense the master-gland of the body. Thus the complicated processes connected with reproduction—the changes that take place at puberty, the changes that bring about the cycles of 'heat' in animals and the menstrual cycle in our own species, gestation, birth and lactation—are all controlled from the pituitary. The pituitary hormones cause the testis, ovary and adrenal cortex to produce other hormones all of which are steroids, derivatives of the carbon-chain shown in Fig. 52. These hormones initiate and maintain the various processes required for the sexual cycle. The pituitary also controls the thyroid, the mammary glands, and the growth of the whole body.

Not only the pituitary but several other organs produce hormones that are proteins. Insulin and the hormone of the parathyroid glands which regulates the calcium content of the

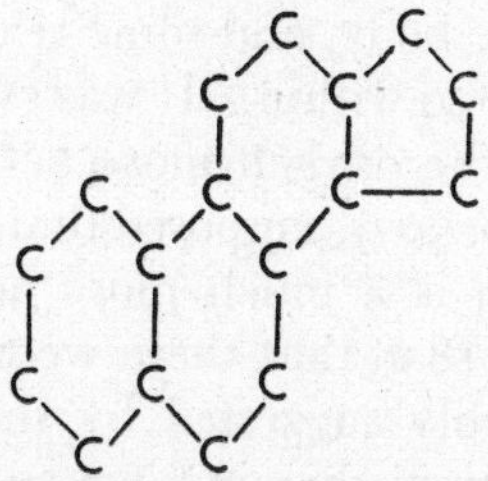

FIG. 52.   The carbon skeleton of steroid molecules.

tissues are examples. Very recently the structure of insulin has been almost completely set out, but we cannot yet connect its structure with its physiological activity.

The Chemical Reactions of the Body

The characteristic activity of nineteenth-century bio-chemistry was the isolation and investigation of the chemical compounds found in living organisms, and this, as we have seen, is still in progress. The characteristic of twentieth-century biochemistry is rather the attempt to discover the chemical reactions which constitute the mechanism of the life-process. Certain fundamental ideas on these questions were, indeed, developed even in the nineteenth century. Thus the knowledge that oxidation was the source of bodily heat is due to Lavoisier (1780–85). That this oxidation took place not only in the lungs but in all the tissues was proved in 1837 by

Magnus, who showed that the oxygen disappeared from the blood during its progress through the capillaries of various organs. The process, viewed as a whole, was seen to obey the usual chemical laws of oxidation. Thus it was shown from about 1870 that a given weight of food and oxygen consumed by the body yielded the same quantity of energy as they could have if the food had been burned in the oxygen outside the body. This work led to the examination of the calorific values of foods, which in turn has led to a scientific knowledge of food requirements and the ability to specify adequate diets for people doing known quantities of work.

The body could then be considered as an engine which burned food and produced heat and work; yet the sort of combustion that went on in the tissues was evidently very different from what goes on in a fire. It was evident more than a hundred years ago that oxygen does not oxidize our food-stuffs outside the body, and some reason had to be sought as to why it should do so within. It was evident that something in the tissues made the oxygen more active. Schönbein, the discoverer of ozone (p. 307), supposed that oxygen in the tissues formed ozone, which is a much more active substance. M. Traube suggested in 1858 that there were *oxygen carriers* in the tissues—an idea readily suggested by the intermediate compound theory of catalysis, then in favour. Thus a substance A, present in small quantity, might first be oxidized, and the product might then oxidize the food-stuff Fd, regenerating A to carry a fresh dose of oxygen,

$$O_2 + 2A = 2AO,$$

$$2AO + 2Fd = 2A + 2FdO.$$

Later he thought that hydrogen peroxide or an organic peroxide could be formed and act in this fashion:

$$A + 2H_2O + O_2 = A(OH)_2 + H_2O_2$$
$$H_2O_2 + Fd = H_2O + FdO,$$

or

$$A + O_2 = AO_2 \text{ (peroxide)}$$
$$AO_2 + Fd = AO + FdO.$$

This idea was supported by the fact that enzymes capable of decomposing hydrogen peroxide are found in many tissues.

Meanwhile there were two other lines of approach to the study of the reactions that went on in the tissues, namely, the study of enzymes and of the nature of the substances oxidized.

Awareness of the presence of organic catalysts in living organisms dates back to 1814, but not much was learnt about them till the closing years of the century. These organic catalysts were generally known as ' ferments '. Pasteur in 1878 distinguished ' formed ferments ', *i.e.* living organisms such as yeast or bacteria, which brought about chemical changes through their life-processes, from ' unformed ferments ', which operated outside the cell—the pepsin of the gastric juice afforded one of many examples of the latter. Buchner in 1897 destroyed that distinction by grinding up yeast and filtering out of it a solution which contained a ferment or enzyme (zymase) which would do the work of yeast in fermenting glucose to alcohol. Since that time it has become clear that the chemical processes within the cell are catalysed by the enzymes which the cell produces. Up to 1898 all the known reactions brought about by enzymes were decompositions, the splitting of complex compounds into something simpler, but in that year the fertile genius of van't Hoff suggested that enzymes, being catalysts, should accelerate a reversible reaction in either direction, and so, if an enzyme caused a compound AB to break up into A and B, it should, under suitable conditions, make A and B recombine to AB. In the same year Croft Hill tried the experiment and found that the ferment that decomposed malt-sugar into glucose would partly convert a concentrated solution of glucose into iso-maltose, a sugar closely resembling though not identical with maltose. In 1886 and in 1901 it was shown that the protein-splitting enzyme pepsin would convert a concentrated mixture of amino-acids into a protein-like substance, plastein. This was further investigated in 1927. It thus became clear that enzymes could be used not only to decompose but to synthesize—and indeed it seems that they can catalyse a very wide variety of reactions. In the early twentieth century there was still a doubt as to whether enzymes were true chemical individuals or whether they were complex compounds in a high state of subdivision (the analogy of platinum-black is obvious), but Willstätter and other workers after 1922 showed that they could be separated in a pure state and crystallized.

Returning to the nineteenth century, we may now consider the history of the question as to what reactions took place in the tissues. The general classification of the body's constituents into ' albuminous substance ' (proteins), carbohydrates and fats was set up by Liebig before 1850. He supposed that albuminous substances were oxidized when muscular energy was produced, while carbohydrates were oxidized to produce heat. Fick and Wislicenus disproved the former statement in 1865 by climbing the Faulhorn on a nitrogen-free diet, and showing that the nitrogen they excreted did not account for the decomposition of enough protein to provide the energy they exerted. This confirmed the very important work of Claude Bernard on glycogen. In 1848 Bernard noted the high proportion of sugar in the liver. He washed the sugar out of the liver, but found that after twenty-four hours more sugar had formed. He extracted from the liver a substance called glycogen, which appeared to be analogous to starch and acted as a storehouse of sugar in the animal in the same way that starch afforded a storehouse of sugar for the plant. It was not until 1905, however, that it was experimentally proved that the liver converted sugar into glycogen.

Bernard in 1859 showed that muscular work caused glycogen to be consumed, and v. Wittich in 1873 showed that a ' ferment ' could cause its decomposition into sugar; and after 1890 it was shown that such ferments were to be found in almost all tissues. It thus became clear that glycogen and its product, glucose, were involved in muscular work. It was also known quite early in the nineteenth century that lactic acid was formed in the muscles when vigorously exercised.

The problem of discovering the chemical reactions by which glycogen was oxidized so as to give the energy that is manifested as muscular energy, heat, and the chemical energy needed for synthesis of the body's constituents, developed into one of the great biochemical researches of the twentieth century. At the beginning of the century we did not know whether glycogen was a single compound or a mixture: in 1946 it was shown that there is more than one compound included as glycogen and that these consist of about 12–18 glucose molecules linked together (p. 277). The simple notion that glucose, liberated from glycogen, is oxidized in the tissues according to the reaction,

$$C_6H_{12}O_6 + 6O_2 \rightarrow 6CO_2 + 6H_2O + \text{Heat},$$

PLATE XIII

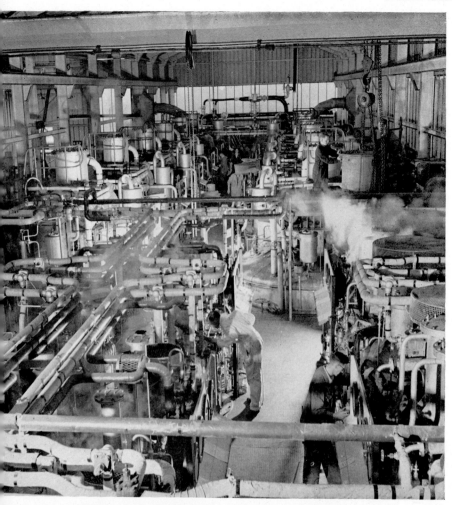

A. — Control Equipment for fermentation processes in tanks of 5,000 gallons and over, used to produce penicillin and other anti-biotics (see p. 291).

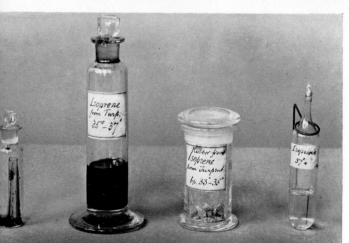

—Tilden's specimens of isoprene and synthetic rubber (see p. 268).

PLATE XIV   A.—Modern Oil Refinery at Stanlow, Cheshire. General view of distillatio
unit (see p. 272).

B.—Part of Retort for Making Anhydrous Hydrofluoric Acid (see pp. 310 ff.).

and that the heat is then turned into work, was too naïve even for 1900. It was obvious that the cell brought about not a conflagration but a gentle and perfectly controlled oxidation. Furthermore, it is now clear that the idea of 6 oxygen molecules simultaneously seizing on a glucose molecule is kinetically absurd. Clearly a reaction of this kind would take place in stages. It was obvious, too, that mere contact of oxygen and glucose would not bring about reaction, for glucose and oxygen can remain in contact for an unlimited time without change.

Work on this difficult problem developed along two lines, the study of the chemical reactions that occurred in muscular action, and that of the oxidations that occur in living tissue generally. The former made the more rapid advance.

Engler in 1904 suggested the notion of an enzyme as an ' auto-oxidizer '. Thus if we call this A and the other oxidizable material B, the A reacts with oxygen to form a compound $A\!\!\begin{matrix} O \\ | \\ O \end{matrix}$ which reacts with B, giving a product BO and liberating A once more. On such a scheme a gentle and steady oxidation could take place. Bach, in 1920–22, added a further suggestion that not only were there enzymes which added oxygen to the oxidizable material in the cell, but also enzymes which could remove hydrogen. Wieland in 1922 proved this idea of dehydrogenation experimentally. He supposed that typical reaction to be:

$$2XH + O_2 \rightarrow 2X + H_2O_2.$$

activated by   hydrogen
oxidase   peroxide

The hydrogen peroxide was supposed to be decomposed by the enzyme catalase, present in many tissues, liberating oxygen again. Warburg and his school, about 1920–30, supported the idea that the oxygen was activated by means of iron compounds present in almost all cells.

Between 1930 and the present day the analysis of the cell-contents has come to indicate that glucose passes through perhaps ten stages in its oxidation. Each of these stages is in equilibrium with its predecessor and successors and is catalysed by an appropriate enzyme, or indeed by a number of these. The result is a slow and controlled oxidation in which the energy evolved can be used with great efficiency. It seems that the process consists not as much in adding oxygen but in removing hydrogen, which is handed on from one molecule to another and is finally oxidized to water. The investigation of this vital life-process has reached the stage where its extreme complexity is becoming apparent: we need not expect it to be solved for many years yet.

Industrial Biochemistry

Biochemistry, the study of the materials of living organism and of the chemical processes that take place in them, has its industrial aspects. For our present purpose we may consider, first, the use of living organisms to make chemical compounds; secondly, the isolation or synthesis of the chemical compounds which take part in the life-process.

Fermentation is perhaps the oldest of chemical processes. The alcoholic and acetous fermentations have already been discussed: the lactic fermentation and others concerned in the making of cheese are of comparable antiquity. A totally new light was thrown on these processes by the work of Louis Pasteur, who between 1854 and 1864 showed that living organisms were the agents of all such changes. His bacteriological methods made the study and control of fermentation possible. The alcoholic fermentation can now be far more regularly and certainly conducted, but we may find special interest in the development of other and wholly new processes for making chemicals by the aid of living organisms.

None of these were developed until biochemical technique became familiar and until the shortages of the war of 1914–18 compelled the search for new sources of supply.

Pasteur studied the fermentation of starch by the *Bacillus butylicus*, which yields *n*-butyl alcohol and acetone. Neither of these substances was in any greater demand than ordinary methods could supply until the production of cordite in wartime quantities demanded increased supplies of acetone. Strange and Graham in Great Britain had in 1913 set up a plant to produce *n*-butyl alcohol and acetone by fermenting potato-starch, but there was then no great demand for butyl alcohol. In 1916 the process was used in the U.S.A. on a large scale; the butyl alcohol was later used to make butyl acetate, which formed an excellent solvent for the nitrocellulose lacquers used for the ' cellulose ' finish of cars. The process was for some time a principal source of acetone, but has now been largely superseded by the production of acetone from petroleum gases (p. 270).

In 1893 Wehmer patented the production of citric acid, formerly made exclusively from citrus fruits, by fermenting sugar-solution with certain moulds. The process was not developed until 1916, when the import of citric acid was restricted by submarine warfare, but it has since remained the chief way of making this product. Amongst other minor fermentative industries may be mentioned the making of gallic acid from tannins, of gluconic and fumaric acids in much the same way as citric acid, of lactic acid from corn-sugar or molasses, and the production of methane by fermenting sewage.

A most important landmark was the isolation of the enzymes, dating from 1897; to-day preparations of diastase are sold on a large scale for de-starching textiles.

The most important process of this kind is, however, the production of penicillin by the growth of the mould *penicillium notatum* in suitable media. This process requires the most careful control and presents great difficulty owing to the instability of the product.

The manufacture of penicillin (actually a mixture of several related chemical individuals) has, however, become a considerable industry. The principle is simply to grow the best strain of the mould *penicillium notatum-chrysogenum* in a nutrient medium and to extract the penicillin from this medium. A carefully selected strain of *penicillium*, grown under sterile conditions, is prepared in considerable quantity and transferred to the fermentors, vats of perhaps 10,000 gallons capacity, containing corn-steep liquor, an extract of maize solubles, together with carbohydrates and some inorganic salts. Air, sterilized to avoid infection with other organisms, is blown through these and they are vigorously stirred. The mould grows as a tangle of fine threads, and when the maximum concentration of penicillin has been reached the culture is filtered and the penicillin extracted with a solvent and re-dissolved back into water. Penicillin is very sensitive to oxidation at any but a very low temperature; the water is therefore removed by freeze-drying. The solution is filtered, frozen and transferred to a high vacuum. The ice slowly evaporates, leaving the penicillin.

Penicillin was synthesized in 1944, but the synthetic method has not displaced its manufacture from the mould and, despite the perfection of the fermentation process, we should be glad of a purely chemical method of manufacture. Some eighty other antibiotics derived from low forms of life have been investigated, but only three or four have been proved to be of value, namely, streptomycin, aureomycin and terramycin, though doubtless the list will be extended.

The study of biochemistry has led to the isolation of numerous substances which play necessary parts in the animal economy and whose deficiency may cause disease. Notable amongst these are the hormones and vitamins, already discussed. Some of these substances, *e.g.* adrenalin, are comparatively simple and have been synthesized in quantities: others, such as the hormone of the thyroid gland or some of the many sex-hormones, have been synthesized only by complex and costly processes: despite this complication the quantity of œstrogens synthesized in 1949 amounted to 1,500 lb. Some hormones, such as the all-important insulin (1921–22), have not been synthesized, and continue to be extracted from animal material. A number of these hormones are prepared from the glands of animals slaughtered for food, and also from those of the large number of whales yearly processed for oil and other products. Certain sex-hormones are separated from the urine of pregnant mares. The methods vary according to the hormone to be extracted, but in general the material, fresh or frozen immediately after slaughter, is extracted with a series of different solvents so selected as finally to arrive at a concentrated solution of the principle. Protein hormones are frequently concentrated by fractional salting-out. The proportion of the hormones in the original material is always very small and their preparation correspondingly difficult: accordingly even a poorly yielding or lengthy synthetic process is preferred to extraction from animal material.

The methods of these syntheses are not essentially different from those of other organic syntheses, but they exploit the very difficult field of steroid chemistry, which has been elucidated only in the last twenty years. Their raw material is chiefly cholesterol, obtained from spinal cords of slaughtered animals or from wool-wax.

The numerous vitamins, a small continuous intake of which

is necessary if health is to be preserved, were formerly extracted from animal or plant material, but were almost all synthesized in the decade 1930–40. Some of these synthetic vitamins are produced on a large scale for addition to bread, butter, margarine and other food-stuffs.

Agricultural Chemistry

From the beginning of modern chemistry the problem on the causes of the fertility of soil has received attention, but until 1804 little was discovered except the fact that certain salts, especially saltpetre (potassium nitrate), promoted growth. The first systematic experimental work was that of Theodore de Saussure, son of the famous botanist. He proved that plants obtained the greatest part of their substance from carbon dioxide and water and only a small but essential portion, including nitrogen, from the soil. His views were not generally followed and up to 1840 it was generally believed that plants obtained their carbon from the humus of the soil.

De Saussure's work was carried on by Boussingault, who was the first to perform field experiments, but he did not succeed in solving the problem of the source from which plants derived their nitrogen. In 1840 Liebig at last convinced the world that plants obtained all their carbon from carbon dioxide, though he believed that the gas not only entered the leaves from the air but the roots from the soil. Liebig at this period did not, however, believe that the soil was the only source of nitrogen and did not regard this element as important. His emphasis was all on the need for the ' mineral ' constituents, potash and phosphates.

In 1843 Lawes and Gilbert began their famous experiments at Rothamsted, where field experiments have been carried on year after year on the same ground up to the present day. These experiments proved the efficacy of artificial manures: they showed that non-leguminous crops, such as wheat or turnips, required a supply of nitrogen compounds, while leguminous crops did not and, indeed, increased the nitrogen content of the soil. In the 1850's and 1860's, then, the importance of nitrogenous fertilizers was realized, and by the end of this period Liebig's view that the chief plant food was ammonia was replaced by the view that nitrates are the material which the plant absorbs. In the next decade bacteriology was becoming important in the hands of Pasteur and others, and in 1877 Schloesing and Muntz discovered that minute living organisms were the means of turning ammonium compounds into nitrates. Warington in 1881–84 showed that the process took place in two stages, the ammonia first forming nitrites, which were then oxidized to nitrates, but he could not demonstrate the active organism, which was done only in 1890 by Winogradsky. But even before the latter date the problem of the nourishment of the leguminous plants had been solved. Berthelot in 1885 had shown that certain micro-organisms in the soil could utilize the nitrogen of the air: Hellriegel and Wilfarth in the following year put forward the view that the bacteria, known to exist in the nodules on the roots of leguminous plants, assimilated nitrogen and handed on the compounds so formed to the plants. Two years later these bacteria were isolated and named *bacterium radicicola*.

Thus were solved the main problems of plant-nutrition. Subsequent research has been chiefly in the biological investigation of the relationships between the competing organisms of the soil. Agricultural science has therefore, in recent years, sought its inspiration in biology rather than in chemistry.

However, the chemists have continued to contribute enormously to agriculture. First and foremost, the gigantic fertilizer industry (Chapter Twenty-five) enables the growing population to be fed. That chemistry had a bearing on the manuring of plants is an ancient notion. Glauber about 1650 believed that saltpetre was the active principle of vegetation—a belief much nearer to the truth than most of the current notions about plants. From about 1750 more attention was given to the application of science to agriculture. The favourite theory was that humus was the essential plant-food, but as a result of the work of De Saussure, Boussingault and Liebig it was supposed by 1840 that the carbon of plants came from the air, their nitrogen from ammonia, their potash and phosphorus from the soil. Liebig was wrong in some details and inclined to pontificate without enough experiments, but he came very near to the essentials of the subject.

In 1837 J. B. Lawes began to experiment upon the plants to discover what were the elements of plant-food. At this early date he discovered the value of spent animal charcoal from the sugar-refineries, consisting essentially of calcium phosphate and carbon, and found that treatment with sulphuric acid increased its value. Bones, and even bones treated with sulphuric acid, had previously been used as a fertilizer, and Lawes's greatest discovery was the value of mineral phosphates. Thus he applied this treatment with sulphuric acid to other phosphatic minerals and so produced the first artificial manure, ' superphosphate of lime '. He manufactured superphosphate and other fertilizers at Deptford on a considerable scale, and from 1843 he employed and worked with J. G. Gilbert, and together they carried out the masterly Rothamsted experiments alluded to above. These demonstrated the needs of crops to be essentially (1) combined nitrogen, (2) phosphates, (3) potash. Combined nitrogen was available in the ammonium sulphate produced from the gas-works (p. 209). Phosphates could be supplied as bones or the superphosphate invented by Lawes, and these are still important at the present time. Potash, however, was not applied, except as woodashes, until 1861, probably for the good reason that there was no satisfactory potash mineral. The Stassfurt deposits (p. 402) of potash were discovered in 1852 and brought into production in 1861, and from that date potash minerals were greatly used on the poor sandy soils of North Germany.

A new source of phosphate was opened up when the basic Bessemer process was introduced by Thomas (p. 202). Basic slags have remained an important source of phosphate, and that from the Bessemer process is about twice as valuable as that from the basic open-hearth process.

The possible supply of nitrogen was greatly augmented by the exports of sodium nitrate from the deposits in Peru and Chile. The existence of ' nitre ' in Peru [1] was known in the seventeenth century, and it was used for making gunpowder, but it was first successfully exported to Europe about 1830. The further development of the industry was slow, but a sharp increase occurred at the time of the Franco-Prussian war. In the years 1880–90 sodium nitrate became of increased importance as a fertilizer and became the chief source of nitrogen for agricultural purposes. The output steadily rose and, as the deposits are not of unlimited extent, towards the end of the

---

[1] The territory in which the nitre occurs was formerly Peruvian, but was ceded to Chile after the war of 1879. Donald, M. B. "History of the Chile Nitrate Industry." *Annals of Science*, 1, 1936, pp. 29–47, 193–216.

nineteenth century it became apparent that they would be
unable permanently to provide the huge quantities of nitrogenous manures needed by agriculture.   Some alarm was
manifested, but the rate of production continued to rise.   Not
only was Chilean nitrate the chief fertilizer, but it was also,
until the year preceding the World War of 1914–18, the only
important source of nitric acid, essential for the manufacture
of high explosives.   As will be seen in Chapter Twenty-five,
the Germans had then brought into production plant for
synthetic ammonia and synthesis of nitric acid therefrom: even
so these processes gave trouble and Germany was saved from
early defeat only by the capture of 300,000 tons of nitrate of
soda at Antwerp, which tided them over until the synthetic
nitric acid plant could meet their needs.   The Allies used
gigantic quantities of sodium nitrate also—nearly 3,000,000
tons in 1916—but the danger of relying on an overseas source
of nitrates, whether for production of food or of explosives, had
become apparent.   Thereafter all the great industrial nations
sought to make themselves independent of such supplies by
setting up synthetic nitrogen plants, and the Chilean nitre
production has somewhat declined, though kept alive by by-
products such as iodine, not obtainable from other sources.

Beside the enormous importance of the fertilizer industry
other contributions of chemistry to agriculture seem small, yet
they are far from unimportant.   The first is pest-control, to
which the study of the various substances toxic to insect-life has
been essential.   The first important discovery of this kind was
the use of carbon disulphide (p. 393) from 1858 as a means of
controlling the phylloxera, or root-aphis, which was destroying
the vines of Europe.   Its success was not, however, outstanding.
The pigment copper aceto-arsenite (Paris green) was used as
a means of poisoning leaf-eating insects as early as 1860, while
lead arsenate, which has replaced it and is now used in
quantities of 20,000 tons or more per annum, came into use in
1892 as a means of combating the gipsy moth in America.
Contact poisons have been greatly developed.   The earliest
seems to have been various oil-emulsions containing kerosene
(p. 270), soap, water and various other substances.   Lime-
sulphur (calcium polysulphide), introduced about 1886, soon
became popular, but in the last twenty years plant-products,
pyrethrum, and the rotenone-containing plants such as derris,

have come to the fore. Synthetics such as dinitrocresol and various thiocyanogen compounds have recently come into use for winter washes.

A large variety of synthetic fumigants for pest-control came into use in the 1920's. Some of these were dusts such as the calcium cyanide (cyanogas) used against rodents, and the arsenates, of which gigantic quantities were required for the campaign against the cotton boll-weevil. Silicofluorides were also brought into use in the mid-'20's.

Numerous volatile fumigants also came into production at this period. Liquid hydrogen cyanide was greatly used for the fumigation of Californian citrus trees despite its considerable dangers. Among other new products, in some cases derived from experience with war-gases, were chloropicrin, the esters of chloracetic acid, and ethylene oxide. The disinfection of corn and other seeds from fungi by means of organic mercurials dates from 1924 and has proved effective.

Among the less volatile insecticides applied in powder form or by spray were derris-root and pyrethrum, the use of which was encouraged in the 1920's by legislation directed against arsenic or lead residues left on food-stuffs. Their active principles were investigated and rotenone, the active principle of derris, was extracted in quantities of thousands of pounds in the late '30's. The war in the Far East, however, cut off supplies of rotenone, but its place was soon supplied by the chlorinated products D.D.T. (dichloro-diphenyl-dichloro-ethylene) and gammexane (γ-hexachlorocyclohexane). The former was first produced in large quantities in 1944, for use against human parasites which might have spread disease among populations disorganized by war. A recent development of promise is the use of systemic insecticides, such as octamethyl pyrophosphoramide, which render plant juices toxic to insects though harmless to mammals. The fluor-acetates developed in America during World War II have proved to be the most effective destroyers of rodents.

The plant hormones may here receive a mention. Certain comparatively simple organic substances, which can be synthesized in quantity, have profound effects on the growth of the plants. Thus solutions of some of them promote root-formation and have revolutionized the propagation of plants from cuttings. More recently others have been found to cause an irregular and distorted growth of leaves; these act as very efficient selective weed-killers, destroying many weeds completely while not affecting cereals and grass. A wide variety of these substances now gives us a considerable control over plant-life, and their investigation is a field of much activity.

The Future of Applied Biochemistry

Organic chemistry exceeds the other departments of the science in the almost infinite possibilities of making new compounds. New techniques continually open up new fields for synthesis. We ourselves are inhabitants of a tissue of organic compounds, and the discovery of substances that can modify our functions and destroy our parasitic enemies is, it would seem, a matter only of time and skill for the synthesis and testing of other organic compounds. The biochemist finds himself in a difficult field: the molecules at the basis of life are very large, complex, unstable and not at all amenable to our present technique. The obvious fields of advance are in the control of food-production and the mastery over those bodily ailments of man and animals that do not arise from constitutional defect: what more we shall see time must be left to discover.

CHAPTER EIGHTEEN

Inorganic Chemistry after 1860

Valency Linkage in Inorganic Compounds

THE progress in inorganic chemistry after 1860 was not quite as spectacular as that of the organic or physical departments of the science, because so much had already been discovered. Most of the common elements and compounds were known, as were also the compositions of most of the common compounds, although there could be no certainty about formulæ until Cannizzaro's system (p. 216) had been adopted. The formula of alum may afford a good example. Thus in 1850 the formula of potash alum was written as KO, $SO^3 + Al^2O^3$, $3SO^3 + 6Aq + 18Aq$: after the new formulæ were adopted it might be written as $Al_2(SO_4)_3 + K_2SO_4 + 24H_2O$. Later, the fact that the constituents were not merely mixed was recognized by writing it as $K_2SO_4.Al_2(SO_4)_3.24H_2O$. But some authors, even in the 1870's, wrote the formula $K_2Al_2(SO_4)_4.$ $24H_2O$, or as $KAl(SO_4)_2.12H_2O$; and, indeed, there was no means of deciding between such alternatives until the method of X-ray analysis of crystals was developed. Thus in the case of alum it was only in 1935 that Beaver and Lipson showed that the two sulphates did not exist in the crystal as individuals and showed reasons, based on X-ray studies, for writing the formula as $KAl(SO_4)_2.12H_2O$. This example, then, illustrates not only the change in the mode of writing formulæ, but our uncertainty until recent years about the structure of very simple inorganic compounds.

The idea of valency, first introduced into inorganic chemistry by W. Odling in 1854, proved successful in that it allowed formulæ to be written according to a rational system. The writing of structural formulæ proved to be an enormous success in the field of organic chemistry, and so between 1860 and 1890, the tendency of the inorganic chemist was to write the formulæ of inorganic compounds along the same lines.

Now Kekulé's structure theory, so successful for organic compounds, depended on the hypothesis of fixed valencies. The valency of carbon is always 4, that of hydrogen 1, and oxygen 2; thus the organic chemist had little need to consider the variation of valency. But the inorganic chemist continually had to do so. Most of the metals had more than one valency, while the non-metals apparently had widely variable valencies. Chlorine, for example, seemed to have valencies of 1, 3, 5 and 7; sulphur of 2, 4 and 6. This gave a much wider choice as to the mode of writing structural formulæ, and what was written could rarely be experimentally substantiated, because inorganic compounds do not undergo those substitution reactions by which the organic chemists were accustomed to prove their formulæ. The structure theory availed pretty well for many inorganic compounds, but there were some classes for which it was inadequate. Thus to write H—S—H for sulphuretted hydrogen was reasonable, but such a formula as

$$
\begin{array}{ccc}
\text{O} & & \text{O} \\
\diagdown\!\!\diagup & & \diagup\!\!\diagdown \\
\text{P} & \!\!-\text{O}-\!\! & \text{P} \\
\diagup\!\!\diagdown & & \diagdown\!\!\diagup \\
\text{O} & & \text{O}
\end{array}
$$

for phosphorus pentoxide, P_2O_5, was not supported by the sort of evidence the organic chemists brought in favour of their formulæ: it was really adopted because it was the only formula that would assign to phosphorus and oxygen the valencies of 5 and 2. Again, the writing of the formula of sodium sulphate as

$$
\begin{array}{ccc}
\text{Na}-\text{O} & & \text{O} \\
\diagdown & & \diagup \\
& \text{S} & \\
\diagup & & \diagdown \\
\text{Na}-\text{O} & & \text{O}
\end{array}
$$

did not explain the great difference between the way in which the metal atoms were linked to the rest of the molecule, so as to be removed by electrolysis, and the way in which the sulphur and oxygen atoms were attached so as not to be separated in this fashion. One may say that the formulæ of inorganic compounds were written so as to satisfy the valency rules and the composition of the compound, but that they did not play a really active part in the development of inorganic chemistry. There were numerous anomalies, moreover. There were compounds which could not be written so as to agree with the normal valencies, *e.g.* carbon monoxide, CO, nitric oxide, NO, nitrogen peroxide, NO_2, aluminium chloride, Al_2Cl_6. There were the cases where whole molecules, which should have no combining power, in fact combined additively with other molecules, and sometimes with great firmness, as in the case of the metal ammines: again, there were groups of very complex compounds, such as the silicates, for which no convincing structures could be written.

The periodic law of Mendelejef (1869), treated in Chapter Nineteen, soon aroused further interest in the problem of valency (p. 218). The maximum valency of an element was seen to be generally equal to the number of its group in the periodic table: thus, carbon in the fourth group had a maximum valency of 4, and sulphur in the sixth group a maximum valency of 6. But the rule was not absolute. Thus the elements of the first horizontal period were anomalous: oxygen never gave its theoretical maximum of 6, nor fluorine that of 7. Moreover, of the nine metals of the eighth group only osmium was known to show a valency of 8. Elements also showed intermediate valencies. There seemed to be signs of a rule that any one element had valencies which were either all odd numbers or all even numbers, but even this did not hold absolutely. It was clear that valency had something to do with the periodic table, but the exact connection was not made clear until the 1920's.

The first important distinction between different types of valency was made by Svante Arrhenius and the other exponents of the ionic theory from *c.* 1885 (p. 367). They distinguished the linkage between the radicals of acids, bases and salts, which broke up into ions in solution, and those of other compounds which did not. Yet the majority of chemists continued to regard this ionic linkage as of the same character as the other. Thus sodium chloride, both as solid and in solution, was regarded as consisting of molecules, a proportion of which broke up into ions, $Na—Cl \rightleftharpoons Na^+ + Cl^-$. Nevertheless the idea of ionization led to great developments in the chemistry of salts and in the method of analysis. Particularly useful was the abandonment of the idea of double decomposition for that of reactions between ions. Instead of thinking of the various reactions which led to the precipitation of barium sulphate from sulphates and barium salts as constituting a whole class,

$$e.g. \quad BaCl_2 + CuSO_4 = BaSO_4 + CuCl_2$$

$$Ba(C_2H_3O_2)_2 + Na_2SO_4 = BaSO_4 + 2NaC_2H_3O_2,$$

and so forth, chemists realized that all these were one and the same reaction, the combination of barium ion and sulphate ion, which was then written

$$Ba^{++} + SO_4^{--} \underset{\text{in solution}}{\rightleftharpoons} BaSO_4 \underset{\text{solid}}{\rightleftharpoons} BaSO_4.$$

The understanding of reactions between salts led to the discovery of the best practical ways of manufacturing them and to a better understanding of inorganic analysis (p. 369). Chemists, and not least industrial chemists, were, however, very slow to adopt the ionic habit of thought. Arrhenius's ideas were put forward in 1885–87, but ionic equations were not commonly visible in students' textbooks before about 1920.

It must be emphasized, however, that ionization was thought of as something that occurred only when the ionizable substance was dissolved in water, and the constituent atoms and groups of solid salts were still generally considered to be linked in the same manner as the constituents of organic compounds. The instinct of scientists is always towards unification; a theory that was to explain the single phenomenon of chemical combination as being the result of two or more different processes was not one that could be accepted until it was clearly proven. Indeed, attempts to distinguish between the mode of combination of the radicals of electrolytes and that of the atoms in non-electrolytes were not seriously considered until the years round 1913.

But there was another class of compounds whose formulæ proved to be quite refractory to explanation by the idea of valency. Copper sulphate, as crystallized from water, has the formula $CuSO_4.5H_2O$. How were the five water molecules attached? Water, being a saturated compound, had no valency-bonds available, nor yet had copper sulphate. What,

moreover, determined the number 5? Chemists were inclined
to ignore this problem. Hydrates were ' loose compounds ',
and a blind eye was turned to their vagaries. But the same
difficulty arose over the metallic ammines, which were not
loose compounds but extremely stable. Some of these ammines
were known in the early years of the nineteenth century, and
their numbers rapidly increased. Typically, the molecule of
an ammine would consist of an atom of a heavy metal, combined with a large number of ammonia molecules, water
molecules and acid radicals. A simple and well-known example was the compound of platinous chloride and ammonia,
$Pt(NH_3)_4Cl_2$. As the century went on many hundreds of
similar compounds were found to exist, cobalt, chromium,
palladium and platinum being the chief (but not the only)
metals that gave rise to them.

The easiest way to account for the presence of all these
ammonia groups was to suppose they formed a chain. Thus
in 1869 Blomstrand (following up an earlier idea of Berzelius)
wrote the above formula as

$$NH_3\!-\!NH_3\!-\!Cl$$
$$\diagup$$
$$Pt$$
$$\diagdown$$
$$NH_3\!-\!NH_3\!-\!Cl.$$

Nitrogen was known to have a valency of 5, so a chain of
ammonia groups,

$$\begin{array}{ccccc} & H & H & & H \\ & | & \diagdown & \diagup & | \\ \cdots\cdots\!-\!\!\!\!&N\!&-\!\!\!\!-\!\!\!\!-\!&N\!&-\!\cdots\cdots \\ & \diagup & \diagdown & & | \\ H & & H & & H \end{array}$$

seemed possible. A great deal was discovered about these
compounds by Jorgensen, who began work on them about
1880. He showed that in some of these compounds the several
acid radicals are attached in different manners. Thus in
chloropentammino-cobaltic chloride, $Co(NH_3)_5Cl_3$, one of the
chlorine atoms does not react when the solution of the salt is
mixed with silver nitrate, while the other two do so. Jorgensen
supposed the chlorine atom which did not react (and therefore
did not ionize) was attached direct to the metal, while the

others were attached to ammonia: he wrote the formula of the above compound as:

$$NH_3\text{——}Cl$$

Not   Cl—Co

ionizable

$$NH_3\text{——}NH_3\text{——}NH_3\text{——}NH_3\text{——}Cl.$$

Jorgensen's formula did not provide any clear explanation why, for example, five ammonia molecules, and not *e.g.* three or seven, should be present in the compound. It did, however, provide a way of writing these formulæ which fitted in with the ordinary valency theories, and also made a distinction between the ionizable and non-ionizable acid radicals.

A totally different theory was advanced in 1891 by Alfred Werner and developed in the years from 1892 onward. The theory was so foreign to the ideas of the time that even after twenty years it was repugnant to orthodox chemists.

Werner supposed that certain atoms tend to attach to themselves a definite number, usually four or six, of other atoms or groups which might be whole molecules or radicals. This number he called the co-ordination number. The resulting complex, he emphasized, is not a salt and does not ionize, but may be the acid or basic radical or a salt. Thus the chloropentamminocobaltic chloride was written by him as:

$$\left[\begin{matrix} & Cl & \\ NH_3 & & NH_3 \\ & Co^{+++} & \\ NH_3 & & NH_3 \\ & NH_3 & \end{matrix}\right] Cl_2$$

The cobalt atom has the co-ordination number of 6. The six groups co-ordinated include one chloride ion. As the cobalt ion has a triple positive charge and chlorine a single negative charge, the complex has a positive valency of 2. This theory strikingly explained the peculiar behaviour of these salts in solution, but it was only slowly adopted; first, because the facts were not always very well known and, since the accepted formulæ of these complex bodies were quite often incorrect, the theory did not explain them: secondly, because the idea of a co-ordination number of 4 or 6, independent of the normal valency, ran quite counter to the ideas of the time. Werner's theory was proved by its prediction of isomers of these ammines. Geometrical isomers and optical isomers had been found in organic compounds; Werner predicted and found them in these ammines. If, as he supposed, six groups were evenly spaced over the surface of the cobalt atom, then if two of these (A) differed from the rest (B), two compounds should be possible and two compounds were formed in such cases. For nearly twenty years he accumulated evidence of this kind, which was attacked and criticized by Jorgensen. But its weight gradually told, and in 1911 the fulfilment of his prediction of optical isomers of one of these bodies really necessitated the adoption of the theory.

At this period three theories of valency existed, each correct

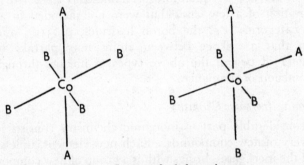

FIG. 53.   Isomers of cobaltammines.

for some types of chemical combination, but all strained by their supporters to cover types to which they did not apply.

(1) There was the Structure-Theory, dating back to Kekulé, according to which the atoms, irrespective of their positive or negative character, were held together by means of a fixed number of linkages characteristic of each atom. This perfectly fitted the facts of organic chemistry, but was wrongly extended to ionizable compounds and co-ordinate compounds.

(2) There was the electrochemical or dualistic theory, dating back to Davy and Berzelius, according to which the atoms were held together by their opposite electrical charges. This theory applied admirably to ionizable compounds but not to organic compounds or co-ordinated compounds.

(3) Finally the co-ordination theory of Werner admirably explained the metallic ammines and various complex salts, but

Werner's extension of it to cover organic compounds seemed to most chemists to be illegitimate.

N. V. Sidgwick, about 1927, showed how the difficulty was resolved by the electronic theory of valency, which showed that all these three different types of linkage really existed. The acid and basic radicals of electrolytes were linked by electrostatic attraction between ions, as suggested by Kossel (p. 350). In other cases the atoms in the molecule were linked by the sharing of electrons in pairs, constituting a valency bond as suggested by Lewis (p. 351). This might be through equal sharing, as in the carbon-to-carbon linkages of organic compounds and many others, or through a pair of electrons both contributed by one atom, the co-ordinate linkage especially found in the compounds that Werner had studied. The treatment of valency by quantum-mechanics has since led to the explanation of a few cases that were not included in any of these categories (*e.g.* the boron hydrides, p. 312), and has shown that a linkage between atoms may partake of the character of two of the above types of linkage through the phenomenon of resonance.

Preparative Inorganic Chemistry

A considerable part of inorganic chemistry consists in the discovery of new compounds. Each new element, unless it be one of the inert gases, brings with it a group of new compounds; furthermore, an enormous number of new compounds of the better-known elements have been prepared in the last hundred years. All have their importance, yet in themselves few are important enough to receive mention in a brief general survey of industrial chemistry such as this book affords. The best that can be done is to glance at a few groups of inorganic compounds that have been discovered or elucidated in the modern period.

The Discovery of Ozone, Hydrogen Peroxide and the Per-acids

We may consider the first two substances together, if only because ozone and hydrogen peroxide were often confused in their early period. Both ozone and hydrogen peroxide were discovered early in the nineteenth century. Thenard discovered hydrogen peroxide in 1818, and after some research showed it to be a ' bi-oxyde d'hydrogéne '. A peculiar smell had long been recognized as resulting from various high-tension electrical processes, and in 1840 C. F. Schönbein put forward the view that the smell was due to a definite chemical substance, ozone. At first he believed it was a new element, similar to chlorine and bromine, but in the next ten years it was proved that when it reacted with substances they combined with oxygen: furthermore, that it could be obtained by electrolysis of pure water and so could not contain anything other than oxygen or hydrogen. In the years 1840–60 there was doubt as to whether ozone was a modification of oxygen or a higher oxide of hydrogen. In 1860 it was proved by T. Andrews and P. G. Tait that the effect of electricity on pure dry oxygen was to cause it to contract and to form ozone, which was therefore a condensed form of oxygen.

The methods of preparing it, *e.g.* the effect of an electrical discharge in oxygen, gave only a mixture of oxygen and ozone and presented a new problem, the determination of the formula of a compound which could not be prepared in a pure state. What was its formula? A density determination of ozonized oxygen would not give the result, because the proportion of ozone in the oxygen was unknown. The proof that its formula was O_3 was due to the discovery that essential oils (unsaturated compounds) absorb ozone. Thus by absorbing the ozone from a measured part of a specimen of ozonized oxygen the proportion of ozone in it could be determined. By heating another part of the mixture the expansion of the ozone when decomposed into oxygen could be determined. It was proved by J. L. Soret (1866), and more accurately by B. C. Brodie in 1872, that 2 volumes of ozone can be converted into 3 volumes of oxygen and that its formula is therefore O_3.

Both ozone and hydrogen peroxide were for a long time unknown in the pure state. Pure ozone was first prepared by cooling and compressing ozonized oxygen until the ozone liquefied (1882), but it is so unstable and explosive a substance as to have found little use. Pure hydrogen peroxide was prepared by distillation under reduced pressure, in 1894.

In and about the decade 1890–1900 a whole class of inorganic compounds, known as per-acids, was discovered. Per-acids are those which can be made from hydrogen peroxide and the acid in question, or which react with dilute sulphuric acid, yielding hydrogen peroxide. Many salts of per-acids are of industrial importance. The first of these to be discovered was persulphuric acid. It had long been known that the dilute sulphuric acid in the anode chamber after electrolysis had oxidizing activity, but the formula of the oxidizing substance was not easily determined. Some took the acid to be $H_2S_2O_8$, others H_2SO_5: actually both acids can be present. However, in 1891, Marshall, while attempting to oxidize cobalt salts by electrolytic methods, obtained a salt of formula KSO_4, which behaved like the oxidizing solutions obtained by electrolysing sulphuric acid. The discovery of this potassium persulphate was followed by attempts to make other ' per-salts '. The per-carbonates were made in 1896–97, perborates in 1898, and others followed: in the same year Caro's acid, H_2SO_5, was isolated. These salts have proved to be of industrial value. Thus perborates in solution behave like a mixture of hydrogen peroxide and borax. They therefore have the detergent effect of the alkaline borax with the bleaching effect of hydrogen peroxide and are much used in washing-powders. This group affords an example of the manner in which the discovery of one member (the persulphate) was rapidly followed by that of a number of analogous substances. Persulphuric acid had been investigated for some twenty years: the pure persulphate was obtained by chance—the hint led rapidly to the discovery of the whole group. This is perhaps the typical pattern of chemical research.

Industrial Use of Ozone

From 1857 an efficient type of ' ozonizer ' was designed by Siemens, and all others are modifications of the same principle. Ozone became industrially important after 1886, when De Meritens showed that it was capable of killing the bacteria in infected water. In 1891 this method was used for sterilizing town water-supplies, and the method is now widely applied on the Continent and America. Ozone has also been used for ventilation, especially in food-storage warehouses, where it inhibits the growth of moulds and bacteria. The belief that ozone is present in and responsible for the fragrance and beneficial effect of sea air is a hardy myth, which seems to have originated in the 1870's and to have been fostered by those responsible for the advertising of health-resorts.

Ozone can now be made at a cost low enough to permit its

use for industrial oxidation, and it has been used for converting iso-eugenol into vanillin (p. 251), and certain steroids into cortisone.

Industrial Use of Hydrogen Peroxide and the Per-acids

The method used for the preparation of hydrogen peroxide throughout the nineteenth century, and to a limited extent to-day, is the action of dilute sulphuric acid upon barium peroxide. The chief process now in use is the preparation of persulphates by electrolysis, their decomposition by vacuum distillation, and the subsequent condensation of the peroxide. Its important technical application is bleaching, while large quantities are used as an antiseptic for medical purposes. Pure hydrogen peroxide, though unstable, can be readily preserved and has been used as a light and concentrated means of storing energy and oxygen in the German V2 and other rocket projectiles.

Simple Nitrogen Compounds

Although the majority of the simple compounds of the common elements had been discovered by 1850, an exception is to be found in hydrogen compounds of nitrogen. Ammonia, of course, had been known for centuries, but neither hydrazine, N_2H_4, nor hydrazoic acid, N_3H, nor hydroxylamine, NH_2OH, were then known or thought of. The first of these to be discovered was hydroxylamine, which was prepared by Lossen in 1855. Hydroxylamine hydrochloride was made by the action of hydrochloric acid and tin on nitric oxide or, better, ethyl nitrate. The free base was only known in solution until Lobry de Bruhn, in 1890, discovered that in absence of water it was fairly stable. It has proved to be important in organic chemistry as reacting with various substances containing the $>CO$ group, forming oximes, which are easily identified and thus afford the analyst a ready means of identifying numerous organic compounds.

Hydrazine, N_2H_4, also finds its principal interest in its reaction with organic compounds. Emil Fischer discovered a substance, $C_6H_5.NH.NH_2$, in 1875 and named it phenyl-hydrazine, implying that it was the phenyl (C_6H_5) derivative of a hypothetical hydrazine, $H_2N—NH_2$. In 1887 Theodore Curtius, who devoted his life to the investigation of these and other nitrogen derivatives, isolated pure hydrazine by hydrolysing triazoacetic acid. The substance was of great interest, but found no considerable uses.

Hydrazoic acid, HN_3, was also discovered by Curtius in the year 1890, and attracted great interest as being the only substance in which one hydrogen atom was combined with more than one other atom. Its formula was taken to be

$$H-N \underset{\displaystyle N}{\overset{\displaystyle N}{\diagup\!\!\!\diagdown}} \Big|\, ,$$

but now it is written as $HN : N \rightleftharpoons N$. It has attained some importance because its salts, the *azides*, especially lead azide, are explosives suitable for and largely used as detonators. Lead azide, first tried as a substitute for fulminate in 1893, was abandoned owing to serious explosions during manufacture. It was reinvestigated about 1913 and in the post-war period came into general use, though it has since receded in favour of certain organic detonating explosives.

Fluorine

One of the sensations of the second half of the nineteenth century was the isolation of the element fluorine. The fluorides and hydrofluoric acid were well characterized in the eighteenth century. Soon after 1814, Ampère suggested to Davy that ' fluoric acid ' was a compound of hydrogen with an element, *i.e.* that it was analogous to hydrochloric acid and not to the oxy-acids. This idea was generally favoured, though there were occasional dissentients. All efforts to isolate the element by methods applicable to the other halogens proved fruitless and chemists began to reconcile themselves to the impossibility of preparing this element; some indeed were inclined to treat their belief as an article of faith. Nevertheless, progress was made. The difficulty was that fluorine reacts with almost all materials. Thus it would react with any substance present, and even with the vessel used for the experiment. About 1856 Frémy came near to solving the problem by electrolysing fused calcium fluoride in a platinum vessel. A gas was evolved, but the platinum was almost instantly perforated and no certain results were obtained. But Frémy had shown, first, that hydrofluoric acid could be obtained free from water, and also that it formed double compounds of fluorides. There followed nearly twenty years of discouragement until 1884, when Henri Moissan tackled the problem afresh. After two years spent in trying several unsuccessful methods, he attempted to electrolyse anhydrous hydrofluoric acid. This does not conduct electricity, but by adding pure dry potassium hydrogen fluoride it was rendered conductive. The vessel was of platinum, closed by fluorite stoppers, and the electrodes were of platinum also. The apparatus was kept very cold ($- 23°$ C.), so minimizing the effect of the fluorine on the platinum. In this way Moissan obtained free fluorine, a substance of astonishing activity.

In the preface to his book, *Le Fluor et ses Composés,* Moissan wrote that in several years' time the preparation will appear quite simple and that all the efforts which its isolation cost him will be forgotten. This has not come about as quickly as the author supposed. Only in the last ten years has fluorine become a manageable laboratory reagent, and the proportion of chemists who have used or seen it remains small. The very expensive platinum tube has been replaced by copper or nickel: the platinum anode may be replaced by graphite. The electrolyte is potassium hydrogen fluoride or the compound $KF.3HF$, in the molten state. The result of the somewhat easier preparation has been the discovery of many new fluorine compounds, notably the oxides, F_2O (1927) and F_2O_2 (1933). Ruff, the discoverer of the latter oxide, has done a great deal of work in this field and has prepared many fluorides of the other halogens, *e.g.* ClF_3 and IF_7.

Fluorine itself was scarcely used in industry until uranium hexafluoride was required in quantity for the purification of that metal in connection with nuclear fission. The Pennsylvania Salt Mfg. Co. began to manufacture and market it in 1946. The process was the electrolysis of potassium hydrogen fluoride and anhydrous hydrofluoric acid with carbon anodes and steel cathodes. Teflon (polytetrafluoroethylene, p. 264) forms a fluorine-resistant material which has enabled the element to be more easily handled. Fluorine is used to make the metallic polyfluorides, used in the manufacture of fluorocarbons. So thoroughly have the problems of handling fluorine been solved that the liquefied gas has even been transported in tank-cars!

Compounds of fluorine, however, have long had considerable value. The use of hydrofluoric acid for etching glass was familiar throughout the nineteenth century. Cryolite (sodium aluminium fluoride) is fundamental to the manufacture of aluminium. An important use of fluorine compounds is in pest control. From 1896 onwards sodium fluoride came into use as a poison for cockroaches and of recent years the silico-fluorides have been used against termites and many plant-pests, and the fluoracetates against rats.

Reactions in Liquid Ammonia

The traditional solvent in inorganic chemistry has been water, but from 1898 onwards E. C. Franklin investigated the properties of liquid ammonia, NH_3. There is an analogy between water, $H.OH$, and ammonia, $H.NH_2$, even in physical properties. Liquid ammonia was shown to be an excellent solvent for salts, to form ammoniates analogous to hydrates. It is, moreover, an ionizing solvent. Franklin distinguished ammono-salts, ammono-acids, ammono-bases. Amides and imides in solution in liquid ammonia behave as acids, others as bases: acetamide is an example of the former, and sodamide of the latter. Ammono-salts result from their reaction, in the above case sodium acetamide, $CH_3.CO.NK_2$.

The discovery of the atomic structure of ammonia and water makes the reason for the analogy clear: each have strongly asymmetric molecules and one or more pairs of electrons which can be donated, forming a co-ordinate linkage.

New Compounds of Boron and Silicon

The inorganic chemistry of the twentieth century has been much aided by numerous physical discoveries. The detection of minute quantities of material has been aided by radio-activity and the manipulation of gases greatly simplified by the availability of liquid air. Thus the analysis of complex mixtures of unstable gases was almost impossible in the nine-teenth century; but with the help of the liquid-air and vacuum technique worked out by the physicists very interesting studies of the silicon and boron hydrides have been made. There are several of these gases, all produced at the same time, e.g. by the reaction of magnesium boride or silicide with dilute acids. They catch alight in air: some are decomposed by water. The problem was as difficult as any the inorganic chemist might undertake.

The nineteenth-century workers discovered that compounds of boron and hydrogen were present in the gas obtained by decomposing magnesium boride with an acid, but this gas contained very little of the boron hydride. Ramsay and Hatfield in 1900 applied the new liquid-air technique and froze the boron hydride out of the gas, but their work was invalidated by the fact that their magnesium boride contained silicon and their boron hydrides were, in fact, largely silicon hydrides. The solution of the problem was due to Alfred Stock, from 1912 onward. He had to find a way of working with these gases, which were decomposed by even traces of moisture and lubricants, such as tap-grease: he had to separate the boron hydrides from the silicon hydrides, of which little or nothing was then known.

The problem was to handle all the gases in a highly evacuated apparatus consisting of glass parts, all fused together, and having specially designed valves that needed no tap-grease. The gases thus came into contact only with glass and mercury. They were distilled from one part of the apparatus to another by cooling parts with liquid air. Instead of identifying substances by boiling-point, they were identified by their vapour pressures. Stock worked out, in fact, the means of carrying out ordinary laboratory operations within a closed evacuated system of vessels. Not only was his technique successful but very influential. The tendency to-day is towards the conduct of chemical operations in closed systems, in contrast to the traditional open methods of the nineteenth century.

Stock's work resulted in the preparation of some seventeen volatile compounds of silicon in a pure condition. Some of these were, of course, previously known, but the information about them was not precise. He isolated six or seven gaseous hydrides of boron and several solid ones. These were not merely so many more new compounds, for their formulæ presented a difficult problem. Boron is tervalent: yet there proved to be no hydride BH_3, and the simplest gaseous hydride was B_2H_6, a formula which, being analogous to that of ethane, C_2H_6, should characterize boron as quadrivalent, like carbon.

Yet boron has only three valency electrons. Naturally there has been a great deal of discussion of this problem, and it seems probable that a special type of valency linkage is found in the boron hydrides. It may briefly be described by saying that it involves the phenomenon of resonance (p. 354) and can be figured as

$$
\begin{array}{ccccc}
\text{H} & & \text{H} & & \text{H} \\
& \diagdown & \diagup & \diagdown & \diagup \\
& \text{B} & & \text{B} & \\
& \diagup & \diagdown & \diagup & \diagdown \\
\text{H} & & \text{H} & & \text{H}
\end{array}
$$

It appears that this ' bridge-linkage ' can only appear in very exceptional conditions and that few other examples are possible. Boron may not be quite unique in this respect, however, as a gallium hydride, Ga_2H_6, has been reported.

Similar methods to those of Stock's enabled Dennis and his collaborators to prepare a number of hydrides of germanium between 1924 and 1930.

This work may be thought to be very remote from industrial practice, yet it was the interest in the chemistry of silicon and the understanding of the reactions of its compounds other than the silicates that led to the important and rapidly developing silicone industry (p. 269). To-morrow it may be the turn of boron.

Some Recent Inorganic Chemical Industries

Most of the greatest advances in the inorganic chemical industry are treated in Chapters Twenty-three and Twenty-five, which deal with electrochemistry and industrial gases respectively.

We may note, however, as a characteristic of the period since 1920 the utilization of many elements which were formerly little more than chemical curiosities.

Conspicuous among these is titanium, by no means a rare element, but not exploited before 1920. In the years from 1920 to 1927 work was done on the use of titanium dioxide as a white pigment. Titanium dioxide precipitated on barium sulphate was at first used, but later this gave place to the pure oxide. This is now perhaps the best of the white pigments, having good covering power and being quite unaffected by hydrogen sulphide or light. In World War II the volatile titanium tetrachloride was made in large quantities as filling for smoke bombs. Titanium is now being used as a structural metal, being as strong as steel, lighter and resistant to corrosion.

Zirconium also came into use in this period. Its oxide became cheaper than tin dioxide and was used in place of it to give opacity to ceramic glazes (cf. pp. 63-4). Zirconium crucibles have also been used for very high-temperature work.

Columbium and tantalum, despite their rarity, have found a niche. Tantalum is extremely resistant to corrosion and has become important for making hydrogen chloride burners and absorption plants. The carbides of both tantalum and columbium have been used for the intensely hard tips of high-speed lathe tools, together with the better-known tungsten carbide, brought into use about 1927. Alloys of tantalum and columbium have been used for tools subject to the heaviest duty and corrosive conditions. Caesium and rubidium have been extensively used in photo-electric cells.

The most startling development in the utilization of the rarer elements was the satisfaction of the gigantic demands for extremely pure uranium, further alluded to on p. 362, in connection with the atomic-bomb project and nuclear fuel.

Analytical Chemistry

Analytical chemistry may be conveniently grouped with inorganic chemistry, with which it is intimately associated. The study of the mineral constituents of the rocks, so actively pursued in the late eighteenth and early nineteenth centuries, was, in fact, the analysis of these materials. So, remarkable as it may seem, the standard fundamental methods of qualitative, quantitative, volumetric and organic combustion analysis were well established by 1850, and textbooks of that period, such as those of Fresenius, are intelligible and useful, and indeed survive in modern editions. The progress of analytical chemistry was much aided by careful work on the determination of atomic weights, which is indeed a form of quantitative analysis. Such men as Stas (*c.* 1860) and T. W. Richards showed what had to be done to obtain results of the highest accuracy, and the analysts followed them at a distance. We have still to chronicle the great advance in analysis that resulted from the study of solutions (p. 369).

During the past century, then, the standard methods of

analysis have been much refined and extended, while some altogether new departments of analytical technique have come into being.

The great increase in the practice of industrial analysis, required for the scientific control of industrial processes, continually calls for increased speed and simplicity, and ideally for the invention of processes that can be carried out by persons of less training than the professional chemist. This tendency led to the development of volumetric analysis at the expense of the slower gravimetric methods. After 1877, new indicators were synthesized by the organic chemists in order to simplify special titrations. Conductometric titrations have now been so far simplified by the use of standardized electrical equipment that they present no more difficulty than the use of indicators. In the twentieth century came the use of organic reagents for detecting and precipitating the metals. The base 'nitron' for precipitating nitrates and the use of dimethylglyoxime for detecting and precipitating nickel date from 1905: 'cupferron' for separation of iron and copper in 1909. Since 1920 a wide variety of organic chemicals giving characteristic spot reactions with metals have much simplified qualitative analysis. These are variants of the traditional methods, but the last hundred years has also seen the introduction of totally new analytical techniques.

First we may note spectrum analysis, originated by Bunsen and Kirchhoff in 1859. Out of this grew the familiar flame-tests for metals, first systematically described by Bunsen in 1866. The study of the absorption spectra of coloured solutions came into use in the '70's, especially for the recognition of dyes, and round about 1900 for the recognition of blood-stains. The interpretation of spectra through the Bohr theory and later by quantum-mechanics greatly stimulated the study of spectroscopy. Infra-red and ultra-violet spectra have been especially developed. Very recently a powerful method has been developed by which the measurement of the intensity of spectral lines can give the proportion of an element present in a mixture. This method has been applied chiefly to the technical determination of small proportions of impurities in metals.

Numerous optical properties of bodies have been utilized by the analyst. The most important is the rotation of the plane of polarized light, which was used to determine the strength of sugar solutions from the 1860's, though the invention of the Jellet instrument (*c.* 1886) marked a new stage in its popularity. The determination of refractive index is useful for the recognition of many liquids and the analysis of mixtures and solutions. The refractometer of Abbe, dating from 1874, made the determination of refractive indices a process to be easily carried out by the industrial chemist.

Colorimetry, the determination of the strength of a solution by measurement of its colour, began in the '90's. The Lovibond tintometer, invented in 1886, made it a satisfactory and sufficiently accurate method, and in recent years it has become a very popular method for industrial analysis owing to its simplicity and speed. Numerous types of colorimeter have been devised, but their results, depending on the judgment of the human eye, are subject to 2–5 % of error. The substitution of a photo-electric cell for the eye reduces this about ten-fold.

Bunsen was not only the author of spectroscopy, but also the chief founder of gas-analysis. The analysis of gases by eudiometry had of course been practised in the eighteenth century, but the working out of a system by which mixtures of gases, especially of the hydrides and oxides of carbon, could be quantitatively analysed was his work. The book on the subject which he published in 1857 stimulated research: shortly afterwards he analysed, with Lyon Playfair, specimens of blast-furnace gas, so pointing the way for research into its practical utilization. Winkler and Hempel improved his methods between 1876 and 1880. The subject attained fresh importance as the analyses of fuel-gases became routine industrial practice. George Lunge, who was a great pioneer in introducing scientific analytical methods into rule-of-thumb industries, was among those who modified the earlier apparatus (1882) so as to allow of quick routine determinations. Many forms of gas apparatus have been devised by other workers, *e.g.* Bone and Wheeler. Other very different but no less important requirements were methods by which the physiologists could analyse respired gases, a type of research which attained much importance in the early years of the twentieth century. J. S. Haldane, who was one of the founders of the modern study of respiration, devised an apparatus which bears his name and is specially adapted to determine minute proportions of carbon dioxide in expired air.   To-day automatic apparatus for analysis of fuel-gases will register the proportion of carbon dioxide continuously on a dial!

The rapid progress of organic chemistry has called for fresh developments in analytical technique.   The well-known combustion-analysis was so far perfected by Liebig in the 1840's that scarcely any change in technique, other than the substitution of gas-furnaces for charcoal, was introduced until the twentieth century.   Perhaps the most important contribution of the latter half of the nineteenth century was Kjeldahl's method for determining the nitrogen content of organic compounds, announced in 1883.

These methods, though accurate, were slow and required the use of more of the compound to be analysed than could in some cases be spared.   Between 1910 and 1916 this disadvantage led Fritz Pregl, when working on certain bile-acids which were obtainable only in minute quantities, to perfect his method of *micro-analysis*, by which quantities of *c.* 0·003–0·005 gm. could be analysed as accurately as the 0·3–0·5 gm. required for the usual process.   Micro-analysis depended on the manufacture of balances sensitive to a millionth of a gramme, but some assay-balances, available when Pregl began his work, had already reached this accuracy.   Since the 1920's micro-combustions have superseded the old methods: but their principle is still that which was worked out by Liebig. Many other analytical processes—almost all indeed—can now be adapted to the micro-scale.

Among other types of analytical process introduced during the last century is electrochemical analysis, in which metals are deposited quantitatively on a weighed electrode.   O. W. Gibbs, in 1864, first applied this method to the analysis of solutions containing copper, while A. Classen in 1882 extended it to almost all the metals; nevertheless its field has remained rather restricted.

Chromatographic analysis is a recent development.   Mixtures of organic materials in solution are allowed to filter through a column of absorbent material, such as aluminium oxide.   Some compounds are absorbed more firmly than others, and by careful washing with solvent the various components of the mixture can be made to settle in separate bands at intervals down the column.   The method was invented in

1906 but fell out of use until the 1930's: it is useful not only for the detection and estimation of complex organic bodies but also for their separation in a state of purity. Chromatography has become a much more important means of analysis since the introduction of paper as an absorption medium. With only a few pieces of filter paper and simple reagents, elaborate analytical studies have been made by this process, even resulting in the award of a Nobel Prize. It is highly satisfactory to observe a notable advance in science being made with apparatus of primitive simplicity.

Forensic analysis, especially the detection of poisons, is of much interest to readers of detective fiction. The foundation of the subject was laid by M. J. B. Orfila as early as 1814. The famous Marsh test for arsenic dates back to 1836. The examination of human remains in order to detect poisons follows the ordinary processes of qualitative and quantitative analysis except in so far as the poison has to be separated from a mass of organic material. In 1850 Stas, the greatest of nineteenth-century analysts, devised the technique which, with some modification, is still followed. The development of micro-methods, especially between 1935 and 1940, has been a great aid to the forensic chemist, who normally has to deal with small quantities of material. Many of the tests employed, e.g. fluorescence analysis, belong rather to physics than to chemistry. Tests for blood-stains are of interest. Spectroscopic examination of suspected blood dates back to the '70's. In the '90's the Teichmann blood-crystals enabled the species of organism from which the blood was derived to be discovered with fair certainty. The precipitin reaction (1901) enabled blood to be certainly identified as human, while in the last few years it has become possible to identify the blood as belonging to a particular group and so to rule out certain individuals as the source of it. Spectrography, especially with the photo-electric spectrophotometer, has allowed accurate analyses to be made of extremely minute samples, almost without sacrifice of material. Forensic analysis is not of course confined to murder cases: for an enormous amount of such work is directed to the examination of food-stuffs and other material for adulterants. All civilized countries have laid down standards of purity of foodstuffs and drugs. The surveillance of these led to the formation of the profession of public analyst, which originated in a very small way in the U.S.A. in 1862, and was fostered by the formation of the Society of Public Analysts in 1874. The public analyst has been the means of transforming the standards of the food-stuffs and drugs supplied to the public.

Instrumentation.

The outstanding characteristic of present-day chemical analysis is instrumentation, especially in industrial practice. A great number of analytical operations can be conducted by automatically measuring some physical property of the mixture and recording this result on a dial or a chart, so enabling much closer checks on processes than individual analyses could permit.

PLATE XV

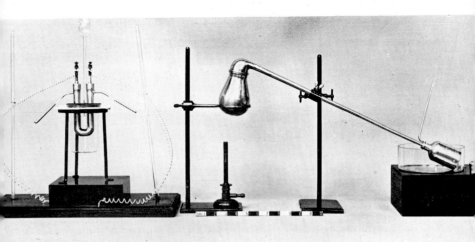

A.—Moissan's Apparatus for the Isolation of Fluorine, 1883. *Reproduction* (see p. 311).

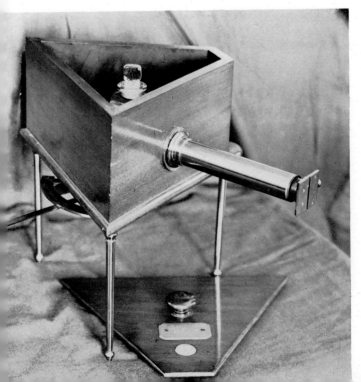

B.—Spectroscope presented by Bunsen to Daubeny at Oxford (see p. 316).

PLATE XVI

Ramsay's Apparatus for preparing Argon, 1894 (see p. 325).

CHAPTER NINETEEN

The Discovery of the Chemical Elements

New Chemical Elements, 1788–1850

THE notion of a chemical element as the ultimate product of chemical analysis was somewhat imprecisely set out in the *Sceptical Chymist* (1661) of Robert Boyle, but was first given practical application by Lavoisier, who in 1789 made a list of bodies which could not then be further analysed. These were: caloric, nitrogen, oxygen, sulphur, phosphorus, carbon, antimony, silver, arsenic, bismuth, cobalt, copper, tin, iron, manganese, mercury, molybdenum, nickel, gold, platinum, lead, tungsten, zinc, potash, soda, ammonia, lime, magnesia, baryta, alumina. Of these ' caloric ' was a figment, derived from an erroneous hypothesis, and ammonia a compound, as were the bases potash, soda, etc., which were even at that time suspected but not yet known to be compounds of metals.

The great period of discovery of new elements was that following 1780. In these years the technique of analysis of inorganic substances rapidly improved, and systematic attention was given to mineralogy. The result was a crop of discoveries of new elements, which by 1850 had brought the number of known elements from the thirty of Lavoisier to no less than sixty-four. The years between 1780 and 1810 were particularly fruitful, introducing to chemistry such elements as strontium, beryllium, boron, the rare earths, the platinum metals, molybdenum, chromium and tungsten. The name of M. H. Klaproth is conspicuous as that of the discoverer of six new elements, though in some cases he did not isolate the pure element but only a compound. The method of discovery was simply chemical analysis of the simplest classical type; this might result in the isolation of bodies that could not be identified with anything known, or in anomalous analytical results, which indicated the presence of some unknown substance. By the year 1850 these methods had done nearly all that they could. The elements as yet undiscovered were, for the most part, present in very small quantity and admixed with other elements to which they had a great resemblance; new techniques were needed for their discovery.

In 1850, sixty-four of the elements that we now regard as such were known: to-day eighty-eight naturally-occurring elements have been isolated, and twelve more have been made by artificial means (p. 359). All but one or two of the balance of twenty-four naturally-occurring elements were discovered through the application of physical techniques to chemistry.

Spectroscopy

The classical methods of chemical analysis were not well adapted to the discovery of small traces of elements in the presence of large quantities of other elements that they resembled; and this was first made possible by the development of the spectroscope by Bunsen and Kirchhoff in 1859. They discovered that when the vapour of a metal or one of its compounds was strongly heated, e.g. by heating the metal or a volatile compound of it in the flame of a Bunsen burner or electric spark or arc, the light given out could be analysed by an arrangement of prisms and lenses into a spectrum consisting of a number of bright lines of different colours. Each metal was characterized by a large number of these lines arranged in a characteristic fashion, and if a conspicuous line not assignable to a known element were to be seen in the spectrum of some newly-examined product, a new element was to be suspected there. Extremely minute quantities of many elements could be detected in this way. The method was established in 1859 and at first appealed to Bunsen as a very sensitive and easy method of analysis, by which the composition of all things terrestrial and celestial could be easily discovered.

At the moment I am engaged in a research with Kirchhoff which gives us sleepless nights. Kirchhoff has made a most beautiful and most unexpected discovery: he has found out the cause of the dark lines in the solar spectrum, and has been able both to strengthen these lines artificially in the solar spectrum and to cause their appearance in a continuous spectrum of a flame, their position being identical with those of the Fraunhofer's lines. Thus the way is pointed out by which the material composition of the sun and fixed stars can be ascertained with the same degree of certainty as we can ascertain by means of our reagents the presence of SO_3 and Cl. By this method, too, the composition of the terrestrial matter can be ascertained, and the component parts distinguished, with as great ease and delicacy as is the case with the matter contained in the sun; thus I have been able to detect lithium in 20 grams of sea-water. For the detection of many substances this method is to be preferred to any of our previously known processes. Thus if you have a mixture of Li, Ka, Na, Ba, Sr, Ca, all you need to do is to bring a milligram of the mixture into our apparatus in order to be able to ascertain the presence of all the above substances by mere observation. Some of these reactions are wonderfully delicate. . . .

Actually the fault of the method was its delicacy; for the analyst wishes to know, as a rule, what elements are present in weighable quantities and to neglect the minute traces which the spectroscope reveals.

The instrument proved invaluable for the detection of new elements. Within a few months most of the conspicuous features of the spectra of the known metals were charted, and in 1860–61 three new elements were discovered by detecting new lines in the spectra of natural products, whereupon it was only a matter of ordinary chemical technique to separate the new elements from the substances in which they occurred. Thus cæsium and rubidium, rare metals resembling sodium and potassium, were discovered spectroscopically by Bunsen in mineral waters in 1860 and 1861 respectively: in the latter year thallium was discovered in the same way by Sir William Crookes in deposits from the lead-chambers of sulphuric acid works. In 1863 Reich and Richter were examining the spectrum of some residues from zinc ores in the hope of finding a source of thallium, and saw an intense indigo-blue line that revealed the presence of a new element, which was then isolated and termed indium. But for the spectroscope all these discoveries would no doubt have been long delayed, and it has since been used in every investigation of supposed new elements.

Discoveries Arising from the Periodic Law

Further discoveries followed the publication of Mendelejef's Periodic Law in 1869. His famous table of the elements (p. 338) was only made possible by leaving gaps for elements as yet unknown. He was so bold as to predict the discovery of these and in certain instances to forecast their properties. This turned the attention of chemists towards seeking these elements, and within the next twenty years three of them were found. Mendelejef named them provisionally by adding Sanskrit numerals to the name of the element which occupied the position in the table below which they were expected to occur.

Mendelejef's predicted ' eka-aluminium ' was realized in gallium, the discovery of which was somewhat curious. Its discoverer, Lecoq de Boisbaudran, found there was a relationship between the spectra of like elements, though he could not express this very exactly: in 1863 he began to look for a missing member of the aluminium-indium-thallium group of elements, thus in a fashion anticipating the idea of Mendelejef. He collected some zinc ore in 1868 but did not work on it till 1874. In the following year he found in it the missing element, which he termed *gallium* after his native land. Mendelejef had predicted the properties of his eka-aluminium in 1869, and in 1875 he showed that his prediction, covering some fifteen properties, was in each instance closely fulfilled by gallium.

In 1879 Mendelejef's eka-boron was discovered by L. F. Nilson and termed *scandium*, while in 1886 his eka-silicon was discovered by C. Winkler and given the name of *germanium*. Germanium was not originally discovered by a spectroscopic observation, but through a failure of an analysis, carried out by its discoverer, to give a satisfactory account of the composition of the silver ore in which it was found. It cannot be said that the periodic table of Mendelejef indicated where these elements would be found: thus eka-aluminium was found associated with zinc, and eka-silicon with silver: and, in fact, the elements of the same periodic group were sometimes, but not always, associated together in their ores.

The most difficult group of elements to deal with are the rare-earths, owing to their great similarity of properties. Until the work of Moseley (p. 345) no one knew how many rare-earth elements existed. About seventy rare-earth elements have at one time or another been described, but there are, in fact, only thirteen naturally occurring, and the other fifty-seven have proved to be mixtures or elements already known. Five of the genuine rare-earth elements had been discovered before 1850; the spectroscope then proved to be a considerable help, and by its aid and the more refined analysis of later years nine others were discovered between that year and 1926, when the now discredited illinium was thought to fill the final gap. The difficulties of this work led to some doubt whether the rare-earth elements were true individuals. In 1886 Crookes examined the spectra of the light emitted by rare-earth elements under bombardment with cathode-rays. He obtained so many different types of spectra that he supposed these elements to be made up of a large number of ' meta-elements ', differing only minutely: it turned out, however, that his results were due to the presence of traces of impurity, which have a profound effect on these phosphorescent spectra.

The elements we have mentioned have proved to be in themselves of small though ever-increasing industrial import-ance, but of considerable interest as filling out the picture of the whole body of elements and their relationships. It is far otherwise, however, with the next group of elements to be discovered, the ' rare ' or ' inert ' gases discovered by Rayleigh, Ramsay and Travers between 1894 and 1902, for these are of considerable industrial as well as theoretical importance.

Discovery of the Inert Gases

This group was discovered through the perfection of physical technique. Towards the end of the nineteenth century physi-cists were much preoccupied with increasing the exactness of their measurements to the highest degree. The densities of gases were being redetermined with great care, and Lord Rayleigh came to examine the density of nitrogen, apparently with a view to discovering whether its atomic weight was an exact multiple of that of hydrogen, as followed from Prout's hypothesis (1815) that the atoms of all elements were combina-tions of hydrogen atoms. In 1892 he found that nitrogen which had been made by removing all other known substances from air was slightly but definitely more dense than nitrogen made from pure nitrogen compounds. In 1894 he read a paper to this effect. William Ramsay then joined in the research. It seemed to them that the nitrogen of the air must contain a hitherto unknown constituent denser than itself, so Ramsay tried to remove the nitrogen from this ' atmospheric nitrogen ' by the action of heated lithium or magnesium, which metals combine with nitrogen to form nitrides. In this way a small quantity of a gas of density 20·1 was isolated: meanwhile Rayleigh reached the same result by adding oxygen to air, sparking it and absorbing the nitrogen oxides with alkali.

Rayleigh and Ramsay published the work jointly. Larger quantities of the new gas were prepared. It proved to be so inert chemically as to form no compounds; so the only way to find its atomic weight was to measure its density and to find out, by determination of the ratio of its specific beats, how many atoms were in the molecule. It proved to consist of single atoms, of atomic weight 39·88. Meanwhile Ramsay obtained another inert gas from the mineral cleveite, which had been supposed to give off nitrogen when heated. He sent this gas for spectroscopic examination to Crookes, who found that its spectrum contained the bright yellow line which Frankland and Lockyer, as long ago as 1868, had seen in the spectrum of the sun and had attributed to an element, unknown on earth, which they had called helium. So the gas from cleveite proved to be helium.

Ramsay was then joined by Travers in a search for more of these inert gases. Another physical technique came opportunely, namely, Hampson's process (p. 423), by which air could be liquefied in quantity. The first portion of liquid air to evaporate yielded the element neon, and the last portion two more elements, krypton and xenon. In 1902 Rutherford and Soddy showed that radium emanation was one of these inert gases. Thus between 1894 and 1902 six new elements were discovered, all monatomic gases and all without any chemical properties. There was no room for them in any of the existing families of Mendelejef's table, but when they were placed at the left-hand border they were seen to form a neutral transition between the electro-negative halogens and the electro-positive alkali-metals. The fact that the atomic weight of all six of these elements fell into this position, and not so as to be interpolated into other families, was the strongest confirmation of Mendelejef's scheme.

The Radioactive Elements

These years between 1895 and 1900, perhaps the most truly epoch-making for science, also saw the beginning of the discovery of another new type of element. We shall see in Chapter Twenty-one how radioactivity came to be discovered by Becquerel in 1896, and how the Curies discovered in the course of their investigation of this phenomenon that certain uranium minerals were more active than pure uranium salts, and inferred that a substance more active than uranium was present. In 1898 the Curies obtained evidence of the existence of a new element, which they called *radium*, in pitchblende, which, however, contained it only in the minutest quantities. In the same year they also obtained evidence of the existence of another new radio-element, *polonium*, in the same material. A radium salt was isolated by them in a state of purity in 1902 (though the metal was not prepared till 1912), but polonium, which was present in even smaller quantities, was not isolated until after 1910. The extraordinary properties of radium concentrated research upon the radioactive minerals, and in the course of the following ten or fifteen years no less than thirty-five radioactive elements were discovered, many of which, however, could not be isolated in weighable quantities. Most of these were isotopes, differing from each other only in their nuclear properties, *i.e.* in atomic weight or radioactive properties; but five of them were new elements in the strictest sense, chemical individuals filling a place in the periodic table that was previously unoccupied—namely, proto-actinium, actinium, radium, radon and polonium. These elements filled up the lower rows of the periodic table, with the exception of the two spaces appropriated to the elements of the alkali-metals and halogen-elements.

Effects of Moseley's Enumeration of the Chemical Elements

In 1913 the work of Moseley greatly simplified the problem of completing the discovery of the naturally-occurring chemical elements. As will be explained in Chapter Twenty-one, Moseley was able to determine the atomic number of an element, *i.e.* its place in the periodic table, directly from the wavelengths of the X-ray spectrum of that element. He thus was able to find out the numbers to which no element corresponded, and so to discover how many spaces in the periodic table were still vacant. Besides the two spaces (85 and 87) mentioned above, there was a space at element 72, and two more at the elements 43 and 75. After the war of 1914–18, which largely suspended research, it was not long before some of these were filled.

The element 72 was clearly a member of the titanium, zirconium and thorium family. Coster and Hevesy, at the suggestion of Niels Bohr, examined the ores of zirconium minerals and, by a lengthy process of recrystallization of ammonium zirconifluoride obtained from this source, separated (in 1922) a new element, which was called *hafnium*.

Attention was next turned to the manganese family, in which there were two missing elements at 43 and 75. No trace of these was found in the ores of manganese, but the examination of platinum ores and columbite, which contained elements of atomic numbers near this value, was partially successful. Element 75 was separated by I. and W. Noddack from molybdenum ore and termed *rhenium*; though rare, it is now available in sufficient quantities for investigation. Both these elements were discovered in 1925. These workers also claimed the discovery of element 43, which they termed *masurium*, but this is now discredited and the place is filled by an element made by radioactive disintegration and termed *technetium*.

Transitory and Trans-Uranic Elements

In the 1930's the chapter of discovery of new elements seemed to be nearly closed. There was still some doubt about masurium and the rare earth illinium, both of which were known only from spectra. The gaps at 85 and 87 were still unfilled; but the symmetry of their positions and the fact that all the radioactive transformations skipped over them suggested to most chemists that they represented nuclei that for some reason could not exist.

In recent years a new field has opened: the preparation in quantity of new elements, and especially those heavier than uranium. Uranium has a higher atomic weight and number than any other natural element; this does not mean that its atomic weight and number is the highest possible, but only the highest possible to an element stable enough to survive the several thousand million years that have elapsed since the formation of heavy elements. We do not know how many elements of higher atomic weight and number may be capable of existing for periods of seconds, months, years or millennia. Even before 1939 work on artificial transmutations and induced radioactivity had proved that trans-uranic elements (*i.e.* elements with atomic numbers higher than 92) could exist, but even in that year no one was prepared to consider the possibility of preparing these elements in weighable, let alone industrially useful, quantities. The rapid realization of this seemingly remote possibility was due to war. The tremendous concentration of talent and resources upon the atomic bomb brought to fruition that which the physicist even of 1935 would have judged to be half a century away: the artificial production of considerable quantities of elements heavier than uranium. Several elements have been made by the action of neutrons or other particles upon other elements. Neptunium (93) is made by the reaction of neutrons with uranium; it is highly radioactive and changes to plutonium (94), which is one of the materials used in the later atomic bombs. Treatment of plutonium with neutrons produced americium (95) and curium (96) and elements 97, 98, 99 and 100; by the time this book appears elements with even heavier nuclei may have been made. From the chemical point of view these elements are very much alike and resemble uranium; and it is probable that actinium begins a new ' period ' which, like that of the rare earths, consists of elements very similar to each other. The possibilities now confronting the chemist are full of interest. The application of gigantic energies to the nuclei of atoms is nearing the stage when it will be possible to bombard the nucleus with particles having an energy about equal to that which binds its constituents. No one can yet say what changes these will bring about or what new elements may be formed.

The intensive study of the products of the decompositions of the uranium atom have revealed the presence of elements 43 (*technetium*) and 61 (*promethium*). Furthermore, artificial radio-elements of atomic numbers 85 and 87 have been discovered, so that all the gaps in the periodic table have now been filled, though no one knows how many elements may be added to its latter end.

Uses of the Newer Elements

Newly-discovered elements often seem to have small promise of usefulness, but in fact there are very few even of the rarest which have not found some industrial use: so much so, indeed, that we need not scorn the simple faith of Samuel Parkes, who wrote in his *Chemical Catechism* (1806):

Q. What are the uses of strontian?

A. Though strontian combines readily with all the acids and possesses alkaline properties, it has not hitherto been employed for any useful purpose. Hereafter it may be found to possess valuable properties, for it exists in abundance and the Author of Nature has formed nothing in vain.

It is hardly possible to go into particulars of the uses of the seventy or so elements discovered since the time of Lavoisier, many of which have now become the ordinary materials of the chemist, but we may first mention the various transition elements, the essential constituents of the alloy steels (p. 203), which have come into use in the last seventy-five years, and especially since 1910. The most important of these are tungsten, molybdenum, chromium, manganese, titanium and vanadium. None of them are particularly rare, but all presented difficulties in extraction which have now been solved, in most cases by alumino-thermic or electrical smelting.

Utilization of the Inert Gases

The inert gases, of which the discovery is described on pp. 325–6, are now prepared on a large scale from liquid air. Their usefulness arises, first, from their chemical inertness and, secondly, from the character of the light they emit in electrical-discharge tubes.

Where inertness alone is required, the commonest of these gases, argon, is chosen; it has been used since *c.* 1919, in considerable quantity, for the filling of electric filament lamps and in the welding of easily-oxidizable materials such as aluminium.

Although helium is present in the air only in the very small proportion of 1 : 200,000, large quantities can be extracted from natural gas. Helium, which has more than nine-tenths of the lifting power of hydrogen and is not inflammable, found a considerable use in the filling of balloons and dirigibles from about 1919 until these were replaced by heavier-than-air craft. It has also been used to mix with oxygen and form an artificial air to be supplied to divers. Helium is less soluble in the blood than is nitrogen, and is therefore less likely to cause fatal accidents through the formation of bubbles in the blood when the pressure is released.

Neon is present in air to the extent of only about 18 parts per million, but it has been extracted on the large scale since about 1909 as a by-product of the making of oxygen and nitrogen from liquid air. The neon lamp began to be used for special purposes, *e.g.* signalling and stroboscopic work, about 1918, but its extensive use for advertising signs dates from about 1927 and has since become an important industry. Argon, helium and neon, alone and with the vapour of mercury, are used for the filling of discharge-lamps and fluorescent tubes; krypton and xenon, despite their rarity, have also occasionally been employed.

The Radium Industry

Radium (*i.e.* radium bromide or other salt of that metal) was in demand for scientific purposes from the time that the Curies announced its discovery, but radium-therapy for malignant growths began about 1908 and became important in the years round 1912.

Radium is separated from the ores of uranium, compounds of which were extracted in some quantity during the latter part of the nineteenth century for use in colouring glass and porcelain. After radium came into demand, uranium ore was sought all over the world for the extraction of the new element. Since atomic energy has been realized the position is reversed and it is once more uranium itself that is in urgent demand. The first source of the ore was the Joachimsthal pitchblende, but from 1913 the carnotite of Colorado became an important source, only to be eclipsed by the deposits of the Belgian Congo.

The radium industry is, of course, quite unlike any other in respect of the minute quantity and high value of its product. The process consisted of precipitating the mixed radium and barium sulphates, converting these into soluble salts and fractionally crystallizing them—a lengthy process. For therapeutic purposes the radium salts were prepared in a substantially pure state, but large quantities of the unseparated radium and barium salts have been used since before World War I for mixing with zinc sulphide to give the luminous paint used for watches and instruments to be read in the dark. For therapeutic purposes radium has been largely replaced by radio-cobalt, made in the atomic pile.

The Rare-Earth Elements

The rare-earth elements also are not without their uses. Welsbach's discovery of the gas-mantle occasioned a demand for thorium, and the residues of the monazite sand from which this element had been extracted formed a convenient source of rare-earth elements. By converting these residues into chlorides and electrolysing them an alloy of some eight rare-earth metals is obtained. This 'mischmetal' has been used, since about 1902, in place of aluminium in the aluminothermic process (p. 386), in order to displace certain metals—e.g. molybdenum, vanadium, niobium and tantalum—from their oxides. Alloyed with iron, it forms the metal of the so-called 'flint' in a cigarette-lighter.

Compounds of several rare-earth elements have been used for colouring porcelain and glass.

The Rarer Metals

Remarkably few even of the rarest metals find no use in industry.

Rubidium and cæsium have been used as 'getters' in radio valves, i.e. substances capable of reacting with any minute traces of gas left therein. Gallium has been used as filling for high-temperature thermometers. Indium is used to protect the bearings of aeroplane engines from corrosion. Germanium is used in transistors. Beryllium, alloyed with forty to fifty times its weight of copper, gives a non-magnetic metal as hard and strong as the finest steel.

Platinum and palladium have long been in use for scientific purposes and for jewellery, but the other and rarer metals of the group have also found their uses. Ruthenium and osmium have been used as catalysts. Rhodium is quite extensively used for plating on silver, for an exceedingly thin film of this metal, while protecting the silver from tarnish, scarcely alters its appearance. Iridium, being very much harder than platinum and more resistant to corrosion, is sometimes used instead of platinum for making crucibles. Columbium is used in special steels, and tantalum, at one time the metal of choice for electric-light filaments, finds a use in the making of very hard and incorrodible tools and chemical plant.

CHAPTER TWENTY

Chemical Theory

The Growth of Chemical Theory

THE principal *motif* of the history of chemistry is its transformation from an art to a science. As long ago as the seventeenth century physics was a science, but chemistry was still an art; thus Beguinus in his *Tyrocinium Chymicum* (1610) calls it " the art of dissolving natural mixed bodies and solidifying dissolved bodies, for the preparation of pleasanter, more health-giving and safer medicines." Such, indeed, was the view of chemistry held in the eighteenth century, and even in the middle of the nineteenth century not a few relics of it remained. Chemistry was mainly analytical and preparative—the separating of the constituents of known bodies and, to a limited extent, the making of new ones. Thus in 1850–60 the majority of our ordinary laboratory reagents were in use, and very respectable results can be obtained by using the methods laid down in the analytical textbooks of the time. Masterly inorganic researches, such as that of Roscoe on vanadium, date from this period.

Thus chemistry in 1860 was still to a large extent a natural history of compounds and a body of techniques for manipulating them. It described a compound, first, by giving a list of its physical properties, telling us whether it was solid, liquid or gas, specifying its boiling-point, melting-point, density, solubility, conductivity and so forth, the emphasis being always on those properties that would enable the compound to be identified: there followed a list of its chemical properties—the circumstances of its decomposition, its reactions with other chemical compounds. This form is still the pattern of our textbooks of inorganic and organic chemistry, though the account given to-day is more numerical and less verbal in its descriptions. That it is, to say the least of it, an unambitious way of considering the different kinds of matter is obvious. To tell us that sulphur is yellow, soluble in carbon disulphide, melts at 114° C., boils at 444° C. and burns with a blue flame savours of an age when the only theoretical connection between such properties was that God at the creation of the world had endowed a certain portion of prime matter with this particular set of attributes. It is the existence of this huge collection of apparently disconnected facts which have to be memorized that makes chemistry a subject so repellent to the theoretically-minded physicist. Chemistry, indeed, remained for a long period at the Baconian stage; it was a natural history, a vast collection of facts united only by certain generalizations which remained as disconnected as the facts themselves.

The Discovery of the ' Essences ' of Chemical Substances

The perfection of chemistry would be its transformation to a Cartesian science, wherein the existence and all the properties of every chemical compound could be deduced mathematically from the fundamentals of physics, *i.e.* the properties of the ultimate particles and the fundamental laws of energy-change. The theoretical chemistry of the past hundred years has brought this ideal in sight. We know, for example, the constitution of a hydrogen atom—one proton and one electron: from this we can now theoretically deduce most of the properties of hydrogen gas. This constitution is as much the ' essence of hydrogen ' as ' a figure bounded by three sides and containing three angles ' is the essence of a triangle. Just as Euclid from this small definition proceeded to the deduction of all the properties of triangles, so are we now beginning to be able to deduce from ' atom consisting of one proton and one electron ' all the properties of hydrogen. The deduction of the properties of more complex substances is obviously a more difficult task and may never be complete: it may always prove to be easier to discover properties empirically and memorize them, rather than to deduce them. But as we attain the understanding of the ' essence ' of each chemical substance—that which makes it to be such as it is—so chemistry will be progressively trans-formed from a natural history to a science of the most developed type.

The Rise of Physical Chemistry

The progress towards this end, not yet attained, has come

about through the attempt to have the most *complete* knowledge of all manner of substances. The preparative type of chemistry was concerned almost entirely with making and chronicling new types of molecules, and little or no effort was made towards the completing of our knowledge of any of the compounds in question. The most precise and complete type of knowledge concerning any body is quantitative knowledge, and such knowledge is attained by measurement.

Chemists before 1850 rarely measured anything except the weights and volumes of the compounds they studied: it was the physicist who applied measurement to every other aspect of phenomena, *e.g.* to light, heat, electricity, in all their manifestations. But the physicists were primarily interested in the property rather than the thing; not in hot water, hot iron, hot sulphur, etc., but in heat, which was common to all these. They tended therefore to neglect the matter in which the phenomenon they studied was manifested; and, indeed, a great deal of good physical work has been made valueless because it related to some impure and indefinite material such as ' turpentine ' or ' glass '. The gigantic progress of modern chemistry has been principally due to the application of the methods of physics to the study of the properties and relationships of the pure compounds studied by the chemists.

This process began by the study of numerous problems apparently quite disconnected. The fact that a knowledge of the densities of gases was required in order to determine their molecular weights necessitated the study of the physics of individual gases. The physicists tended to deal with the most ' perfect ' gases, those that showed the greatest regularities, while the chemists tended to study the actual behaviour of all the gases they knew and to try to make sense of their departures from the norm. Again, the liquefaction of gases was a useful chemical technique and, until the most modern period, was developed by chemists rather than physicists.

The chemist has always concerned himself with solutions, for solid bodies do not come into intimate contact with each other and so do not easily enter into chemical reaction. The theory of solutions was therefore investigated by the chemists and, as we shall see, between 1870 and 1890 the analogy of a dissolved substance to a gas became apparent and was fruitful in results.

Electrolysis had from the first year of the nineteenth century been an indispensable chemical process, and electrical measurements applied to it led finally in the 1880's to the epoch-making ionic theory and the new department of electrochemistry (p. 367).

The chemist likewise finds that his transformations involve energy changes—for chemical changes are the immediate source of the motive power both of organisms and machines. The study of the energy changes produced in chemical reactions built up the science of chemical thermodynamics.

All these researches were grouped as ' physical chemistry ', and a generation ago they formed a series of almost disconnected studies. To-day they are beginning to be linked, for most of them are seen to be potentially aspects of the physics of ultimate particles. At their most general they seem very remote from the factory, yet, in fact, almost every department of physical chemistry has had its repercussions upon industry, either by increasing the chemist's understanding of his science or, in some cases, by direct solution of industrial problems. A case in point is the investigation of the relation between the chemical elements. It started by theoretical studies of the relation between the atomic weights and other properties of the elements: to-day, eighty years after, it has brought into being the vast industry of nuclear fuel; to-morrow it may transform the problem of power for industry.

CHAPTER TWENTY-ONE

The Road to Nuclear Power

The Periodic Law

THE early valency and structural theory (p. 218) was of much more use in organic chemistry than in inorganic, because carbon has an invariable valency and is bound by linkages which are always of the covalent type (p. 351), whereas the majority of other elements have variable valency and most of their compounds are of the ionic type, not bound by a definite linkage but by electrical attraction. Thus up to 1869 inorganic chemistry progressed rather by the preparation of new compounds than by any theory that might indicate why those compounds, rather than others, were formed. Inorganic chemistry appeared to be somewhat disconnected—lists and descriptions of compounds of elements seen to be analogous, but not adequately classified.

Very little attention had been paid before the year 1865 to the possibility of discovering regularities in the relations between atoms of different elements. The concept of an atom was that of a minute very hard body with a definite weight and combining power. All the properties of an element and its compounds were recognized, hypothetically, as deriving from the properties of the atom, but, since there did not appear to be the remotest possibility of discovering the latter's properties, no interest in the matter was shown. In 1864 J. A. R. Newlands and W. Odling both drew up tables (Fig. 54) in which the elements were classified according to their atomic weights, but neither of these men made a serious effort to develop the notion. Lother Meyer in 1869 perceived clearly the rhythmic recurrence of properties as one passes from the lightest elements to the heaviest, but he was overshadowed by the great Russian, Dmitri Ivanovitch Mendelejef, who developed the idea in far greater depth and detail. Mendelejef's discovery of the Periodic Law was perhaps the most pregnant single achievement of the century. It revealed that the atoms of the sixty-five elements then known were related in a regular manner. They could no longer be thought of as arbitrary unconnected kinds of matter, but rather as having some common factor which might one day be elucidated. Mendelejef showed that if the elements were arranged in order of atomic weight, similar elements recurred at regular intervals throughout the list. He expressed this as a table (Fig. 55) and showed that like elements fell into vertical groups or families, provided

" "	" Zn 65	Ag 108 Cd 112	Au 196·5 Hg 200
Na 23 Mg 24 "	" " "	" " Sn 118	Tl 203 Pb 207 "
Al 27·5 " Si 28	" As 75 "	U 120 Sb 122 "	" Bi 210 "
P 31 S 32 Cl 35·5	Se 79·5 Br 80 "	Te 129 I 127 "	" " "
K 39 Ca 40 "	Rb 85 Sr 87·5 Zr 89·5	Cs 133 V 137 Ba 137 Ta 138	" " "
" "	Ce 92 Mo 96	" "	" "
Ti 50 Cr 52·5	" "	" "	Th 231·5 "

FIG. 54. William Odling's table of the elements. Note that many of Mendelejef's groups appear on the horizontal lines. Several wrong atomic weights, *e.g.* of Ta, V, U, obscure the merit of the scheme.

that a few gaps were left for certain elements which he boldly asserted were still to be discovered. He predicted the chemistry of these missing elements on the basis of that of the families in which they were to appear: enormous interest was roused when some of these elements were discovered and proved to be such as he had predicted (p. 323).

Mendelejef's discovery brought order into inorganic chemistry. It was a great thing that, for example, calcium sulphate was to be seen, not merely in relation to other calcium compounds and other sulphates, but to all the sulphates of the

Séries	Groupe I R^2O	Groupe II RO	Groupe III R^2O^3	Groupe IV RH^4 RO^2	Groupe V RH^3 R^2O^5	Groupe VI RH^2 RO^3	Groupe VII RH R^2O^7	Groupe VIII RO^4
1	H = 1							
2	Li = 7	Be = 9.4	B = 11	C = 12	N = 14	O = 16	F = 19	
3	Na = 23	Mg = 24	Al = 27.3	Si = 28	P = 31	S = 32	Cl = 35.5	
4	K = 39	Ca = 40	— = 44	Ti = 48	V = 51	Cr = 52	Mn = 55	Fe = 56; Co = 59; Ni = 59; Cu = 63.
5	(Cu = 63)	Zn = 65	— = 68	— = 72	As = 75	Se = 78	Br = 80	
6	Rb = 85	Sr = 87	?Yt = 88	Zr = 90	Nb = 94	Mo = 96	— = 100	Ru = 104; Rh = 104; Pd = 106; Ag = 108.
7	(Ag = 108)	Cd = 112	In = 113	Sn = 118	Sb = 122	Te = 125	I = 127	
8	Cs = 133	Ba = 137	?Di = 138	?Ce = 140				
9								
10			?Er = 178	?La = 180	Ta = 182	W = 184		Os = 195; Ir = 197; Pt = 198; Au = 199.
11	(Au = 199)	Hg = 200	Tl = 204	Pb = 207	Bi = 208			
12				Th = 231		Ur = 240		

FIG. 55. An early version of Mendelejeff's Table of the Elements.

calcium group—beryllium, magnesium, strontium, barium—and also in relation to the selenates and tellurates. Secondly, this grouping of the elements showed a regular connection between the valency of an element and a position in the periodic table. Thus the principal valencies of most elements were their group-number, and eight less their group-number: this did not, in fact, explain the valencies of the elements fully but was obviously an aspect of some wider law. Mendelejef's table was based on *atomic weight*: it related the whole chemistry of an element to the weight of its atom; it thus became certain that the properties of the atoms were the source of all the chemical properties of the elements, though it was some thirty years before there was any evidence that the atom was even a composite body.

Mendelejef's work was followed by a burst of activity in inorganic chemistry, designed to follow up the clues that his periodic table afforded. New elements were searched for among the minerals of the elements whose families presented gaps, and several were found (Chapter Nineteen). Elements which did not seem to fit in with Mendelejef's scheme were reinvestigated, and in almost every case the result was to vindicate it. A few small anomalies, however, remained. The position of certain pairs of elements seemed to be reversed. Thus iodine obviously belonged to the fluorine family, or ' halogens ', and tellurium to the oxygen family, which *preceded* the halogens in the periodic table; yet the atomic weight of iodine was *less* than that of tellurium. Chemists were confident that some error would be found and the positions would be reversed, but no amount of research could make it so. This, and a few similar cases, showed that it was not the atomic weights themselves, but something closely approximating to them, on which the properties of the elements depended. Some forty-five years, indeed, had to elapse before the true relationship was found.

New Types of Chemical Union

About 1887 a revolutionary idea was brought into chemistry, namely, the ionic theory, which resulted from the efforts of the physical chemists. Of this more will be said in Chapter Twenty-two, but it cannot be left out of the story of the atom and molecule. Everyone had recognized that there were great differences between the properties of acids, bases and salts and those of other compounds. Thus we may compare two compounds of chlorine: sodium chloride, which is a salt, and benzyl chloride, which is not. Sodium chloride is soluble in water, its solution conducts electricity, it is non-volatile, most of its reactions are instantaneous, and its molecular weight, measured in solution, appears to be little more than half that indicated by its formula, NaCl. Benzyl chloride is insoluble in water, a non-conductor of electricity, volatile, reacting only slowly with the reagents that affect chlorides, and is of normal molecular weight. A group of chemists, notably Svante Arrhenius and Wilhelm Ostwald, connected these properties and explained them by the supposition that in solution a considerable proportion of the molecules of these acids, bases and salts broke up into their constituent atoms or groups, which bore a large electrical charge and were termed ions. Thus common salt, NaCl, when dissolved in water, was supposed to break up into the ions Na^+ and Cl^-.

This, the ionic theory, was so effective in explaining many of the properties of acids, bases and salts that chemists were forced to adopt it, though it seemed clean contrary to their notions about chemical combination. It raised a new complication, moreover—for it was now necessary to explain why some compounds broke up in this way and others did not: it seemed that there were two different ways in which atoms could enter into chemical union. Indeed, the work of Werner (p. 305) on co-ordinate compounds seemed to indicate a third way, a grouping of saturated molecules and ions about a central atom, which served to explain the constitution of the puzzling metallic ammines, but not to be applicable to other types. Thus there was a serious need for new light upon the nature of chemical combination.

In the 1880's and 1890's the physical chemist's interest in the atom receded, for there arose a school that gave little attention to, and indeed decried, the reality of atoms. They were inclined to say that the matter behaves *as if* it were made up of atoms, but disinclined to treat these atoms as real until there was more concrete evidence of them. Those physical chemists who relied on thermodynamics—calculations about energy relationships—to rationalize their view of chemistry, tended to sneer at the organic chemists, who were content to treat their atoms as so many solid balls connected by wires and were finding this apparently crude conception to give valuable results. Both schools were, of course, exploiting different properties of the atom. Thermodynamics gave a true statistical account of the energy changes of atoms and molecules while neglecting the arrangement of these atoms. Organic chemistry was gaining a true account of the arrangement of atoms, neglecting their energy relationships. Meanwhile, physics was shaping a third approach.

The Electron

The story of the electron opens with Faraday, who showed that when a chemical compound was broken up by electrical current the same quantity of electricity was always associated with the production of one 'chemical equivalent' of the product. This was really evidence that electricity consisted of 'atoms' or indivisible equal portions—evidence of the same type as was taken to prove that matter consisted of atoms. But this idea was not yet grasped: the atom was thought of as taking up a unitary portion of electricity because of its constitution rather than that of the electricity—just as a pint-pot takes a pint of beer because it holds a pint and not because beer cannot be had in portions less than a pint. However, when the idea of ions became familiar, it was clear that there existed a *unitary charge of electricity* and that one or more of these charges was associated with each atom of an element when ionized; though the idea that electricity could not exist except in the form of these unitary charges did not follow and was not generally accepted. The word 'electron' was coined in 1879 to describe this unitary charge, but did not attain much currency until the years from 1897 onward, when a particle was identified with the electron and the elucidation of the structure of the atom began.

It was one thing to name a unitary charge of electricity, but quite another to demonstrate that such a thing existed apart from ordinary matter. Yet as early as 1859 the discharge of electricity through a highly evacuated tube was demonstrated, and (Sir) William Crookes, after 1876, showed that this discharge consisted of rays which behaved like a stream of particles of high velocity carrying electrical charges. He could not weigh the particles nor measure their charge, and he thought of these rays as matter in a fourth or 'radiant' state. The crucial experiment of weighing these particles was accomplished in 1897 by (Sir) J. J. Thomson and, on the Continent, by Kaufmann and Wiechert. Thomson proved the weight of each of these particles to be only 1-1850th of the weight of the lightest of atoms, that of hydrogen, and he showed that they could be elicited from every kind of matter. This work established that these electrons, as they were called, were constituents of every kind of matter. Their charge was negative, and atoms are electrically neutral; so it followed that there was some positive electricity in or about the atom. Thomson suggested that it might form a sphere of positive electricity in which the electrons were embedded, and it was not until 1911 that it was known to be concentrated in a particle, minute relatively even to the atom itself.

Radioactivity

In 1895 Röntgen discovered X-rays, which were thought to be something to do with fluorescence of the glass of the X-ray tube. In February, 1896, Henri Becquerel tried to find out whether other fluorescent bodies emitted X-rays. He tried the highly-fluorescent double sulphate of potassium and uranium and found that this emitted rays that affected a photographic plate even when nothing was done to make the salt fluoresce. At first there was very little idea as to the nature either of X-rays or radioactivity, as the emission of rays by uranium and some other bodies came to be called. A very important step was made when the Curies found that the uranium ore, pitchblende, was much more radioactive than uranium, and correctly deduced that it contained a more radioactive substance. From 1898 to 1902 Mme Curie worked on the separation of the active constituent of pitchblende and by a most laborious process separated the element radium in a nearly pure state. In the first decade of the century many other radio-elements were discovered.

This totally new phenomenon was very hard to understand; for here were elements emitting energy which had no recognizable source. Early in 1901 it was thought that this energy must come from within the atoms. In 1903 Ernest Rutherford and Frederick Soddy made one of the great discoveries of science, namely, that the atoms of these radioactive elements were breaking up, changing into other atoms, and in doing so could give out three kinds of ' rays ':

(1) Alpha-particles, which were shown to be electrically-
charged helium atoms;

(2) Beta-rays, which were electrons; and
(3) Gamma-rays, which were radiation even more pene-
    trating than X-rays.

Soddy showed in 1911 that, when an alpha-particle was
given out, the new element produced was two places lower in
the periodic table than the element which had emitted the
particle, and in 1913 A. S. Russell showed that a beta-ray
change produced an element one place higher. These rules
are known as the Displacement Law. The final product of all
these radioactive changes was shown to be lead. In 1913
Soddy in England and T. W. Richards in America showed
that the atomic weight of specimens of lead which had been
extracted from uranium minerals was lower (tending to 206)
than that of specimens of lead derived from thorium minerals
(tending to 208). These specimens were otherwise identical
and no one could regard any of them as being anything but
lead. Thus it became clear that the identity of an element and
its position in the periodic table did not depend merely on its
atomic weight, and that this position must be determined by
something else: a conclusion reinforced by the fact that a beta-
ray change involved no measurable alteration of atomic weight
but produced a new element with a different place in the
periodic table.

Here we meet the now familiar idea of the isotope. B.
Boltwood (1906) and B. Keetman (1908) found that the radio-
element ionium was apparently identical with thorium in
chemical properties, though not in atomic weight or radioactive
behaviour. Similar evidence accumulated in the next few
years and, after the Displacement Law had been established,
Soddy generalized the evidence, asserting that elements might
differ in atomic weight and radioactive properties, yet occupy
the same place in the periodic table and be identical in other
properties. Such elements he named *isotopes*.

Radioactivity was not merely a great discovery but a first-
rate tool of research. The trail of an alpha-particle or an
electron could be photographed in the cloud-chamber, invented
by C. T. R. Wilson. When such a particle passes at an
enormous velocity through the air it detaches electrons from
the molecules it encounters. If the air is supersaturated with
moisture a line of cloud condenses along the trail, and this can

be photographed; thus it became possible to shoot high-velocity particles at matter and see what happened to each of them singly. This later became the method of studying the first atomic transmutations.

The Nucleus

Meanwhile (Lord) Rutherford tried the experiment of discharging alpha-particles through thin sheets of metal-foil. A very small proportion of these were sharply deflected and even returned in the direction from which they came. He had already shown that the most powerful magnetic and electric fields that he could command deflected these particles only to a small extent; it was evident, therefore, that inside the atoms of the foil there was something with a gigantically greater field of force than he could command in the laboratory. This ' something ' was evidently very small, even in comparison with an atom, because only a very small proportion of electrons were considerably deflected in passing through the foil, so that the majority of the particles missed this body altogether. It had a mass at least comparable to that of an alpha-particle, which is thousands of times heavier than an electron. To this ' something ' Rutherford gave the name of the *nucleus* of the atom. So the picture of the atom, as held about 1912, was of a cloud of electrons of no known arrangement surrounding a heavy nucleus, minute compared to the atom as a whole and having nearly all the mass of the atom and all its positive charge. The unit of positive charge was that of the hydrogen nucleus, which Rutherford called the *proton*.

The next stage was to discover the charge on the nuclei of the atoms of the various elements. This must take us back to the discovery of X-rays in 1895. These rays, which were produced when cathode-rays were projected on to a metal or other target, remained a mystery for some time, and it was only in 1912, when it was shown that they could be diffracted by a crystal, that they were certainly known to be radiation like light but of shorter wavelength—though this had been long suspected. (Sir) William and (Sir) Lawrence Bragg (whose work is described in Chapter Twenty-two) showed that the spectrum of a beam of X-rays could be obtained by reflecting it from a crystal, the regular rows of atoms in which acted as a diffraction grating. H. G. J. Moseley in 1913 used this method to examine the different spectra of the types of X-rays which were obtained by bombarding each of the elements with cathode-rays, and he found that the wavelength of the X-rays emitted by each element depended in a simple way upon the atomic number of the element (*i.e.* its place in the periodic table). He could thus calculate the atomic number of each element from his experimental results. This meant that he could *measure* the place of an element in the periodic table by an experiment, and so could easily find what atomic numbers were unrepresented; that is to say, what places remained to be filled and therefore what elements remained to be discovered

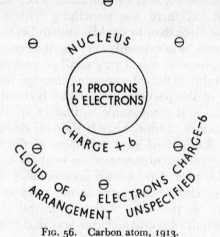

FIG. 56. Carbon atom, 1913.

(p. 323). That was a great step, but Moseley's work also led to the acceptance of the view that the atom was made up of:

(1) A cloud of electrons equal in number to its atomic number.

(2) A nucleus with a total positive charge equal to the atomic number.

On this view carbon, the sixth element in the table, had a nucleus of positive charge 6 units, surrounded by a cloud of 6 electrons. Six protons weigh as much as 6 hydrogen atoms and the atomic weight of carbon is 12, which means that its atom is twelve times heavier than a hydrogen atom; so it was assumed that the carbon nucleus consisted of 12 protons and

6 electrons: this makes its mass twelve times that of a hydrogen atom and its charge 12 − 6, i.e. 6 positive units. This part of the theory has been altered since the discovery of the neutron.

The arrangement (Fig. 56) seemed an odd one. If the nucleus had an intense positive charge, why was not the cloud of negative electrons attracted into it? The first and fairly obvious answer was that the reason might be the same as that which explains why the earth does not fall into the sun— namely, that the electrons were revolving with great velocity about the nucleus, forming a miniature solar system. But this could not be allowed, for according to classical electro-dynamics electric charges revolving in orbits must generate radiation and lose energy. It would follow that an atom made up of negative electrons revolving about a positive nucleus should collapse in a burst of radiation—which did not corre-spond to anything that had been observed.

The Rutherford-Bohr Atom

The solution of this difficulty was provided by a brilliant idea of the Danish scientist Niels Bohr, namely, the application of the quantum theory of Max Planck to the Rutherford atom. In 1900 Planck put forward the notion that a vibrating body which gives out radiation gives it out in discontinuous portions, or *quanta*, whose energy is equal to the frequency of the vibra-tion multiplied by a constant. This notion explained a number of phenomena about radiation, specific heat, photo-chemistry, etc., which were quite inexplicable by the physical laws which had been found to hold for large-scale phenomena. The quantum theory, in the years 1900–10, was revealed as the only effective way of dealing with minute-scale phenomena, and ' classical ' dynamics was shown to be merely an expression of the statistical behaviour of countless particles obeying quantal laws.

In 1913 Bohr proposed that the electrons should be supposed to rotate about the nucleus, and that this should be made reasonable by assuming that each electron could have only certain fixed energies, each corresponding to so many quanta, and could only rotate in orbits of diameter corresponding to those energies; electrons therefore gave out energy (as quanta of radiation) only when they moved from one orbit to another. While they were in any one orbit they did not radiate nor lose energy and so showed no tendency to slow down and fall into the nucleus. This theory supported itself by its great success in explaining spectra, *i.e.* the kind of light that atoms gave out. It showed why this light was not of all wavelengths but only of certain fixed wavelengths (which appeared as spectral lines) and, furthermore, explained the relationship between many of these wavelengths, an advance which a couple of years before would have seemed incredible.

Bohr's theory soon led to the understanding of the meaning of the periodic table. The successive horizontal periods corresponded to the quantum number relating to the outermost electron: the vertical group number corresponded to the

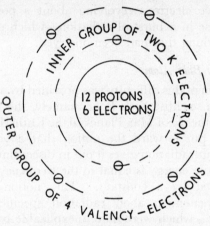

FIG. 57.   Carbon atom, 1920.

number of electrons in that outermost group. The connection between valency and the periodic table soon began to be apparent. These outermost electrons were the binding factors in chemical combination: thus the number of them available for chemical combination corresponded to the number of linkages that the atom could form with other atoms.

These ideas came in rapid succession in the ten years following 1913. They explained the constitution of the atom, the characteristics of the spectra, the structure of the periodic table and the different kinds of valency, and so brought about the greatest revolution in chemistry that has ever been. But as yet it was not clear why the successive groups of the table should contain 2, 8, 8, 18, 32 ...... elements, or in other words why the possible number of electrons of each successive quantum number were:

Quantum number	Maximum number of electrons in the group
1	2
2	8
3	18
4	32

This was explained by Pauli in 1925. It had been found that the statement *e.g.* that the outermost electron of the sodium atom was specified by a quantum number 3 was not enough to describe it. As early as 1916 Sommerfeld showed

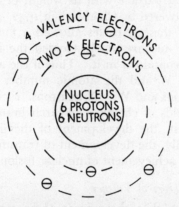

FIG. 58. Carbon atom after discovery of neutron, 1932.

that the fine structure of the hydrogen spectrum indicated more 'energy-jumps' than Bohr's theory allowed for. He showed that not only did the diameter of an electron's orbit correspond to the 'total' quantum number, but that its eccentricity and the precession of the axis of the orbit had to be described by a second, the angular quantum number. Later it was shown that a third quantum number had to be introduced to describe the magnetic properties of an electron, and a fourth to characterize its spin. Pauli put forward the simple rule that no two electrons in the same atom can have all their quantum numbers the same. This principle allowed the size of each group in the periodic table to be predicted.

Through Bohr's theory and its modifications several great chemical principles are explained. Chemical inertness is due to the tight binding of electrons resulting from symmetry of the electronic pattern, chemical activity to loose binding; chemical affinity corresponds to the amount of energy liberated when a more symmetrical pattern of electrons is attained: the periodicity of the elements to the repetition of the electronic patterns.

The chief changes in our ideas concerning the atom after 1930 were, first, the simplification of our ideas concerning the nucleus through the discovery of the neutron; secondly, the development of wave-mechanics, which modified the Bohr theory in various ways and led to a still further understanding of the periodic table.

The neutron, a particle with its weight of a proton but no charge, was discovered by Chadwick in 1932. It was seen that the existence of these particles allowed a formulation of the make-up of the nucleus which avoided the improbability of electrons being contained in it. Thus if the atomic weight of the element be W and the atomic number N, the nucleus contains N protons and W − N neutrons.

Two great fields of chemical research branch off from the Bohr atom: first, the development of the understanding of valency; secondly, the development of transmutation, leading to the crowning achievement of nuclear fission.

The Electronic Theory of Valency

We have seen that there were three types of chemical combination that had been known since the end of the nineteenth century.

First, there was the combination of the acid and basic parts of a salt: this allowed of the separation of the two parts of the compound into ions when it was dissolved in water. The work of Bragg (Chapter Twenty-two) showed that in the solid state these ions were not associated into molecules but simply packed into a crystal. It seemed, then, that a salt was simply an association of ions and combination of this kind was simply ionization. A difficulty arose, however, with weak electrolytes (e.g. mercuric salts or weak acids), which certainly existed both as ions and as molecules.

Secondly, there was the type of combination found in non-ionized compounds, and most conspicuously in organic compounds.

Thirdly, there was the combination that took place additively between whole molecules, particularly familiar in the complex salts and hydrates. This had been termed co-ordinate valency by Werner (Chapter Eighteen).

Even before the establishment of the Rutherford-Bohr theory of atomic structure it had been suggested that electrons were concerned in binding the atoms of chemical compounds. Drude in 1904, for example, and Ramsay in 1908, put out some fertile suggestions on the subject. In 1916 came two very important ideas which have proved to be close approximations to the theories held to-day.

The first was that of Kossel, who supposed that two atoms, A and B, could be bound together by one (A) transferring one or more electrons to the other (B). Thus A becomes a positive ion and B a negative ion; these adhere by their electrostatic attraction:

$$A + B \rightarrow A^+ + B^- \rightarrow [A]^+[B]^-.$$

In terms of the Bohr theory, the transfer of electrons brought each of the atoms concerned to the stable state characterized by a complete shell of eight electrons.

Thus a chlorine atom has seven electrons in its outer ring, a sodium atom has one: they react by transfer of the electron from the sodium atom to the chlorine atom. Both are thus

SODIUM ATOM   CHLORINE ATOM

SODIUM ION   CHLORINE ION

left as ions with complete outer shells of eight electrons. In the same year G. N. Lewis suggested that by the sharing of electrons the same state of stability could be reached. So if two atoms whose outer groups fell short of 8 were to share one or more electrons they could both attain the stable structure with an outer group of eight.

$$: \overset{..}{\underset{..}{Cl}} \cdot + \cdot \overset{..}{\underset{..}{Cl}} : \quad \rightarrow \quad : \overset{..}{\underset{..}{Cl}} : \overset{..}{\underset{..}{Cl}} :$$

Two chlorine atoms   A chlorine molecule

Finally, Sidgwick, about 1927, showed that the above process could explain Werner's co-ordinate valency and show how saturated molecules could combine. In such a case the pair of electrons constituting the valency bond are contributed by one atom only. A simple case is the combination of boron trimethide and ammonia, the former lacking its full complement of electrons, the latter having a pair not utilized in chemical combination:

$$\begin{array}{cc}
H_3 & H_3 \\
C \quad H & C \quad H \\
\overset{..}{} \quad \overset{..}{} & \overset{..}{} \quad \overset{..}{} \\
H_3C : \overset{..}{\underset{..}{B}} + : \overset{..}{N} : H \rightarrow H_3C : \overset{..}{\underset{..}{B}} : \overset{..}{N} : H \\
\overset{..}{} \quad \overset{..}{} & \overset{..}{} \quad \overset{..}{} \\
C \quad H & C \quad H \\
H_3 & H_3
\end{array}$$

It was thus shown that the molecules of Werner's co-ordinate compounds were held together by electronic linkages similar to those found in other types of compounds.

Since these systems were proposed it has become clear that there are many gradations between these three types of valency. Electrons need not be equally shared: thus we can find all grades between complete transfer, equal sharing and one-sided donation (see p. 306).

In the late 1920's and early '30's the molecule began to be thought of not merely as an arrangement of atoms but as a structure held together by electrons, which might have a greater concentration at one point and less at another. Such a molecule is said to have electrical polarity. This idea appeared in more than one field of work. In the first place, Debye and others proved by physical methods that many molecules had polarity—were *dipoles*, as it is said, and it was shown that a measure of this polarity was to be found in the refractive index of compounds.

PLATE XVII

B.—Aston's Mass Spectrograph (see p. 357).

A.—Artificial Transmutation of a Nitrogen Atom, *Blackett*, 1932
(see p. 360).

PLATE XVIII

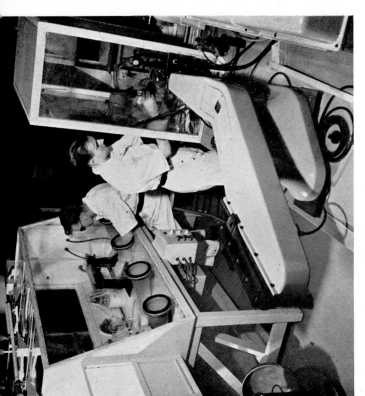

B.—Laboratory Work with Radioactive Materials. Special fume cupboards and glove boxes protect technicians from contamination with radioactive material. With highly active sources remote control is used.

At about the same time (1925) Lapworth, Ingold and Robinson developed the hypothesis that certain groups in organic compounds were attractive or repellent to electrons and could cause a drift of electrons from or towards the other parts of the molecule, and thus explained the reasons why certain parts of certain molecules were or were not attacked by certain reagents. The conclusions reached in that way were confirmed by determining the polarity (dipole moment) by physical methods (1931). This was a new and fruitful development in organic chemistry, which had previously been treated as purely a matter of structure: at about the same period the theories concerning that structure were to be most remarkably confirmed by a physical technique.

The Mapping of Molecules

The approximate size of atoms and molecules had been known early in the century (p. 371), but Bragg's technique for the measurement of the units of crystal-structure of diamond and graphite, in which the atoms were believed to be chemically combined, indicated the distance between the centres of combined carbon atoms. This method can be applied to a great many compounds, and in this way (and by other methods which confirm it) the distances between the atoms in molecules have been found; they vary from about 0·5 to 5 Angstrom units, according to the atom and mode of linkage. The mapping of the shape of molecules has likewise been developed (since 1933) by a refinement of the Bragg-Laue process, which subjects all the features of the pattern of X-rays diffracted by a crystal to a very long and laborious mathematical analysis. The result has been to confirm almost completely the conclusions which the organic chemists had drawn from the chemical behaviour of these substances concerning the general structure of their molecules: but it is not merely a confirmation, for it gives the exact distances between the atoms and also their mutual orientation, and so tells us more than could have been deduced by the classical methods of organic chemistry.

By the early 1930's we had the means of knowing the size, shape and, in a general way, the electronic make-up of the molecules: it still remained, however, to find a mathematical method of calculating the positions and motions of these electrons. This, if it is possible, may be the key to the physical chemist's ideal of being able to calculate the properties of a compound, physical and chemical, from the data given by its formula. This ideal is still unattained and, for most substances, a distant objective: yet the successes of the new quantum mechanics which has developed in the last twenty years are making it look possible.

Quantum Mechanics

How are calculations about electrons to be made? Not in the same way as we make calculations about billiard-balls or pendulums, for electrons are described by quantal laws, and billiard-balls and pendulums by classical dynamics. The mathematics involved are formidable to the chemist; suffice it to say here that no attempt is made to indicate the position of an electron at any moment, but rather to indicate the probability of finding an electron at a particular point in the molecule. Thus Fig. 61 gives the *contours* of increasing electron density in the molecule of anthracene, but not the position of individual electrons, the quest for which is proved by the uncertainty principle to be unattainable or even meaningless. How far is this mathematical theory going to be useful? At present only the simplest molecules, such as that of hydrogen, H_2, can be rigorously handled by it, and it is very difficult to suppose that the wave-function of anything so complex as the molecule of *e.g.* indigotin (p. 240) could be discovered and made use of. None the less, even though quantum mechanics has not yet attempted the complex description of a chemical compound, it has been effective in elucidating many of their properties, hitherto obscure, and especially the intermediate types of valency linkage.

One idea which has been of great value is that of resonance. It frequently happens that the structure of a compound can be written down in more than one way using the simple electron-sharing or electron-transfer notions described above (p. 352). Benzene is a case in point. It is found in such cases that the observed properties of the compound, or the distances between the atoms, or its physical properties indicate a stronger binding than corresponds with any of the canonical forms. The quantum-mechanical study of these cases generally confirms that there will be a greater energy of binding, and, because the form of mathematical analysis used closely resembles that used in describing the phenomenon of resonance in mechanics, the term resonance has been attached to this particular aspect of molecular structure. It must not be thought there is implied any corresponding dynamism in the molecular state. The molecular structure is to be regarded as uniquely determined; just as much as in the older formulation, but fixed in a pattern not susceptible of expression by a simple printed formula, or communicable except as the sum of the percentage ' contribu-

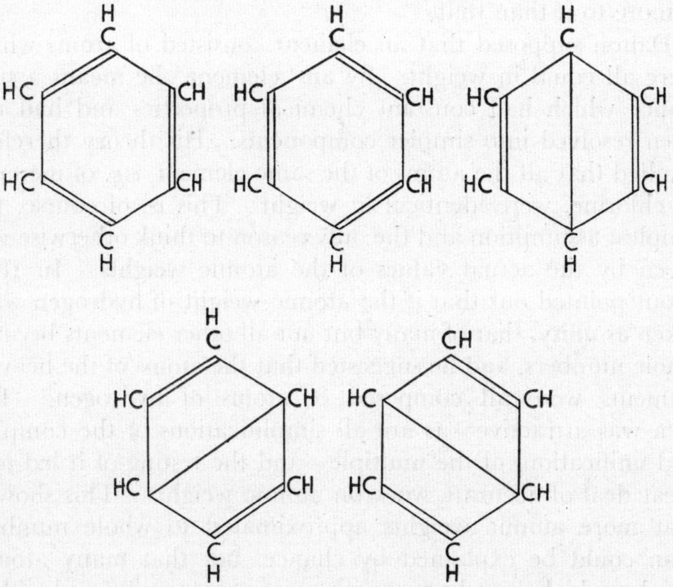

Fig. 59. Five structures of benzene leading to resonance.

tions ' of canonical forms which provide a starting point for a mathematical analysis.

The ordinary formulæ are still valid in most respects and they provide a basis for the understanding of the more complex concepts. So far, although the quantum mechanical study of structures has predicted very little in quantitative terms, its qualitative implications have enormously increased our understanding of the details of molecular constitution. The day is not yet in sight when the chemist will be able to start from the data of structures of the carbon, hydrogen, oxygen and nitrogen atoms and the formula of penicillin, and will compute at his desk a method for synthesizing it, instead of proceeding by conjecture, trial and error in the laboratory. Nevertheless, such ideas as that of resonance have sharpened the mind's eye of the chemist to a remarkable extent during the past quarter of a century.

Isotopes

In the 1920's the notion of isotopes, already alluded to in Chapter Nineteen, became more important. It was there discussed from the point of view of atomic structure, but there is more to it than that.

Dalton supposed that an element consisted of atoms which were all equal in weight. By an ' element ' he meant a substance which had constant chemical properties and had not been resolved into simpler components. His theory therefore implied that all the atoms of the same element, *e.g.* of mercury or chlorine, were identical in weight. This is, of course, the simplest assumption and the only reason to think otherwise was given by the actual values of the atomic weights. In 1815 Prout pointed out that if the atomic weight of hydrogen were taken as unity, that of many but not all other elements became whole numbers, and he suggested that the atoms of the heavier elements were all composed of atoms of hydrogen. The idea was attractive—as are all simplifications of the complex and unifications of the multiple—and the testing of it led to a great deal of accurate work on atomic weights. This showed that more atomic weights approximated to whole numbers than could be explained by chance, but that many atomic weights which were known with great accuracy differed widely from whole numbers. Thus oxygen, nitrogen, carbon, sodium and others had atomic weights which were very nearly whole multiples of the atomic weight of hydrogen, while chlorine (present accepted value 35·46) and others had not. It is curious that no one envisaged the possibility that some elements might consist of several similar but not identical types of atoms, always mixed in the same proportions, until Crookes in 1886 put forward this very idea. But the evidence from spectra (p. 323) by which he tried to support the theory proved unsound and the idea was generally forgotten.

We have already seen that the course of radioactive transformations proved that two elements of different atomic weight could occupy the same place in the periodic table (p. 344). At the same period (1913) it was proved by positive ray analysis that the gas neon contained atoms of two different weights, and F. W. Aston succeeded in separating neon into two portions of slightly different density. Specimens of lead of different atomic weight were isolated from thorium and from uranium minerals. This proved the existence of isotopes, and the final step was to separate from a pure chemical element or compound two specimens of an element differing in atomic weight. In 1920 Harkins succeeded in separating hydrogen chloride into two portions differing slightly in density; but Aston's and Harkins's separations were, however, very far from complete.

In 1918, A. J. Dempster invented an apparatus which would separate charged particles of different masses and so enable the isotopes in an element to be separated and characterized, but this was eclipsed by the mass-spectrograph constructed by Aston in 1919. This instrument, by a combination of electrical and magnetic fields, could focus a beam of flying atoms in such a manner that atoms of the same weight and electrical charge were all projected on to the same point. By focusing the beams of atoms on a photographic plate, lines were obtained each corresponding to atoms or compounds of particular atomic or molecular weight, and in this and similar ways, between 1919 and 1935, all the elements were examined to discover whether they were mixtures of isotopes. It appeared that only about twenty of the ninety elements consisted of one kind of atom, the others containing from two to nine different kinds of atoms. Thus tin, the atomic weight of which is $118 \cdot 7$, contains nine different kinds of atom with atomic weights varying from 112 to 124. Aston's instrument, incidentally, proved to be an admirable means of determining atomic weights, as the relative abundance of the different isotopes could be judged from the intensity of the trace they gave on the photographic plate. It is to-day a valuable tool for chemical analysis.

It now seemed that Prout's hypothesis had a sound basis, for a hydrogen atom consisted of one proton and one electron and all other atoms were then thought to consist of n protons [1] and n electrons, where n was some whole number. Thus an atom of sodium containing 23 protons and 23 electrons should be

[1] The neutron was not yet discovered.

exactly 23 times as heavy as a hydrogen atom. But in fact this was not the case and the atom of sodium was not 23·000 but 22·894 times as heavy as a hydrogen atom. Interest now centred on the reason why Prout's hypothesis did not apply more exactly than experiment showed. The atoms of the very light elements and the heaviest elements were heavier than would be expected,[1] and the majority of the elements with atomic weights between 20 and 200 were lighter. This divergence was attributed to the energy lost in their formation. According to Einstein's relativity theory, the loss or gain of 9×10^{20} ergs of energy is accompanied by the gain or loss of 1 gm. of mass. It appeared then that the elements of middling atomic weight had been formed from their constituent particles with the liberation of much more energy than the heaviest and lightest elements. The source of the atomic energy liberated in nuclear fission (p. 361) is the conversion of heavy elements into elements of middling atomic weight: a small fraction of the mass of the heavy element is converted into the gigantic quantity of energy that is seen in the atomic explosion. A similar conversion of the lightest element, hydrogen, into somewhat heavier elements is the basis of the hydrogen bomb and yields far more energy.

But to return to our isotopes. Before 1930 no one had succeeded in separating from any chemical element or compound pure or even approximately pure specimens of the isotopes it contained, but in 1930–32 Urey and his co-workers proved that hydrogen had a heavy isotope of atomic weight 2, which has since been given the name of deuterium. This is present in ordinary water to the extent of 1 part in 5,000, and in the years between 1932 and 1939 its separation was rapidly perfected and it became an article of commerce. The methods of electrolysis and distillation were chiefly used and in 1938 Clusius invented the simple process of thermal diffusion. A hot wire passes axially through a vertical tube containing the gas or vapour from which the isotopes are to be separated. The lighter isotope collects at the upper end of the tube, and although the separation is far from complete successive diffusions are capable of effecting it. By such means not only ' heavy hydrogen ' but heavy nitrogen, carbon, sulphur, oxygen and chlorine were obtained.

[1] On the basis of $O = 16$.

Meanwhile radioactive isotopes were being prepared by other methods (p. 329), and in the last five years the development of the uranium pile (p. 362) has made these available in relatively large quantities. These isotopes are of great practical importance in biochemistry and many other types of research as a means of 'labelling' a particular portion of an element. Their chemical and biological behaviour is exactly the same as that of the normal element, but they can be distinguished from any other specimens of the same element that may be present by a determination of atomic weight or density, or by their radioactivity, if any. Here is a simple example of the problems that can be solved in this way.

An animal eats fat and oxidizes it, forming carbon dioxide and water and producing energy; it also has fat-deposits in its body. Does it oxidize only the fat that it eats, or does some come from the deposits? The research workers prepared fat which had some deuterium atoms in its molecule in place of some of the hydrogen atoms and fed this to a mouse, whose products were preserved and which was later killed and examined. Analysis of its fat-deposits and the water produced by its respiration showed that about half the fat eaten was deposited and half the fat oxidized came from the deposits, which proves that these deposits are not permanent reserves but entrepôts through which fats are continually moving. In this manner it has been shown that all the bodily tissues—even bones and teeth—are in constant equilibrium with the blood-stream and tissue-fluids, which continually remove material and deposit fresh.

The method has also been applied to many chemical reactions of non-living substances, and has revealed the same sort of dynamic properties in ordinary mixtures previously regarded as inert. Thus we commonly think of chlorine as having no effect on sodium chloride; but if we bring gaseous chlorine into contact with a solution of the compound of sodium with radioactive chlorine, the radioactive chlorine is soon found in the gas. If we represent the atom of radioactive chlorine as Cl and of ordinary chlorine as Cl, it is evident that the reactions

$$Cl_2 + Cl^- \rightleftharpoons Cl.Cl + Cl^-$$
$$\text{and} \quad Cl_2 + 2Cl^- \rightleftharpoons Cl_2 + 2Cl^-$$

go on rapidly and continuously; thus we can infer that in a

solution containing ordinary salt and chlorine the chlorine atoms are continually passing into chlorine ions and vice versa. Here is a fact we should have otherwise been unable to establish, namely, that many mixtures are all the time undergoing chemical change, though none could be detected by the classical methods. Yet this is not true for all mixtures. Thus we may ask whether the atoms of sulphur dissolved in carbon disulphide are all the time exchanging places with the sulphur atoms in the solvent molecules, and experiments with radioactive sulphur show that they are not.

Transmutation and Atomic Energy

Returning to the notion of the Bohr-Rutherford atom, as held in the 1920's, it is easy to see that it promised the possibility of transmutation. The nucleus was known to decompose in the course of radioactive change, but Rutherford was the first to demonstrate (1919) an artificial transmutation by observing atom traces by their scintillations on a fluorescent screen. About this time (1911–12), as we have already mentioned, the Wilson cloud-chamber gave us a way of photographing the tracks of atoms which can show us the results of the collisions of these minute particles. P. M. S. Blackett photographed the tracks that were made by alpha-particles, shot out by radium, as they traversed nitrogen gas. One trail showed a fork and the angles revealed that a nitrogen atom had swallowed up an alpha-particle, shot out a proton and had thus been transformed into an isotope of oxygen. So the artificial transmutation of single atoms became a possibility. The great interest of this work was that it indicated the manner in which the nucleus behaved when bombarded. It did not break up as a flint would break when hit by a bullet; it seemed to swallow the bombarding particle whole and then to shoot out something quite different.

In 1932 was made a crucial discovery, that of the neutron. (Sir) James Chadwick, when bombarding beryllium with alpha-particles from polonium, discovered that the former element shot out particles which proved to have the same mass as a proton but no electrical charge. These were named neutrons and proved to be a most valuable means of transmuting elements. They were easily swallowed up by atoms because they were neutral and were therefore not repelled by the intense electrical potential of the nucleus. In 1934 came a further step. Mme I. Joliot-Curie and her husband, F. Joliot, showed that certain elements, after bombardment by alpha-particles, became radioactive. Bombardment with neutrons or other high-speed particles proved even more effective. In general terms, the result was that the nucleus of the atom bombarded swallowed up the bombarding particle and formed a new and unstable isotope of itself (or of some other element) which then decomposed in the same way as do the natural radioactive elements. Great interest was aroused. The next stage was to seek ways of producing high-speed particles from something else than the rare and expensive radium. The solution was found in various instruments which accelerated electrons, protons or deuterons (nuclei of 'heavy hydrogen' atoms, p. 358) by means of electric and magnetic fields. The best known of these is the cyclotron, in which the particle is made to describe a very long path in the form of a flat spiral between the poles of a magnet while it receives repeated accelerating impulses from a strong electric field. By bombardment with such high-speed particles almost all the elements were made into radioactive varieties. The uses of these are discussed on pp. 359–60.

In 1938 came the discovery of nuclear fission (how great we none of us knew, or indeed know). To bombard uranium with neutrons seemed an interesting experiment because it might be transmuted into new elements with atoms even heavier than the uranium atom, which is the heaviest of the atoms of natural elements. Fermi began this work in 1934, and puzzling results were obtained. It was only in 1939 that Meitner and Frisch showed that a new kind of decomposition took place. The uranium atom sometimes did what was expected, merely to swallow the neutron and later eject a particle; but sometimes it split into two roughly equal parts moving with enormous velocity and shot out several neutrons. It was at once seen that this could be the key to the tapping of the energy of the atom. If splitting of one uranium atom produced two or more neutrons, each of which could split another uranium atom, so producing further neutrons, the splitting of one atom should break up the whole mass with a terrific outburst of energy. But in fact it did not. There then seemed to be two possible reasons for the failure of uranium to explode. The piece of uranium might be so small that the neutrons escaped before they collided fruitfully with another uranium atom; or there might be enough atoms of other elements in ordinary uranium, not specially purified, to absorb most of the neutrons formed and thus to intercept them before they split a uranium atom. Such was the state of affairs in 1939. The possibility of the liberation of atomic energy was realized, but it was thought that only in a very large mass of very pure uranium could fission take place and maintain itself.

War broke out, and in Germany, England and America the possibilities of an atomic bomb were appreciated and the most gigantic of researches was undertaken, regardless of cost and against time. Germany dropped out when the Allied air attacks reduced her industrial potential, and the U.S.A. was able to provide the enormous resources required for the work. The full story would be altogether disproportionate to the space this book can afford.

Uranium consists of three isotopes; 99·3 % consists of the isotope of atomic weight 238 (U-238), 0·7 % of the isotope of atomic weight 235 (U-235), and only 0·008 % of the isotope of atomic weight 234.

When U-238 is bombarded with neutrons of moderate energy its atoms absorb the neutrons and ultimately form a new element, plutonium, which had never existed in measurable quantity before these experiments began. Both U-235 and plutonium are fissionable material—that is to say, they are capable of exploding in an atomic bomb. So to make fissionable material it is necessary either to separate U-235 from the U-238 with which it is mixed or to prepare plutonium in an atomic pile. Both have been accomplished, but the latter is the method of choice.

Very pure uranium metal was encased in aluminium shells and embedded in graphite (or immersed in heavy water). Many tons of graphite and uranium were built into a ' pile ' surrounded by heavy concrete walls to screen off radiation. A weak neutron source (radium and beryllium) was used to start it off. The neutrons break up a few U-235 atoms: some neutrons from these break up more U-235 atoms and so keep up the supply of neutrons. Most of the neutrons are slowed down by collision with the graphite (or heavy water) and are then absorbed by the U-238 atoms, forming plutonium. The pile evolves enormous quantities of energy and its temperature has to be kept down by cooling: this energy has been used for industrial purposes in experimental plants. The uranium is removed mechanically from time to time and the plutonium is separated from it. The fission-products of the uranium are intensely radioactive and no human being can go near the products because the intense radiation destroys the blood-forming cells and causes death within a few days. The complex chemical processes of separation have therefore to be conducted by automatic machinery; the disposal of the fission-products presents a serious problem.

The culmination of the century's research into the nature of the atom and molecule is the gift of gigantic power. The problem of deciding on the use to be made of it is not a scientific one, but belongs to the moral region in which man sees as dimly and moves as clumsily as he saw and moved not a century but a millennium ago.

CHAPTER TWENTY-TWO

The Arrangement of Molecules

Kinetic Theory of Gases

WE have seen how the structure, first of the molecule, then of the atom, came to be discovered during the past century. We are now to consider researches that led to the discovery of the way in which the smallest particles of matter that can exist in the free state—namely, molecules—are disposed relatively to each other.

The first purpose of the atomic theory was to explain the composition of compounds, and for this purpose it was not necessary to discuss whether molecules were at rest or moving, or to consider whether they were arranged in any particular fashion. The original approach to this problem, which later became of the first importance to chemistry, was made through investigation of the nature of heat by physicists. Lavoisier and his followers thought of heat as consisting of material particles, minute atoms of ' caloric ' occupying the spaces between the atoms or molecules of bodies. The modern view that heat is nothing else than a mode of motion had been suggested by Francis Bacon in 1620 and was several times revived during the next two centuries. Benjamin Thompson (Count Rumford) showed in 1799 that unlimited heat could be produced from ' motion ' without any change of weight resulting; in the 1840's the extensive work of James Prescott Joule (c. 1840–50) on the mechanical equivalent of heat carried general conviction; and by 1850 these studies were developing into the kinetic theory of gases. The physicists showed that a great many of the properties that gases had in common, and a great many of the phenomena of heat, could be deduced from the assumption that gases consist of molecules which are in unceasing chaotic motion and which are so small and relatively so far apart that their diameter is negligible compared with the space between them. The energy of motion of these molecules was the heat-energy of the gas. The molecules were, for the purpose of this theory, assumed to be spherical, perfectly elastic and impenetrable and to exert no forces upon each other.

The physicists were doing what science so often does, namely, inventing an ideal system (the 'perfect' gas) about which calculations could be made and their results compared with those of experiments upon the real systems—namely, the gases isolated by the chemist. It was shown that this ideal system would conform exactly to Boyle's Law, Charles's Law, Avogadro's Law and the diffusion laws, and therefore had a strong claim to be considered as a true account of a gas that conformed to those laws. But, in fact, no actual gas conforms to them exactly. The more rarefied a gas, the smaller its molecules, and the higher its temperature, the more nearly it approximates to the ideal 'perfect' gas described by the gas-laws; but it was at once evident that, although the kinetic theory, as then held, gave a good account of gases in general, it did not give a true account of any particular gas. So from the 1860's much work was concentrated on discovering how real gases differed from the ideal kinetic picture. It became clear in these years that their molecules did move rapidly and chaotically as the theory demanded, but that they were not of negligible volume and that they either attracted or repelled each other to an appreciable extent.

Thomas Andrews made an important advance when he studied exactly how various gases deviated from Boyle's Law. In 1869 he put forward the theory of the critical state, showing that every gas had a certain 'critical temperature' above which no pressure could convert it into the liquid state. Andrews and others then made clear the actual effect of pressure upon gases—that at high pressures they were not as compressible as Boyle's Law indicated, and that at low temperatures they were more compressible. This work was given a theoretical foundation by J. D. van der Waals, who published in 1873 a *Dissertation on the Continuity of the Liquid and Gaseous State*. The law that describes the relation between the pressure and volume of a perfect gas is that, for a given specimen of gas, the product of the pressure (P) multiplied by the volume (V) is always the same. Van der Waals described the behaviour of ordinary imperfect gases by adding to P a constant representing the mutual attraction of the molecules, and by subtracting from V a constant representing the volume of the molecules; the equations he obtained in this way described the behaviour of real gases much more accurately than did the equation for the perfect gas. He thus initiated two new researches, the study of the forces of attraction between molecules and the study of the size of the molecule itself, to neither of which problems had any serious attention previously been given. Van der Waal's equation did not, however, describe the temperature, pressure and volume relations exactly. Numerous other workers tried to discover more complex laws that would apply exactly to every gas, but none were more than moderately satisfactory. The problem is really a very difficult one, because the molecules of most gases are very complex structures. To predict their exact behaviour, all their possible modes of motion—rotation, various types of vibration, dissociation, ionization—would have to be taken into account, and the problem is too complicated for human reason. None the less the kinetic theory of gases, especially as modified by van der Waals and others, is a valuable approximation to a description of real gases, and one that enabled much of their behaviour to be understood. We may say, in fact, that the mutual relation of molecules in the gaseous state was pretty well understood by 1880, though of course an enormous field for development remained, especially with regard to the exact quantitative prediction of the behaviour of gases. The theory of liquids, solutions and solids was in a much less advanced condition.

The chief importance of this work for chemical industry was its clarification of the problem of the liquefaction of gases which, when solved as described in Chapter Twenty-five, led to so many and extensive developments in the industrial preparation of oxygen, hydrogen, carbon monoxide, nitrogen, ammonia and nitric acid.

Since heat is not a property of gases alone, it followed that the particles of liquids and solids must likewise undergo some sort of motion, the energy of which constituted their heat-energy, but the theory of these motions did not develop quickly.

Theory of Solutions

The next development towards the knowledge of the arrangements and motions of the molecules was the theory of solutions.

Several studies of this subject and many accurate measurements had already been made by 1880. Thomas Graham's discovery of osmotic pressure was the beginning. It seemed that a dissolved substance exerted a sort of pressure within the solution and methods of measuring this pressure accurately were devised by Pfeffer in 1887.

Meanwhile another line was pursued by F. M. Raoult, who between 1878 and 1882 studied the lowering of the freezing-point of a liquid when a substance was dissolved in it and showed that, other things being equal, the lowering of the freezing-point was in inverse proportion to the molecular weight of the dissolved substance: in 1886–87 he showed that the lowering of the vapour-pressure of a liquid when a non-volatile substance was added obeyed the same law. Raoult regarded these methods as valuable ways of measuring molecular weights (p. 218), as indeed they were, especially after the technique of determining the freezing-point to $0 \cdot 001°$ C. had been developed by Beckmann (1889).

The genius of the Dutchman van't Hoff transformed these researches of Pfeffer and Raoult into a first-class principle of science. He showed that Pfeffer's results implied that a substance in the state of solution was quantitatively analogous to a gas: that, for example, the osmotic pressure of a gram of a substance dissolved in a litre of water was numerically the same as the pressure of a gramme of the substance in the form of gas confined in a vessel of the capacity of a litre. Furthermore, he was able to show, by thermodynamic reasoning, that Raoult's results were a necessary consequence of this principle. It could then scarcely be doubted that substances in solution consisted of freely-moving molecules like those of a gas. Yet there was still a difficulty. Solutions of organic substances conformed exactly to van't Hoff's and Raoult's laws for osmotic pressure and alteration of freezing-point and vapour-pressure; but solutions of salts in water did not, and they always gave a higher osmotic pressure and greater alterations in freezing-point, etc., than these laws predicted. This divergence from theory was the source of an even greater generalization, the ionic theory, resulting primarily from the researches of Svante Arrhenius, confirmed and extended by those of van't Hoff and Wilhelm Ostwald.

Arrhenius, a Swede, was interested, like Raoult, in trying

to find the molecular weights of non-volatile substances, and to that end he studied the electrical conductivities of solutions. Work on the subject had been done by Michael Faraday (1832–33), by J. W. Hittorf (1853–59) and F. Kohlrausch (1874). Faraday had given the name of *ion* to the parts into which the electrolyte was separated during electrolysis. The results of Hittorf and Kohlrausch seemed to indicate that, when a salt in solution conducted electricity, the two ions (*e.g.* sodium ion and chloride ion in a solution of common salt) moved independently, but they did not draw from this any definite conclusions about the state of salts in solution. In 1883 Arrhenius studied the way in which the conductivity of solutions altered with the dilution of the solution. He came to the conclusion that, with respect to conductivity, the salt seemed to consist of an active and an inactive part, the former always being a certain fraction of the total. He did not yet specify how these parts were constituted. In 1885 van't Hoff saw that the osmotic pressure, etc., of dilute solutions of many salts approximated to twice the values expected from their formulæ, and in 1884–85 Ostwald found that Arrhenius's ideas explained the anomalous results that had been obtained concerning the affinity-coefficients of acids.

These men, between them, arrived at the theory of electrolytic dissociation, commonly known as the ionic theory, according to which a proportion of the molecules of electrolytes (acids, bases and salts) was broken up in solution into electrically-charged ions. Thus common salt in solution was not considered to consist of NaCl molecules but, rather, of a comparatively small proportion of these in equilibrium with a large proportion of sodium ions, Na^+, and chloride ions, Cl^-. At infinite dilution the solution was presumed to contain only ions and water.

The ionic theory explained the properties of solutions of electrolytes. Not only did it explain the values found for their conductivities, osmotic pressure, freezing-point, boiling-point and catalytic effect, but also for the first time showed up and elucidated a number of remarkable chemical differences between acids, bases and salts and all other classes of bodies. The fact that we can describe a salt by the names of the metals and acid from which it is made—that *e.g.* a dilute solution of copper sulphate has a set of properties common to all copper salts, another common to all sulphates, and no others—was easily understood if all copper salts broke down in dilute solution into copper ions and all sulphates into sulphate ions.

The ionic theory of solution produced enormously valuable results in the later '80's and the '90's. It was not, however, received with universal acclamation. To the plain chemist the statement that sodium chloride in solution broke up into sodium ion and chloride ion seemed to be as much as to say that it broke up into sodium and chlorine, which was obviously nonsense. The theory was greatly helped by Wilhelm Ostwald, who had just started the *Zeitschrift für Physikalische Chemie* and who published therein the earliest papers on the ionic theory. After Nernst in 1889 had successfully applied the theory to the E.M.F. of voltaic batteries hardly anyone to whom physical chemistry was intelligible still doubted.

The ionic theory proved to be the key to the understanding of analytical chemistry. Before the '90's analysis was a sort of skilled craft, in which ' tips ' and recipes empirically found to be successful were handed down from master to pupil. Ostwald's *Scientific Foundations of Analytical Chemistry*, published in German in 1894, transformed it from an art to a science.

The effect of the theory upon industry was immense. Electrolysis had been a sort of empirical art, a rather uncertain and tricky way of making a few compounds that could not be made otherwise. The ionic theory gave the explanation of its processes and the means of forecasting and calculating the best conditions. Thus we must attribute the rise of electrochemical processes after 1890 not only to the new availability of cheap electricity but also to the understanding of its chemical uses and significance. These developments are so important as to require a separate chapter (Chapter Twenty-three) for their study.

But, apart from these practical uses, the idea of the ion as a permanent constituent of matter was a new step towards our understanding of the world. The ionic theory, then, completed the broad outlines of the theory of solution. Little study had, however, been given to the structure of solids and liquids.

Structure of Solids

The theory of the structure of solids scarcely entered into nineteenth-century chemistry. The characteristic of solids that gave the first clue to their structure was their crystalline form. This was a property that could be studied mathematically. Only certain types of geometrical figures were assumed by crystals, and a mathematical analysis of these showed that they were all figures that could be built up from space-lattices, *i.e.* units of pattern endlessly repeated throughout the crystal. The geometry of these lattices was worked out by a series of crystallographers between 1842 and 1894, and in the end all the known crystal forms were assigned to some one of the 230 types of lattice which the mathematicians showed to be possible. But this work indicated only the existence of lattices in the crystal: it did not show how the molecules were disposed in the lattices, or even whether the lattices were of molecular dimensions. Thus it was supposed, quite reasonably but wrongly, that the cubic crystals of common salt contained the molecules of salt evenly spaced at the intersections of a cubic network. This lattice theory, in fact, explained with precision the whole of the characteristics of crystal geometry, but it gave no information as to the size of the molecules or their type of motion or how they were oriented.

The Numbering of Molecules

A new era of knowledge of minute structure opened with the twentieth century. Before that time we had ideas only of the general distribution of molecules. We could not point to gas, solution or solid and draw the pattern formed by the molecules: we could only indicate the general character of the disposition of those molecules. Indeed, we knew very little about the individual molecules; we could not weigh, measure or count them—and, in fact, there was no small justification for those who were disinclined to regard them as real in the sense that *e.g.* a billiard-ball is real. But from the turn of the century it became possible to accumulate reliable information about the individual molecules and atoms, and the first step was the attempt to count the number of molecules in a known quantity of matter.

That the atom and the molecule must be extremely small was known on several counts; thus oil films on water as thin as 10^{-8} cm. had been recorded, and these could not be thinner than a molecule—though they might be a great deal thicker.

The first effort to calculate the numbers of the molecules from the properties of gases was that of Löschmidt in 1865, but little attention was given to the question until the years between 1898 and 1914, especially the period 1908–10. The first successful method was based on discovering the charge on one electron. It can easily be seen that this gives us the number of molecules in a given weight of matter. We know, *e.g.*, how much electricity is needed to decompose silver nitrate so as to produce a given weight of silver (w). That quantity of electricity (Q) is equal to the total charge on all the silver ions in question, each of which is associated with one electron. So if we could divide Q by the charge on one electron (e) the result would be the number (n) of silver atoms in the weight of silver (w) deposited, and w/n would be the weight of an atom of silver.

To discover n, therefore, we need to know e, the charge on one electron. J. S. Townsend and J. J. Thomson worked on this difficult problem between 1897 and 1902, in which year their results led to the conclusion that there were about 4×10^{19} molecules in a cubic centimetre of gas at normal temperature and pressure. Much attention was given to the problem in the years round 1908–10. The most accurate method was probably that of Millikan, who from 1908 to 1910 made accurate determinations of the charge of an electron. His method was to give an electrical charge to a mist of minute oil-drops. One of these was allowed to enter an illuminated chamber, where it was viewed by a microscope. By means of the electrical attraction of a charged plate the charged drop could be kept hanging in mid-air: on cutting off the electrical field it began to fall, and the speed of its fall was measured. From these data the electrical charge on the individual oil-drops could be measured, and all the oil-drops were found to have charges that were exact multiples of the lowest charge found on any; this lowest charge was therefore taken to be that of the indivisible unit of electricity, the electron. Millikan's best experiment indicated that 1 gram-molecule of any compound (*e.g.* 18 gm., about $\frac{1}{2}$ oz., of water) contains $6 \cdot 063 \times 10^{23}$ molecules, and that the lightest atom, that of hydrogen, weighed $1 \cdot 66 \times 10^{-24}$ gm.

Similar results were gained by Jean Perrin from *c.* 1908 by studying the way in which fine particles suspended in a liquid settled out, and treating their behaviour as analogous to that

of the molecules of a gas. Thus a suspension of very fine
particles in a liquid does not settle to the bottom, but the
particles become more crowded as the bottom is approached.
In the same way the particles of a gas (*e.g.* air) do not settle
down to the ground but the molecules become more crowded
together as the surface of the earth is more nearly approached,
a fact which we usually express by saying that the air becomes
denser at lower altitudes. By counting the particles in the
suspension at different levels, by means of a microscope,
Perrin arrived at a rule connecting the numbers of the particles
at any level with their masses: by applying that rule to the
gas he deduced the masses of the gas molecules.

Not only Millikan's and Perrin's but about seven methods
in all concurred in giving similar results, and others have since
been added. One of the most interesting and easiest to understand is based on radium, and was developed by Rutherford
and his co-workers in 1908–10. Radium shoots out particles
of helium at a rate which, over a short period, can be regarded
as steady. A very minute but known weight of radium is held
near a fluorescent screen. Flashes appear on the screen as
each helium atom hits it, and these can be counted. From the
results it was calculated that 1 gm. of radium emits
34,000,000,000 helium atoms per second, or $34 \times 86,400 \times 365 \times 10^9$ atoms per year. Next an appreciable quantity of
a radium salt was sealed in a tube: this was opened after a
year and the helium measured. The volume produced was
0·156 c.c. per gram of radium per year. This quantity of
helium must contain the number of atoms named above,
which shows that 62×10^{22} helium atoms must be contained in
1 gram-molecule (22,400 c.c.) of helium.

This work told us the numbers and the weights of atoms
and molecules: at about the same period efforts were made to
discover their size. It was now known that 2 gm. of hydrogen
contain approximately 62×10^{22} molecules. Suppose this
hydrogen to be concentrated as much as possible by freezing
it: the molecules could then be thought to be in contact like
close-packed billiard-balls. It is obviously possible to calculate
from their number and the density of solid hydrogen that each
of these spheres would be about 4×10^{-8} cm. in diameter. A
number of more accurate methods have since been used, and it
is now known that this is too large a figure and that the

diameter of most atoms is between 0.2×10^{-8} and 3×10^{-8} cm.: molecules made up of many atoms are, of course, correspondingly larger. We can never enunciate an exact figure for the diameter of an atom, because an atom has no surface; it is a nucleus surrounded by a cloud of electrons, and the probability of meeting an electron does not abruptly cease at any point but falls off rapidly as we recede from the nucleus; for practical purposes, however, the size of an atom is that of the territory into which other atoms do not penetrate on account of their mutual repellent forces, and it is this territory of which we estimate the volume and which we represent as a sphere in our models of atoms and molecules.

So by 1912 we had a good knowledge of the size and weight of atoms and the number of them in a given quantity of matter; furthermore, we knew something about their available energy and, within close limits, their average velocities. In 1890 the atom had seemed doubtfully real: in 1912 we had knowledge concerning it so precise as to put at rest any doubts as to whether the atomic theory were only some kind of mathematical convention. But our knowledge was still very deficient concerning the part that the motions of the atoms within the molecule played in the behaviour of matter, and these were obviously important from the point of view of chemistry. Moreover, our knowledge concerning the lay-out of the molecule itself was unsatisfactory because it was the result of deductions from chemical behaviour, unconfirmed by the observations of physics: furthermore, there were a great many molecules, especially outside the organic field, concerning the structure of which we knew almost nothing. Our knowledge of matter in the solid state was also slight: the crystallographers gave us strong indirect evidence of the existence of space-lattices, but what relation the chemist's molecules had to the crystallographer's lattices remained obscure. Suddenly the whole of this field was enlightened by the discovery of a wholly new technique, the Bragg-Laue method of crystal analysis, a method which has developed in many directions and has almost transformed many departments of chemistry.

X-ray Analysis of Crystal Structure

The mathematical theory of space-lattices was virtually completed by Barlow in 1894. In 1895 came the discovery of

X-rays (p. 343), and from then to 1912 there was much research and controversy on the question as to whether or not these were electromagnetic waves, of the same nature as light but of shorter wavelength. They resembled light in most particulars but they were neither reflected by polished surfaces nor refracted by lenses; they could not be polarized nor yet diffracted even by the finest gratings that could be ruled. Ewald had been considering what effect the lattice of a crystal should have on light, and Max von Laue in 1912 asked himself what would happen if electromagnetic waves of about the same wavelength as the distance between the units of the crystal-lattice were to impinge on a crystal. It seemed reasonable to suppose that the wavelength of X-rays and the distance between atoms in a crystalline solid might be of the same order, and v. Laue's pupils, Friedrich and Knipping, at once tried the experiment. The crystal, in fact, proved to be a grating of the right fineness to diffract X-rays, and a beam of X-rays when passed through a crystal on to a photographic plate was found to give a central spot and a large number of weaker spots, grouped symmetrically round it (Plate XX, A). This single experiment at once proved that X-rays were electromagnetic waves, and when its implications were developed it led to a way of analysing X-rays into spectra and also enabled the internal structure of the crystal to be discovered and, above all, measured. Now, the problem of deducing the structure of the crystal from the pattern of spots on the photographic plate was, and still is, a formidable one, and the analysis of crystals would have progressed but slowly had not (Sir) W. H. Bragg invented the X-ray spectrometer (Plate XX, B), in which a beam of X-rays was reflected from the various planes of atoms inside the crystal. The beam was most strongly reflected when the angle was such that the radiation reflected from the various planes did not undergo interference: the angle at which the reflected beams left the crystal was discovered by means of an ionization chamber, the air in which was rendered electrically conducting when the X-ray beam entered it. This method led to much simpler calculations than those required for the analysis of the pattern given by von Laue's method, and by 1913 Bragg had worked out the structures of the most important types of crystals. The war of 1914–18 slowed up the work, but during it one important advance was made, independently by

P. Debye and P. Scherrer in Zürich (1916) and by Hull in America (1917). This was the use of powdered material instead of large crystals, in which form many materials could not be prepared. Technique advanced in many other directions, but the greatest improvement was the measurement not only of the angles through which the X-ray beams were reflected but also of the intensity of each beam. When intensity as well as angle was considered very complex crystals could be analysed. This method had been foreshadowed by Bragg as early as 1914-15, but in fact it was not brought into practical use until 1926 onward. The use of beams of electrons instead of X-rays was introduced in 1928 by Davisson and Germer, and also by (Sir) G. P. Thomson.

These methods opened up the new subject of Crystal Chemistry. It became possible through these completer analyses of crystals to calculate the places of the individual atoms in the molecules that composed them. Now there were many substances the structure of the molecules of which had not been discoverable by chemical means (p. 220); these were chiefly insoluble and non-volatile substances with large molecules, and these proved particularly amenable to X-ray analysis.

From an early period, however, (1913) the new technique had led to important discoveries about chemical combination.

First of all, it was clear that the crystals of most salts contained no molecules but only ions. Thus common salt, whose composition was expressed as NaCl, did not consist of an assemblage of NaCl molecules but of equal proportions of Na^+ ions and Cl^- ions packed into a lattice such that each ion was surrounded by six of the other kind. There was no reason to assign any sodium ion to any chlorine ion and it appeared that the molecule, NaCl, existed neither in the solid state nor in solution, but only in the vapour of salt.

Secondly, the facts revealed by crystal analysis required the new conception of *giant molecules*. In diamond, for instance, the molecule and crystal were seen to be identical, every carbon atom being chemically linked to its neighbour: graphite consisted of layers of giant molecules laid one over another like a pack of cards. The idea that there were pure substances which did not consist of large assemblages of identical molecules was altogether new to chemistry and proved invaluable in

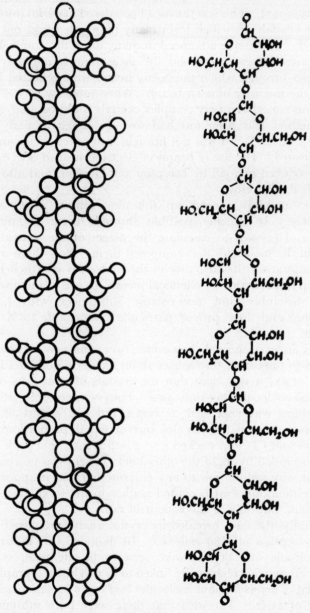

FIG. 60.   Four of the two hundred or so units composing the cellulose molecule.

opening up the study of bodies of this type, *e.g.* silicates, rubber, silk and thermo-setting plastics.

Thirdly, the analysis of certain crystals which consisted of giant molecules with a regular repeating structure revealed the distances between the atoms (or ions) in the molecule, and so gave us the length of the valency bonds and the angles they made with each other.

Bodies that are not in the strict sense crystalline but have some sort of repetition in their structure were also studied by X-ray analysis. Many organic compounds with large molecules are of this type. Thus such carbohydrates as starch and cellulose consist of chains of glucose residues (Fig. 60). Before 1920 such bodies as rubber or gelatin were thought to be structureless: to-day the study of the structure of such humanly important materials as rubber, keratin, silk, cellulose and the like is a department of science vital to industry. Herzog, Jancke and Polanyi in 1920 showed that the cellulose molecule consisted of a series of minute identical links and calculated their dimensions; these links have since proved to be pairs of glucose units. Rubber was shown to consist of chains of atoms that could unfold when stretched and fold up again when released (p. 268). W. T. Astbury from 1931 made remarkable researches on silk and wool. He showed that the silk fibre had an internal pattern that repeated itself in intervals of 3·5 and 7 Angstrom units. Silk was known to be made up of units of the amino-acid serine, and this, if linked as in Fig. 46, would give precisely the right pattern of reflections. This was really the first direct evidence as to the structure of a protein. Such studies have thrown a great deal of light on materials of biological interest and are obviously very important to the textile industries; these have recently been conducting researches thereon which are now beginning to issue in practice.

When the more powerful methods came into use it became possible to make a complete picture of the lay-out of a molecule. By very laborious calculations, based on the angles and intensities of the X-ray beams, the probability of an electron being found at each point of the molecule could be assessed. The probability was obviously greatest at the centre of each atom's territory: so a map such as Fig. 61, showing the contours of electron density, is in fact a map of the positions of the atoms in the molecule. One of the earliest studies of this kind was Robertson's work on anthracene (1933). Its greatest triumph was the elucidation of the unknown structure of

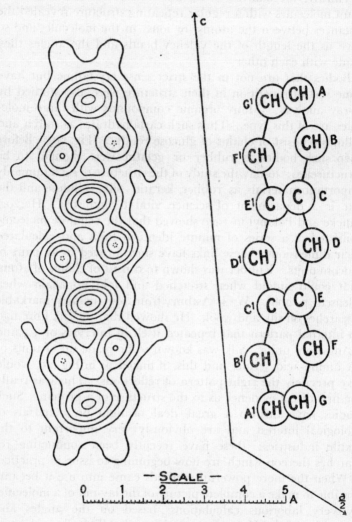

FIG. 61.   Structure of anthracene (Robertson).

penicillin. This work has not at present superseded the organic chemist's classical method of discovering formulæ, because of the great length of time and amount of work involved in the calculations. It is anticipated, however, that this will be much reduced by the use of the new calculating machines of the electronic type.

A very important class of bodies about which the chemist

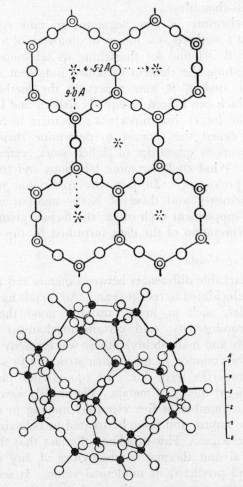

FIG. 62. Silicate structure (Bragg).

formerly knew very little are the silicates. The chief constituents of many rocks, clay, brick, ceramics, glass, etc., are silicates. The simplest chemical formulæ of these had been discovered by the ordinary methods of analysis that have been in use for a hundred years and more, but the results did not tell us much about, let us say, the reason why mica is so different from felspar. Bragg's methods revealed the complicated structures of these bodies (Fig. 62) and so opened up a new field in chemistry.

Crystal chemistry is now beginning to rank equally with the chemist's methods as a means of discovery of formulæ. If some method is found for shortening its laborious character and diminishing the element of skilled judgment required of the crystal analyst, it may supersede the methods of the chemist, which can indeed be equally tedious and less certain. We must not forget that important substances such as strychnine long defied the chemist to determine their structure despite enormous quantities of skilled work, extending over a century. What could be more laborious and tedious than efforts so prolonged? In fact, the traditional methods of organic chemistry and those of X-ray analysis or electron diffraction supplement each other, the former giving the clue to the interpretation of the data furnished by the latter.

The Theory of Metals

The remarkable differences between metals and non-metals have been elucidated in recent years. All metals have a group of properties, such as lustre, opacity, good thermal and electrical conductivity, and certain mechanical properties (*e.g.* ductility and malleability); there was formerly no indication as to the common factor in their structure to which these common properties were due. In 1900 Drude put forward the electron-gas theory of metals. The metals were supposed to contain a number of free electrons moving in the spaces between the atoms, and these he treated as behaving like the molecules in a gas. This explained the fact that the ratio of the electrical and thermal conductivities of any metal was constant and predicted its numerical value. It seemed that Drude's theory must have a basis of truth, but it failed to account for many properties of metals. Many alternatives and modifications were suggested and argued, but none were satisfactory until Sommerfeld in 1927 treated the behaviour of the free electrons, supposed to be present in metals, by wave mechanics, which is the only appropriate way of making calculations about electrons. We may think of the metal as consisting of an assemblage of positive ions immersed in a cloud of electrons not bound to any particular ion. The crystals of the metal are held together by the attraction of the cloud of electrons and the positive ions. This accounts for the fact that metals can be deformed and still keep their strength, for the 'electron-gas' still holds the atoms together however they move. Metals, of course, have a crystal structure, and so within each of the crystals of which metals are made up the positive ions form a lattice structure.

The electron-gas theory of the nature of metals has not yet led to any startling practical results, but is a useful guide in the selection of metals to compose alloys intended to have particular properties.

Structure of Liquids

Liquids, throughout the nineteenth century and until recently, were generally thought to be without structure, the motions of their molecules being supposed to be wholly chaotic, as are those of gas. However, the discovery in 1888–89 of the remarkable substances (*e.g.* azoxyanisole) which melt first to 'liquid-crystals', which have the fluidity of liquids and the optical properties of crystals, and then at a higher temperature form a normal liquid, showed that fluidity was not incompatible with structure. But it is only in the last ten years that liquids in general have been shown to consist of molecules ordered in an imperfect fashion. Thus considering any particular molecule of a liquid, its immediate neighbours are not quite regularly spaced around it. Their neighbours, again, are not quite regularly spaced, so that within a short distance of any molecule considered all regularity with respect to that molecule disappears. A liquid may be visualized as a body of continually-shifting imperfect crystal structures. Such an arrangement can only exist if there are gaps or spaces in the packing of the molecules: to these gaps are to be attributed the ability of liquids to flow.

Rheology

The great majority of forms of matter undergo deformation and flow when subjected to sufficient strains; this flow and deformation may be industrially valuable, as when metals or plastics are shaped by pressure, or deleterious, as when materials give way under strain. In any case the prediction of the effect of such strains is of the greatest importance. In the last fifteen years much work has been done in analysing and describing the way in which such different kinds of matter as metals, rubber, clays, doughs, paints, cheeses, road-surface compositions respond to strain, and to formulating structures that correspond to their properties, brittle, plastic, elastic and the like. This new science of Rheology has already a large literature and much practical value, though theory yet lags behind.

CHAPTER TWENTY-THREE

The Electrochemical Industries

The Availability of Electricity

ELECTRICITY has been applied to the chemical industries in two principal ways, first for the decomposition of compounds by electrolysis, and secondly for the achievement of high temperatures.

Before the year 1800 it was realized that electricity had chemical effects, but the static machines and Leyden jars of the period gave far too little electricity for chemical preparations, let alone for manufactures. The first useful electric battery was made by Volta in 1800, and in the next thirty years or so the general principles of electrolysis were worked out, culminating in Faraday's laws (1833–35) and Daniell's studies of electrode reactions in the succeeding decade.

The manufacture of primary batteries may be considered to be a chemical industry. The first electric batteries were inconvenient or expensive, and the Daniell cell (1836) and the Grove cell (1839) were the first convenient means of obtaining useful quantities of electricity. The Leclanché cell appeared in 1865 and was much used for electric bells. After the filament lamp appeared dry batteries were more and more needed, and the ordinary Leclanché dry cell was brought out in 1888. The storage battery, or accumulator, was not of use until generators provided cheap electricity to be stored. The lead accumulator was invented by Planté in 1859, but the great development of storage cells came only with lighting-plant and the motor car. The alkaline storage cells developed from the work of T. A. Edison (1900).

From about 1840 large quantities of electricity began to be required for electro-plating, and the expense of battery zinc and electrolyte was a serious one. Industry quickly appreciated the significance of Faraday's truly epoch-making discovery in 1831 of the possibility of generating electricity by moving a conductor in a magnetic field, and many magneto-electric machines were devised and used to supply current to electro-plating baths. All suffered from the fact that they employed permanent magnets, which gave but a weak magnetic flux, and so Wilde's idea of using electro-magnets and Werner Siemens' idea of energizing these means of the current generated by the dynamo itself (1866) must be thought of as giving us the essentials of the modern generator. Gramme's improvements of the armature (1872) provided a generator suitable for large-scale chemical operations, but it was the work of T. A. Edison that, about 1880, produced a really efficient generator. From this time electric lighting and transport began to require electrical energy in quantity.

The year 1886 may be taken as the beginning of the great electro-chemical industries. The cheapest electric power was and is still generated at centres where the energy of falling water is available, and consequently some sections of the chemical industry moved to these centres, and especially to the region around Niagara Falls, where the generation of electricity began as early as 1881. Since that time the consumption of electrical power by the chemical industries has so increased that they now consume nearly a fifth of the electricity produced in America.

Electro-plating

Electrolysis was discovered almost at the same time as the electric battery. The copying of objects by electrotype was perhaps its first industrial use, but this was soon overshadowed by the development of the electro-plating of silver and gold. The use of solutions of cyanides as the electrolyte was the key discovery, made by John Wright in 1840. The process was taken up by the Elkingtons, who had been making electrotypes, etc., since 1836, and rapidly became a great success. Electro-plating was far less laborious and expensive than the making of Sheffield plate by sweating together plates of copper and silver, and the Victorian age was enabled to rejoice in a show of the precious metals. Silver- and gold-plating were the most important, but copper-plating was used as a foundation for silver, and also to copy objects of art by electrotyping. Nickel-plating came into commercial use in 1869. At present the chief use of electro-deposition is for chromium-plating, which began

PLATE XIX

Cyclotron at Atomic Energy Research Establishment, Harwell, 1949 (see p. 361).

PLATE XX

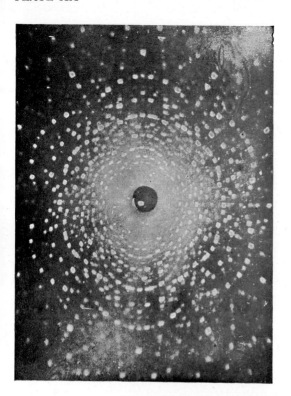

A.—Laue Photograph of Nepheline (see p. 374).

B.—Original X-ray Spectrometer used by W. H. and W. L. Bragg (see p. 374).

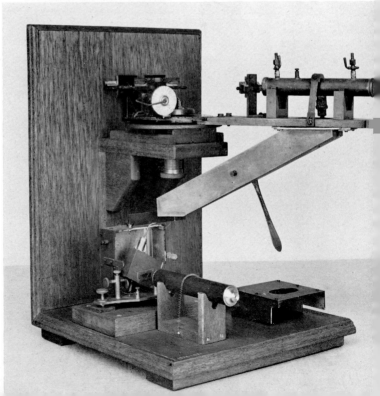

to be used for special purposes about 1925. Somewhat earlier the electro-deposition of iron was used for the repairing of worn machine parts, and this has since been greatly developed. Cadmium-plating became important soon after 1920. Plating with platinum, rhodium, bright zinc and bright nickel followed in the '30's. Electro-deposition of tin is now replacing the ancient methods of tinning.

Electro-plating with precious metals could flourish even when electricity was expensively produced from batteries, for the amount of electricity used was relatively small and the product was costly and could bear the expense.

Refining and Winning of Metals

The earliest large-scale use of electricity in metallurgy was for the refining of copper. The process consists of making impure copper the anode in in electrolytic cell, and pure copper the cathode. Copper from the anode passes into copper ions, which deposit the metal on the cathode: any gold and silver present, together with some other impurities, sink to the bottom as an insoluble slime, or 'anode mud'. J. B. Elkington used this process in 1865 at Pembray, in South Wales, then the centre of the copper trade. A few years later this was taken up in the U.S.A.: in 1877 Siemens and Halske designed a dynamo specially to provide the current needed for this operation. At this period the electrical industry began to demand the purest copper for its conductors and was for the first time in a position to supply the electricity needed to refine it. Gold was refined by this type of process from 1878, and silver from 1884, and indeed it has become a standard method for purifying such metals as are not affected by water. In recent years nickel and lead have been extensively refined in this way.

Where cheap electricity is available certain metals can be produced in a very pure state by converting their ores into a solution and electrolysing it. Copper ores have been treated in this way since 1886 but the method became important only after 1912, and for the purpose of utilizing very low-grade copper ores. The process has the advantage that the metal needs no further refining.

The making of zinc by distillation was always an expensive process and yielded a somewhat impure metal. Since the war of 1914–18, however, an increasing quantity of zinc (now some 25 % of the total) has been made by roasting the ore, dissolving it in dilute sulphuric acid and electrolysing the product. Cadmium and antimony and manganese can also be made in this way and electrical processes—in America at least—are steadily replacing the traditional methods of metallurgy.

Aluminium

The making of aluminium at a low cost was a great event in industrial history, not only for its value as a light and strong metal but also as a means of making many other metals, otherwise inaccessible, which in their turn made possible the wonderful special steels of modern times.

Aluminium compounds have, of course, been well known for a long time, and many attempts were made to find an easy process for the preparation of the metal. H. St. C. Deville's process (1854) involved the heating of aluminium chloride with sodium, itself expensive and made with difficulty by distillation methods; in the 1870's aluminium cost about $10 a pound and was of rather low purity. An enormous number of other processes were devised, but none were successful until, in the first half of 1886, both P. L. V. Hérault in France and C. M. Hall in America discovered the modern process—the electrolysis of a solution of aluminium oxide in fused cryolite. The process came into production in 1888 and has remained remarkably the same in principle for sixty-five years, though much has been discovered concerning the purifying of the materials. The automobile industry, after 1900, created a huge demand for aluminium, and the aircraft industry has augmented the demand for it and for various light alloys made from aluminium together with magnesium and beryllium—metals that are also prepared electrolytically.

Aluminium has a very high heat of combustion and reacts violently with oxides of other metals, forming aluminium oxide and setting free the metal. This reaction was brought into use by Goldschmidt in 1898 and soon became of great importance. The mixture of aluminium powder and magnetic iron oxide is known as *thermit*. When fired it produces half its weight of molten steel at a high temperature. This molten steel was used from about 1899 for welding; thermit itself has since been adopted as a filling for incendiary bombs. About 1905 the process was adapted to the industrial production of hitherto inaccessible metals, *e.g.* chromium, manganese, tungsten and molybdenum, by the simple process of igniting a mixture of aluminium powder and the oxide of the metal. Many alloys also, such as ferro-titanium, ferro-vanadium, ferro-boron, manganese-copper, chromium-manganese, etc., were made by igniting mixtures of aluminium with the oxides of the component metals; these alloys were then mixed with steel to form new steels of special hardness, toughness, heat-resistance, etc. Such steels have opened up new fields in engineering practice.

The need for a metal at once very light and very strong was not fully satisfied by aluminium. For the manufacture of aeroplanes and airships something stronger was needed and was found in the alloys of aluminium and magnesium. Duralumin, an alloy of aluminium with a little magnesium and manganese and about 4% of copper, has the remarkable property of becoming fairly soft on quenching, and thereafter slowly becoming hard and stronger than mild steel. This alloy was developed in 1909–11, and in the last decade a great variety of light alloys of this type have been devised for various purposes.

Magnesium compounds are very plentiful, but little effort was made before the 1940's to develop the manufacture of the metal, because it was believed to be too easily corroded and too inflammable to be of much use. For many years it was made in small quantities by electrolysing the fused chloride, and in Germany about 1910 an improvement was made by adopting an electrolyte of fused potassium and magnesium chlorides with a little ammonium chloride. In the concluding years of the 1914–18 war production was increased, but only to an annual figure of some hundreds of tons, mostly used for flares and tracer-bullets. Light alloys of magnesium were investigated in the '20's in Germany and America and became important after *c.* 1930.

The second world war caused an enormous demand for magnesium, both for incendiary bombs and for aeroplane parts. The modern method combined the extraction of bromine and of magnesium from natural brine. The magnesium chloride was separated from sodium chloride and calcium chloride by a somewhat complex process of crystallization. The magnesium chloride was dried in hydrogen-chloride gas, fused, together with potassium or sodium chloride, and electrolysed. The fused magnesium floated to the surface. The large-scale production of the metal has brought the price down to a twentieth of its cost in 1915.

Another light metal usually produced by electrolysis is beryllium. Its industrial development began in Germany and America in 1916, when beryllium-copper ores were first used. It was not until World War II that its use became extensive. The alloy of copper with some 2% of beryllium and a little nickel or cobalt is soft after annealing and quenching: it can then be machined and hardened by heating to 240°–300°. It is unique as having a high electrical conductivity together with great strength and resistance to fatigue.

Electrolytic Alkali

The next important industry to use electrical methods was the alkali industry. The making of chlorine in this fashion had been patented as early as 1851, but it was not until 1890 that the Germans began the electrolytic production of caustic soda and chlorine. It was taken up soon after in England and, towards the end of the decade, in the U.S.A., the critical date for whose electro-chemical industry was 1894, when the great hydroelectric scheme of Niagara Falls came into operation.

The electrolysis of a solution of sodium chloride, common salt, yielded caustic soda and hydrogen at the cathode and chlorine at the anode—all three very saleable substances; but the chief difficulty was to separate the caustic soda from the salt present in the same solution. This problem was solved in several ways from the year 1890 onward. Either the cathode was placed in a compartment isolated from the rest of the electrolyte by a porous diaphragm, or it consisted of a pool of mercury in which the sodium dissolved and was later extracted by the action of water or steam. The mercury-cathode processes produced an alkali of a new standard of purity.

The alkali industry depends on the separation of the sodium and chlorine of common salt. These appear in different forms in different processes. Thus the Leblanc process produced sodium carbonate and hydrochloric acid: the Solvay process gave sodium carbonate and the useless calcium chloride. The electrolysis of sodium chloride solutions yielded sodium hydroxide, hydrogen and chlorine, while the electrolysis of fused salt yielded sodium and chlorine only. Thus for production of soda-ash for the glass industry and domestic soda the Leblanc and Solvay processes were well adapted, while the electrolytic processes met the demand for caustic soda and chlorine. It was difficult to satisfy the demand for one of these without over-producing the other. World War I called for both these products in quantity and greatly expanded the use of the electrolytic processes, especially in the U.S.A. After the war caustic soda was a saleable product, but the use of chlorine, after the military demand had ceased, had to be developed. The electrolytic process very soon replaced the old Weldon and Deacon processes for the making of bleaching powder. This was soon seen to be a wasteful method of transporting chlorine and the tendency to use it in the elementary form has increased in the last thirty years, so that the production of bleaching powder is now a minor industry. Even before World War I liquid chlorine was being transported by tank-car, and after it the liquid was widely distributed in this way both for bleaching and for the sterilization of water. The growth of industrial organic chemistry also greatly increased the demand for chlorine, and by 1930 it was caustic soda which was being over-produced. It must be remembered, however, that although the electrolytic process had much advanced it was still producing less than half the American caustic soda and not 5% of the sodium carbonate. In more recent years, however, the demand for chlorine has so far increased as to give a large surplus of caustic soda, which is converted into sodium carbonate, so that, on the whole, the ammonia-soda process is now slowly giving way to the electrolytic, production from which in America has been doubling itself every five or six years.

The advent of the electrolytic process facilitated the production of the compounds formed from its products, caustic soda and chlorine. If the products from the electrodes were allowed to mix, hypochlorites were produced. Solutions made in this way came into use as antiseptics about 1904 and have been used for disinfecting water, for which, however, free chlorine is now the usual agent. If the mixing of chlorine and alkali takes place at a high temperature chlorates are formed, and this is the usual modern method of preparing potassium chlorate for explosives, etc., and sodium chlorate, used as a weed-killer and oxidizing agent. Chlorites, formerly a mere curiosity, are now used for bleaching some cellulose products.

Sodium metal was made on the industrial scale in 1854 by Deville's method of heating sodium carbonate, coal and chalk; but the yield was very poor. In 1890 Castner brought out his method of making the metal by electrolysing caustic soda. This greatly lowered the price of the metal and enabled it to be used to make cyanides, needed for the extraction of gold from its ores, and sodamide, used in the synthesis of indigo. Deville's process survived only for a few years, and Castner's held the field until about 1920, when the Downs cell enabled sodium to be made by electrolysing fused sodium chloride, a more difficult but less expensive process.

Hydrogen is also evolved in the making of electrolytic caustic soda. It can be used in the hydrogenation of oils or the making of synthetic ammonia, etc., if plant is available nearby; it is, however, a bulky gas which does not bear the costs of transport. Large quantities are obtained from the methane of natural gas cracked at 200–300 atm. and 500° C.

At this point we may refer to the industrial production of fluorine, an element which can only be made by electrolysis. Its reactivity is such that its manufacture presented great difficulty and, although it was prepared by Moissan as long ago as 1886, it is only in the last decade that it has been brought into industrial use (p. 310).

High-temperature Reactions in Electric Furnaces

The electric furnace opened up a new field, that of chemical reactions at high temperatures. All furnaces used before the '80's had derived their heat from fuel burning in air; much of the heat evolved was used up in heating the products of combustion and the inert nitrogen of the air, so that the final temperature was never very high. Perhaps 1,200° C. was as high a temperature as could be reached by material heated in ordinary furnaces, though some of the Siemens regenerative furnaces may have brought their contents to 1,400° C. Furnaces fed with oxygen could have reached higher temperatures, but oxygen was too expensive even for blow-pipe work before the development of the Brin process in the '80's, and has never become cheap enough for feeding furnaces.[1] The temperature attained in a furnace heated by an electric arc or the passage of an electric current through its contents may be anything up to 2,000° C. and is limited [2] mainly by the difficulties of finding materials, for furnace and crucible, refractory enough to withstand these temperatures. Furthermore, electric heating introduces no chemical substances into the furnace and difficulties due to oxidation or reduction by furnace gases do not occur. The quantity of electricity consumed is large and these industries have therefore developed where water power is available and electricity cheap, and especially around Niagara Falls.

The first electric furnaces were attempts to utilize the very high temperatures of the electric arc. Siemens's furnace, constructed in 1878, capable of melting 8 lb. of platinum, seems to have been the first. The induction furnace, in which a rotary magnetic field induces in metal currents which heat it to any desired extent, was invented in 1887, but since it operates only on metallic conductors its chemical importance has been slight. Moissan's arc-furnace (1894), though only on the laboratory scale, marked an advance.

The kind of electric furnace most important for industrial chemistry was that in which a mass of conductive material is raised to a high temperature by currents passing through it. The aluminium furnace is kept hot in this fashion, though the primary purpose of the current is electrolysis. Thus the manufacture of aluminium at least indicated the possibility of heating large masses of material by the electric current. Of this type were the furnaces used for making phosphorus, silicon carbide, calcium carbide, ferro-alloys and graphite, all inventions of the years 1888–95.

One of the earliest processes (1888) depending on electrical heating was the electrical process for phosphorus, in which calcium phosphate, silica and coke are heated by an electric current passing through the mass, whereupon they react to form calcium silicate, carbon monoxide and phosphorus, which volatilize and are condensed. This process has been so far cheapened and improved that phosphorus made by it

---

[1] Air enriched with oxygen has however sometimes been used.
[2] Small arc-furnaces reach much higher temperatures, 3,000° C. or more.

is now converted directly into phosphoric acid to be used in food-stuffs and, as polyphosphates, in detergents.

A very recent development is the high-frequency electrode furnace used for heating and melting non-conductors, such as organic materials.

Calcium Carbide and its Products

The first compound to be manufactured on a really large scale in the electric furnace was calcium carbide. The compound had been known since 1863 and had been several times prepared. In 1892 Thomas L. Willson of Spray, in the United States, and Moissan, in France, both discovered the present way of making it. Willson was a manufacturer of aluminium and thus was readily able to set up plant to manufacture it. In Europe, Héroult also began its manufacture about the same time. The process is simple in principle: a mass of quicklime and anthracite or high-grade coke is heated by the passage of a very large current through the conductive carbon, so raising the mass to a temperature estimated at *c*. 2,000° C.; at this temperature calcium carbide is formed and melts to a liquid, which in the older furnaces was allowed to solidify to a block but in the more recent furnaces is tapped and run off.

The first object of manufacturing calcium carbide was to produce acetylene gas, used for lighting. Although after about 1910 acetylene lighting diminished to a very small industry, from 1904 onwards the gas was used in ever greater quantities for oxyacetylene welding. In 1907 calcium cyanamide, CaN_2C, began to be made from calcium carbide by heating it in an atmosphere of nitrogen; this was sold as a fertilizer or converted into ammonia or into cyanides. The last named is its chief chemical use to-day, as the direct synthesis of ammonia (p. 429) has replaced the cyanamide process. Acetylene is not now exclusively made from carbide, for it is also manufactured by the cracking of lower hydrocarbons or by the partial combustion of methane.

The most important use of acetylene is as a starting point for organic syntheses. It gives a new source of compounds containing two or four atoms of carbon, which were formerly derived from alcohol or acetic acid. The process by which acetylene may be combined with water in presence of mercuric salts to form acetaldehyde, which can be oxidized to acetic acid, was tried as early as 1905, but only became an important industry about 1916, when World War I and the development of the rayon and cellulose-lacquer industries after it brought about a shortage of acetic acid and acetone. The difficulties of the process were then overcome and to-day far more acetic acid is made from acetylene than by the distillation of wood. Very important to-day are the unsaturated hydrocarbons, vinylacetylene and divinylacetylene, that can be made from it and serve as a basis for synthetic rubbers. Acetylene also readily forms vinyl compounds, which can be polymerized to valuable flexible plastics (p. 263). Thus a part of the synthetic-rubber industry and a very important part of the plastics industry derive from the carbide process. Acetylene can also be converted into a solvent, trichlorethylene, much used for degreasing leather and for incorporating in industrial soaps. None the less, acetylene from calcium carbide as a source material is being overshadowed by the olefinic gases from petroleum-cracking.

Carbon Disulphide

Taylor's electrical carbon-disulphide plant (1901) may be mentioned as a pioneer in this connection. Carbon disulphide (discovered in 1796) had long been in demand as an insecticide, for it was one of the chief means of combating the ruinous invasion of the European vines by the American *phylloxera*, an aphis infesting the roots. The demand for it was increased by the slowly-developing viscose process for the manufacture of artificial silk (p. 256). Its manufacture by the action of sulphur vapour on externally-heated carbon was unsatisfactory; so the method of passing an electric current through a mixture of coke and sulphur proved to be a most valuable one. Carbon disulphide production was enormously increased by the growth of the rayon industry and the increased use of carbon tetrachloride, both as a solvent and an effective fire extinguisher. Much of this is now, however, made by chlorinating natural gas.

Abrasives

Silicon carbide, which is familiar under the trade name of carborundum, was discovered accidentally by E. C. Acheson in 1891 and was brought into production in 1893. The process consists of heating pure quartz sand and coke by the passage of a large electric current, and has been but little modified with the passage of years. Silicon carbide is extremely hard and withstands very high temperatures: thus it has proved itself of the utmost importance both for sharpening and precision grinding, and it is, moreover, the most satisfactory refractory substance for furnace linings, etc. Fused alumina and boron carbide are other important abrasives made in the electric furnace, as is also the intensely hard tungsten carbide, which has revolutionized machine-tool practice.

Graphite

Graphite, one of the crystalline forms of carbon, has been used for pencil-leads since at least 1565, the year after the discovery of the Borrowdale deposits by German miners prospecting for copper. It was a rather rare mineral before the nineteenth century, but during that period new sources were discovered, chiefly in Ceylon and India. Girard and Street, in 1893, seem to have been the first to make graphite by heating carbon electrically, but the first successful process was that of E. G. Acheson, who in 1895 adapted his carborundum furnace for the purpose and found that the so-called amorphous carbon (e.g. anthracite or coke) could be converted into graphite by passing an electric current through it so as to raise it to a very high temperature. This process not only provided graphite for pencil leads and crucibles, but it could yield a form of graphite which, on treatment with gallotannic acid, was resolved into very fine particles (deflocculated Acheson graphite); this, suspended in oil or water, formed a most valuable lubricant.

Much difficulty had hitherto been experienced in making anodes for the electrolytic processes which came into use in the 1890's. These anodes were subject to the action of acids, chlorine, etc., and carbon was the only suitable conductive material. At that time it was hard to obtain carbon in compact masses from which large anodes could be cut. Sometimes slabs of the hard carbon deposits from coal-gas retorts were sawn up to make anodes, but suitable pieces were difficult to come by. Acheson moulded these anodes from carbon (e.g. petroleum coke), bound with a little molasses or tar, and graphitized them by stacking them in the core of his graphite furnace and raising them to a high temperature. These electrodes were influential in bringing about the success of many of the new electrolytic processes.

The advent of the atomic pile brought about a demand for large quantities of very pure graphite. No such material had previously been made, and it is understood that its production was one of the major difficulties of that tremendous task.

Carbon is now an important material for the construction of refractory furnace parts, *e.g.* for the hearths of blast-furnaces, and furnaces for use with ferro-alloys.

Electrolytic Oxidation and Reduction

When solutions are electrolysed, electrons enter the solution at the cathode and are withdrawn at the anode, which processes have the effect of reducing the compounds in contact with the cathode and oxidizing those in contact with the anode, and this without introducing any new substance into the solution. A number of industrial processes of this character have been brought into use since 1900. The best known is the electrolytic preparation of hydrogen peroxide, introduced about 1905 and now the standard method (p. 306). The first stage is the electrolysis of cold sulphuric acid, leading to its oxidation to persulphuric acid, $H_2S_2O_8$, from which hydrogen peroxide is formed by distillation.

Another important process, developed about 1919, is the manufacture of white lead by electrolysing lead acetate solution in a cell with lead anodes. The electrolyte is divided by diaphragms: that round the anode consists of sodium acetate, that round the cathode of sodium acetate and carbonate. The lead anodes dissolve to acetate which is precipitated by the carbonate ions travelling to the anode. This process is claimed to produce white lead comparable with that of the ancient but still surviving stack processes (p. 83). Other processes now employed are the oxidation of chlorates to perchlorates, manganates to permanganates, ferrocyanides to ferricyanides, chromic salts to chromic acid.

A good many organic oxidations and reductions have been recently used, *e.g.* the oxidation of anthracene to anthraquinone and the reduction of glucose to sorbitol and mannitol, used as moistening agents (humectants) and for organic syntheses. An important development is the anodic oxidation of aluminium, patented in 1914 by Bengough in England. This process gives to aluminium a hard protective film which can be dyed without impairing the lustre of the metal.

Deuterium

Deuterium, the hydrogen isotope H^2, and its oxide, ' heavy water ', were discovered in 1932. Ordinary water contains about 175 deuterium atoms per million hydrogen atoms. On electrolysis the deuterium atoms are evolved more slowly than the hydrogen atoms and thus, by long electrolysis, the heavy-water content of common water is increased, a first step towards the separation of the pure material, which is of great importance for the making of certain types of atomic piles (p. 362).

CHAPTER TWENTY-FOUR

The Conditions of Chemical Reactions

Early Ideas concerning Velocity of Reaction and Equilibria

ABOUT 1800 there was a controversy as to whether the relative quantities of chemical reagents that were brought together influenced the nature and proportions of the products of the chemical reaction between them. There were those who supposed the actual composition of the compounds produced might be modified by altering the proportions of the reagents: others believed that the composition of these was unaffected but that the proportion produced might be altered by an excess of one of the reagents. That, for example, silver chloride might contain more or less silver, according to the proportions of the reagents used to make it, was shown to be false, but that the nature of the products of a reaction and the proportion of a reagent transformed could be influenced by altering the quantities of the reagents was, in fact, true. This question began to be reconsidered from 1850 onward.

That some chemical actions proceed very rapidly and others very slowly was obvious to every practical chemist, but at this period there was no explanation of this fact other than the general notion that these reactions were most rapid in which the reactants had the greatest ' affinity '.

When the chemist spoke of the rate or speed at which a reaction proceeds he was thinking of the proportion of the reagents that undergo reaction in a given time: it was still necessary, however, to give a definition of reaction-velocity and to try to measure it. In 1850 Wilhelmy studied the conversion of a solution of cane-sugar into glucose and fructose in presence of acids: this was an easy case to study because cane-sugar has a measurable optical property, its rotation of polarized light, the change in which indicated the progressive disappearance of the cane-sugar. Wilhelmy's work was not followed up until many years had elapsed.

It was well known, even at this time, that some chemical

397

reactions did not complete themselves but came to an equi-
librium-point, where action seemed to cease. A. W. Williamson, also in 1850, suggested the fundamental idea that in these cases there was a dynamic equilibrium. He supposed that, *e.g.* compounds A and B might react to form compounds C and D, and that these compounds C and D, as soon as formed, might begin to re-form A and B: the final result would be a mixture of A, B, C and D, unchanging in total composition but in which the chemical reactions, $A + B \rightarrow C + D$ and $C + D \rightarrow A + B$, were both proceeding at the same rate, so that no change in the composition of the mixture resulted. This idea did not at first receive the attention it deserved. Thus P. E. M. Berthelot and P. St. Gilles, who in 1863 worked out the effects of concentration and temperature on some equilibria, did not treat them as dynamic. The idea of the velocity of a chemical reaction and the laws that govern it were well worked out by A. Vernon Harcourt and W. Esson in 1866–67. They were, however, not concerned with equilibria, and the first solid contribution to the theory of these reactions was the formulation of the idea of active mass, and the law of mass-action by Guldberg and Waage, whose work was first published in Norwegian in 1864 but did not attract attention until it was issued in French in 1867. The law they enunciated was essentially that the ' chemical action of a substance at any moment was proportional to its active amount ', *i.e.* that the rate of reaction of a substance was proportional to its concentration.

This law of mass-action was a useful guide to the prediction of the conditions under which the maximum yield of any substance could be obtained. Thus, for example, it showed that if we wished to turn the greatest possible proportion of an acid into an ester, according to the reaction

$$\text{Acid} + \text{alcohol} \rightleftharpoons \text{ester} + \text{water},$$

we should not use the reactants in the proportion indicated by the equation (one molecular weight of each), but use a larger proportion of alcohol and remove the water as far as possible. For, since at equilibrium the rate of reaction must be the same in each direction, it followed that

$$\frac{(\text{concentration of acid}) \times (\text{concentration of alcohol})}{(\text{concentration of ester}) \times (\text{concentration of water})} = K,$$

where K is a numerical constant. Thus the increase of concentration of alcohol and diminution of concentration of water must make the concentration of acid at equilibrium small and the concentration of ester large, as was required.

This law dealt with only one of the factors that alter the velocity of a reaction or the proportion of the reactants in an equilibrium mixture—namely, the concentration of the reactants. It would tell us the effect of adding an excess of one reagent, of diluting or concentrating the mixture, or of altering the pressure on gases undergoing chemical reactions. But it did not indicate the effect of temperature on the reaction, nor did it give any information about the time-factor, *i.e.* the actual speed of the reaction or the length of time that would be needed before equilibrium would be attained.

The effect of temperature on equilibrium reactions was worked out through the application of thermodynamics to chemistry, and the actual speeds of the reactions are studied by the comparatively new science of chemical kinetics.

Chemical Thermodynamics

Among the great principles which have built up modern chemistry are those of thermodynamics. The two chief aspects in which chemical phenomena can be understood are the aspects of *structure*, already discussed in Chapters Fifteen and Twenty-two, and of *energy*, which is the concern of thermodynamics. Structure is easily visualized and the problems of the structural side of chemistry are easily comprehended, if not easily solved; but in seeking to investigate chemical energy the nineteenth-century chemist entered an unfamiliar field. It is obvious, of course, that chemical energy is a conception without which chemistry cannot be understood. Clearly the speed and extent of chemical changes are dependent on the energy-changes that take place: chemical changes (*e.g.* the burning of fuels) are, moreover, the source of almost all the energy on which an industrial civilization depends. Furthermore, the ' structural ' and the ' energetic ' treatments of chemistry were independent, and the consideration of chemical changes from the point of view of energy was possible in spite of the complete ignorance of their intimate mechanism that prevailed until very recent times.

It has been known for centuries that chemical actions produce heat, and even in the later part of the eighteenth century measurements of the heat produced in various reactions had been made by Lavoisier.

In 1840 Hess enunciated the law that if a stated quantity of substance A was converted into substance B the same quantity of heat was evolved or absorbed, irrespective of the number of intermediate steps by which the conversion was made: this law is really only a special case of the law of Conservation of Energy, which, however, was not clearly stated before the next decade. From about 1852 Julius Thomsen, at Copenhagen, and M. Berthelot, in France, determined a great number of heats of reaction. These men were impressed by the idea that the reactions which proceed with the greatest speed are those which evolve most heat. This theory was put forward between 1852 and 1869, but it was only an approximate rule and went too far in making the heat produced in a reaction the measure of 'chemical force'. If this theory were correct, there could be no reversible reactions; if A changes to B and produces heat, then when B changes to A a heat is absorbed and the system becomes cooler. In the latter case there should be no 'chemical force', yet there are thousands of cases of equilibrium changes where the reaction proceeds in both directions at once.

The work of Thomsen and Berthelot was more practical than theoretical, and although thermodynamics began with the Law of Conservation of Energy, enunciated by various workers, and especially by Helmholtz about 1847, it was not applied to chemistry until the years 1868–78, first by A. Horstmann and later by the American J. Willard Gibbs. Gibbs was a mathematical physicist whose treatment of thermodynamics assumed the full rigour of mathematical form. He is said to have made only one public speech, which consisted of the four words "Mathematics is a language." It is—and he did not translate. In the 1870's chemists were generally ignorant of any but the elementary parts of mathematics, and simple arithmetic was considered to be a sufficient equipment for their work. So, although the theoretical calculations of Gibbs concerning chemical thermodynamics were remarkably complete, they were so far sundered from the habit of thought and conceptions of the practical chemist that they were, in fact, neglected and much of their content was rediscovered piece-meal.

The Practical Results of Thermo-chemistry

The work of Thomsen and Berthelot on heat of combustion was soon followed by the practical measurement of the quantity of heat given out by the combustion of a given weight of fuel—a most important piece of knowledge for the buyer. Berthelot's bomb-calorimeter of 1881 was followed by a host of alternative instruments in the '80's and '90's. Oxygen-bomb calorimeters are still the instruments of choice for the determination of the calorific value of fuels.

The determination of the heats of various chemical reactions were important as data for the thermodynamics of gas-reactions, which receive separate treatment in Chapter Twenty-five.

Heterogeneous Equilibria

Willard Gibbs set out a great part of chemical thermo-dynamics, but his name is particularly renowned in connection with the Phase Rule. This generalization deals with hetero-geneous systems, *i.e.* those whose various parts are separated by boundaries. Thus a mixture of ice and water, or an emul-sion of oil and water, or a liquid in contact with its vapour, is a heterogeneous system. The homogeneous parts of which such a system is composed (*i.e.* ice, water, vapour) are called phases. Gibbs's rule is that " it is necessary to assemble at least n molecular species in order to construct a heterogeneous system at equilibrium consisting of $n + 1$ phases."

Gibbs certainly cannot have realized the extreme importance this generalization would acquire. In addition to a wide variety of uses in chemical research, it enables us to conduct large-scale distillations and crystallizations in such a manner as to obtain the maximum quantity of product, a matter absolutely essential to chemical industry. It enables us to understand the formation of the various components of alloys on which modern metallurgy is largely founded. Whether the changes concerned in reaching the equilibrium are physical or chemical does not matter: the phase rule is applicable to every phenomenon where there is more than one phase in equilibrium. Despite its great importance this work of Gibbs remained neglected for ten years. In 1886, however, van't

Hoff directed the attention of Bakhuis Roozeboom thereto, and to him we owe the exposition of the phase rule as a practical guide to the work of the chemist, pure and applied.

The Phase Rule and the Preparation of Salts

The process of crystallization is an ancient method of obtaining salts from solutions (pp. 77, 118), but the phase rule was the first means of systematizing our knowledge of the process. The simple cases of purification by crystallization called for no further aid from theory, but where one salt was to be obtained from a complex mixture the phase-rule diagrams enabled the industrial chemist to enunciate the exact procedure for obtaining the desired product.

The first industrially important investigation of this kind seems to have been that of van't Hoff and Meyerhoffer (1897–99) on the conditions in which carnallite (hydrated potassium magnesium chloride) can exist in equilibrium with aqueous solutions. This led to the knowledge of the most advantageous way of obtaining potassium chloride from this mineral, the chief source of potash in the famous Stassfurt deposits. Later the theory of cyclic processes for the separation of pure salts from mixtures was worked out by Blasdale (1918), F. A. Freeth (1924) and others, leading to valuable economies in heat and materials.

Metallography

That metals consisted of masses of small crystals had been known since the seventeenth century, but modern metallography may be thought to date from 1864, when H. C. Sorby made excellent micro-photographs of specimens of iron and steel. His work, however, attracted little notice. This microscopical examination of polished and etched surfaces of metal, showing the crystals of different constituents, began to be taken seriously in the 1880's and '90's and became general practice only after 1900.

The freezing of metallic alloys was studied about the turn of the century, and the first application of the phase rule to the various crystalline compounds of iron and carbon contained in iron and steel was made by Roozeboom in 1900. This set the pattern of research concerning alloys, and the results of studies of cooling-curves and of microscopy were incorporated into the central notion of phase-rule equilibria.

The next great development followed from the X-ray analysis of crystal structure. In 1921 Westgren began the study of the structures of the crystals of the constituents of alloys. Thus the constitution of metals came to be understood and Hume-Rothery, in 1926, was able to connect the structures of alloys with their electron-atom ratios. From 1921 onward methods of making large single crystals of metals were worked out, and thus the individual properties of the constituent crystals became known. From 1922 Polanyi and others have studied the way that these crystals are deformed by strain. At present much attention is being focused on the effects of irregularities and deficiencies in the crystal pattern.

The effect of these and later researches upon metallurgy has been to lead it some of the way along the path from the status of an empirical art to that of a true science.

Homogeneous Equilibria

The study of thermodynamics gave us not only the phase rule, which treated of heterogeneous systems, but also the means of studying homogeneous systems, such as a mixture of gases or of liquids in chemical equilibrium, and both of these fields were cultivated by van't Hoff, most fecund originator of chemical ideas.

In 1884 he published his *Études de dynamique chimique*. The first half of this deals with chemical kinetics (p. 405), the second with the application of thermodynamics to chemical equilibria. The mathematical treatment of the subject was still unfamiliar and generally repugnant to chemists, but one important rule which could be expressed in non-mathematical language had a great influence. This was the *Principle of Mobile Equilibrium*. It states that a rise (or fall) of temperature will displace the equilibrium of a chemical reaction in such a way as to favour that system whose formation is attended with an absorption (or evolution) of heat.

Le Chatelier in the same year (1884) put forward the principle in a wider form, indicating that if any constraint is put upon a system at equilibrium, it will so change as to diminish that constraint. This applied not only to heat changes but also to pressure changes and, in fact, included the

Law of Mass Action. Thus if a system at equilibrium is cooled, the equilibrium will alter in the direction which brings about the evolution of heat: if the system is compressed the equilibrium will alter so as to decrease its volume and so diminish the pressure. The principle proved to be extremely valuable to the industrial chemist, who is normally concerned to obtain the greatest yield of a product from his material. Thermodynamics was capable of telling him the conditions of temperature and pressure at which the greatest final yields could be attained and of predicting how large that yield could be. Further radical developments in thermodynamics were brought about by Nernst from *c.* 1894, and his Heat Theorem may be thought to have completed the essentials of the science of chemical thermodynamics.

The practical developments of thermodynamics began with the twentieth century. Chemical processes in industry, as in the laboratory, had been commonly conducted at atmospheric pressure: but thermodynamics indicated that many equilibrium-reactions which gave an unprofitably small yield at low pressures might give a valuable yield at high pressures: it also opened up the possibility of operations at very high temperatures, then becoming attainable as a result of the development of electrical power. This fitted in very well with the pressing need then felt for the fixation of nitrogen—*i.e.* the conversion of the nitrogen of the air into ammonia or nitrates, which could be used as fertilizers and for the production of explosives. From the first decade of the twentieth century the utilization of high-pressure reactions has been developed in all the great industrial centres. These reactions are discussed in Chapter Twenty-five.

But thermodynamics is not enough for the study of chemical reactions, because it considers only the conditions of a system at equilibrium, not the process by which such a system reaches equilibrium. Thermodynamics might tell us that, if a mixture of certain gases was maintained at 500 atm. pressure and 200° C. until equilibrium was attained, 80% of it would be transformed into some product we require, but it would not tell us whether a second or a year was required for the transformation. But the time factor is intensely important to the industrial chemist, who is not so much concerned with getting the maximum yield from a given amount of material as with turning out the greatest quantity in the least time with a given expenditure on plant. Into many of his processes the question of equilibrium does not enter. He is therefore more nearly concerned with chemical kinetics, the study of the speed of chemical reactions.

Chemical Kinetics

That the time a chemical reaction takes to complete itself is influenced by many factors was a known fact long before there was any theory of how that influence operated. All practical chemists, since the days of the alchemists, have known that heat accelerates chemical reactions, and from the beginning of the nineteenth century it was known that small quantities of certain substances (catalysts) that took no apparent part in the reaction could do the same.

Nothing was known about the actual process of chemical change. The chemical equations stated that certain substances met and others were produced. The internal mechanism of chemical reactions seemed to lie beyond conjecture; in fact, the nineteenth-century idea of chemical reaction was like an innocent maiden's notion of human reproduction. The parties met, there was a marriage and a new body was produced: into the intervening steps it was not possible to enquire.

We cannot, even in 1955, give any connected account of any chemical reaction in such a way as to follow the individual or even general course of the atoms and electrons throughout: but we know a number of the factors that play a part in the mechanism of chemical reaction, and we can make a number of useful calculations concerning them.

The elucidation of the nature of the factors that influence the speed of a chemical reaction and of their mode of operation began to make progress from the 1880's. Once more it was van't Hoff, in 1884, who laid the foundation of the subject. The kinetic theory indicated that molecules were in continual motion. One condition of their reaction was, then, obvious: if the reaction involved two or more molecules of the reactants, two such molecules must meet, and the relative probability of their meeting under various conditions of proximity (i.e. concentration) and speed of motion (i.e. temperature) was calculable. Van't Hoff calculated the effect of changes in concentration and temperature on the number of collisions between molecules and formulated definite laws about the way the speed of a reaction would fall off as the reacting substances became used up. But it was easier to work out these laws than to find reactions whose velocities agreed accurately with the laws that had been worked out. He saw that there were ' perturbing factors ' and he hoped to study them, but in fact they were very little investigated for some forty years.

In 1889 Arrhenius contributed the most valuable idea of chemical kinetics, that of *active molecules*. The slow rate of many reactions was a clear proof that molecules capable of reaction did not react whenever they collided. Arrhenius suggested that a molecule would react only when it had a high degree of energy. The molecules of a given substance at a given temperature have a fixed *average* energy, but Arrhenius saw that in the course of the vast number of collisions which the molecules were continually undergoing there would at any instant always be a small number with energies either much greater or much less than the average. He supposed that only those molecules reacted which had energies greater than a certain amount; the greater the energy required for reaction, the smaller would be the proportion of these ' activated ' molecules, and hence the slower the reaction rate. This fruitful concept was not followed up at the time and further developments were delayed some forty years until the discovery of chain-reactions caused renewed activity in the field of chemical kinetics.

It had been suggested as early as 1913 that an activated molecule might react and pass on its extra energy to another molecule, which would thereby be activated and would at once react and pass its energy on to a third; this process could, it seemed, continue *ad libitum*, so that the reaction would proceed along a chain of thousands or millions of molecules until it was broken either by the collision of the active molecule with some other kind of molecule, which would absorb the energy and not pass it on, or by the chains reaching the wall of the vessel. Although subsequent work has shown that chains of this type, where *energy* is handed on from molecule to molecule, do not in fact occur, yet other types of chain-reaction are much more common than was realized.

A remarkable example of the light that can be thrown by chemical kinetics on an apparently very simple reaction is the combination of hydrogen and oxygen to form water, on which large numbers of scientific papers, not to mention a book, have been written. The high-pressure explosion of hydrogen-oxygen mixtures was investigated by M. Berthelot as early as 1870, when he was President of the French Committee of National Defence, and received great study by Dixon and his collaborators after 1880 but had not then been related to other problems of reaction-velocity. The reaction $2H_2 + O_2 = 2H_2O$, as commonly written in school textbooks, implies that the three molecules, two of hydrogen and one of oxygen, all collide together at the same instant. The chances of such a ' three-body ' collision occurring are small, and in fact an investigation of the reaction shows that this simple picture is quite untenable. The reaction is a very complicated affair which goes by different mechanisms at different temperatures and pressures. It has some remarkable features; for instance, in the region of $570°$ C. a mixture of the gases will react quite smoothly at a certain pressure, although at greater *or* lower pressures the mixture will explode. It is in this temperature region of about $540°–600°$ C. that a chain-reaction is proceeding in the gases. It is quite probably initiated by the formation of a very small number of hydrogen atoms, which can then react as follows:

$$H + O_2 = OH + O.$$

The OH and O radicals formed are as unstable and highly reactive as the H atom itself and react immediately thus:

$$OH + H_2 = H_2O + H$$
$$O + H_2 = OH + H.$$

The net result is that one H atom has produced *three* equally reactive radicals (one OH and two H's), which proceed to multiply further. The radicals are removed by competitive reactions which do not produce other radicals, but only water. If these competitive reactions do not remove the radicals as quickly as they are formed, then the reaction-chain is said to be ' branched ', and the reaction will in fact be explosive. If, however, the ' chain branching ' is under control, then the reaction will go quite smoothly and steadily. The existence of explosive conditions at pressures above and below that at which reaction proceeds smoothly is due to there being two quite different mechanisms by which active radicals are removed.

The problem of chemical kinetics is to try to discover all the factors that influence a chemical reaction and, if possible, to deduce the rate of that reaction from what we know about molecules. We know enough about a few simple molecules to be able to do this, but the mathematical treatment is very complex and it will be a long time before we can calculate, *e.g.* the rate of reaction of petrol-vapour and air. The difficulty lies in the number of factors that determine whether a collision between two molecules will result in a chemical reaction. The molecule is not a simple particle. It consists of two or more atoms, each of which consists of a nucleus and many electrons; the molecule can spin on its axis, it can vibrate, its electrons can take up energy; its energy may be stored in one part of it rather than another. For a fruitful collision certain parts of the molecule concerned must meet, and these parts must be in a particular energy state. We also suppose that the contact must endure for a certain time. Merely to recognize the existence of these factors is of much value in solving the problems of the practical conduct of reactions, but the difficulty of taking them all into account in a mathematical expression is a formidable one.

This work has mostly been carried out during the last twenty-five years on inorganic gas-reactions; but other schools of thought have made much progress in discovering the mechanisms of the reactions of organic chemistry.

Since about 1925 A. Lapworth, C. K. Ingold and R. Robinson have investigated the effect of the concentration of electrons in different parts of the molecule (p. 353). Some groups attract the electrons in the rest of the molecule, others repel them: and the ease of detachment of the electrons determines the part of the molecule which will be attacked by a reagent. We have here the notion of the reacting molecules having electrical attractions for each other, an idea which indeed goes back to the time of Berzelius, but is only now receiving exact treatment.

Another school of research had investigated the influence of free radicals. The recognition of free radicals as involved in gas-reactions made it easier for the organic chemist to accept their transitory existence in the reactions of more complicated organic compounds. In some very special cases free radicals of surprising stability can be made. The idea that every valency bond must have an atom attached to it and that free valency bonds cannot exist was an axiom in organic chemistry until 1900, when Gomberg showed that hexaphenylethane,

$$\underset{\displaystyle C_6H_5}{\overset{\displaystyle C_6H_5}{C_6H_5-C-C-C_6H_5,}}\quad\overset{\displaystyle C_6H_5}{\underset{\displaystyle C_6H_5}{}}$$

broke up in solution into triphenyl-methyl,

$$C_6H_5-\underset{\displaystyle C_6H_5}{\overset{\displaystyle C_6H_5}{C}}-$$

which possessed a free valency bond. It behaved quite differently from other hydrocarbons, reacting additively with free oxygen, halogens, nitric oxide, sulphur dioxide, e.g.

$$C_6H_5-\underset{\displaystyle C_6H_5}{\overset{\displaystyle C_6H_5}{C}} + NO \rightarrow C_6H_5-\underset{\displaystyle C_6H_5}{\overset{\displaystyle C_6H_5}{C}}-NO.$$

In the nineteenth century it had been taken as axiomatic that if any atom or molecule were liberated with one of its normal valency bonds unoccupied by another atom it instantly combined with another similar atom or molecule to form a double molecule. Thus the triphenylmethyl molecule should have combined to form hexaphenylethane, yet in fact the opposite process occurred. Other bodies were found to be similar in behaviour to triphenylmethyl, but the real problem remained largely unexplained. From 1922, however, it was shown that free single atoms could exist for an appreciable time. Hydrogen, oxygen and chlorine normally exist as double molecules, H_2, O_2, Cl_2; but it was demonstrated that by means of electrical discharges they could be broken up into H, O and Cl atoms which could persist for periods of the order of a second or so before recombining. The gases in the atomic state are highly reactive, combining at room-temperature with many elements upon which the normal gas is quite without effect. From 1929 Paneth and his co-workers showed that the organic radicals methyl, —CH_3, and ethyl, —C_2H_5, could be obtained in a free state for a brief period. The reason why these do not immediately recombine is now clear. The electric discharge, or whatever means is used to make the free atom or radical, activates it, *i.e.* endows it with a high degree of energy. For example, two such activated hydrogen atoms cannot recombine because the molecule that would be produced would have far too much energy to hold together; so the atoms can only recombine if something else can intervene to take this extra energy away. This may be the wall of the vessel or a molecule of some foreign substance: alternatively the energy may be given off as radiation.

Since 1934 it has been shown that, when some organic compounds are strongly heated or exposed to ultra-violet light, they break down into these free radicals, which then recombine to form the various decomposition products. We have here some evidence that the formation of free radicals is one of the mechanisms through which chemical reaction may occur.

Summing up the condition for a chemical reaction, it seems that the reactant molecules must acquire an abnormal amount of energy, either by collision or by absorbing radiation. If two different molecules have to meet in order that the reaction may take place, there may be a number of conditions to be fulfilled as to their internal state and external orientation.

The actual change in the molecules may either be a splitting into free radicals, which then recombine provided that their energy is taken away, or a breaking into ions (electrically-charged portions) which recombine in the same manner, or sometimes a 'normal' reaction of molecules of the classical type.

It is clear that the type of chemical equation that we still write in school textbooks, with up to a dozen molecules on the left-hand side, does not represent the facts, but is simply a convenience for working out calculations about quantities of reagents and products. Thus the well-known equation

$$2KIO_3 + 5H_2SO_3 = I_2 + 2KHSO_4 + 3H_2SO_4 + H_2O$$

should no longer be regarded as implying that in order to bring about the change seven molecules have to meet simultaneously—which would be wildly improbable. Such equations as these merely summarize the total result of a number of successive changes, each taking place by the collision of two molecules or ions, or at most three.

A molecule is a system of electrons, and so it should prove possible to predict by quantum mechanics what is likely to occur when two molecules collide. The probability of the particles acquiring the necessary energy to bring about a particular chemical change can, in theory, be worked out from the properties of the atoms, and in fact the velocity of a number of simple reactions has been theoretically calculated in this way. We are beginning, for the first time, to envisage the prediction of not only the course and extent but also the speed of chemical reactions—a further step towards the transformation of chemistry into mathematical physics.

None the less this transformation has not proceeded very far. The mechanism of some very simple gas-reactions, *e.g.* the combustion of hydrogen and of carbon monoxide, has been given probable explanations but not yet predicted *a priori*. Much light has been thrown on the combustion phenomena of hydrocarbons, which are the basis of the generation of most heat and power. A vast amount of work has been done on these comparatively complex reactions and a mass of facts and generalizations have been acquired. Yet, although the researches (*e.g.* of Tizard and Pye, 1924) on detonation and knock have been very profitable to the automobile industry, we cannot yet claim to be able to state in chemical terms what occurs in a hydrocarbon flame.

Catalysis

In the early years of the nineteenth century it had been noticed that many chemical reactions were conditioned by the presence of comparatively minute quantities of a substance that appeared to be chemically unaltered by the change. Berzelius, in 1835, drew attention to these phenomena and gave them the general name of catalysis and postulated a *catalytic force*.

One of the earliest examples can be taken from the reaction of hydrogen and oxygen to form water. A mixture of these gases remains for an indefinite period at room-temperature without any apparent change, but if a piece of spongy platinum is introduced the gases react at its surface, forming water: the platinum rapidly becomes hot and in a short space causes the mixture to explode. The platinum is quite unaltered. The Döbereiner lamp based on this principle was invented in 1823. It had but small success because the arsenic present as impurity in the zinc was evolved with the hydrogen and inactivated or ' poisoned ' the platinum catalyst. The effect of platinum on hydrogen and oxygen is classed as heterogeneous catalysis because the platinum is not admixed with the gases, but only in contact with them. A familiar example of homogeneous catalysis may be taken from starch, a solution of which remains unchanged until a little acid is added, whereupon the starch reacts with water and produces the sugar glucose. The acid remains unaltered.

The most conspicuous instances of catalysis are the effect of metals on gas-reactions, the effect of acids on a variety of reactions and the effect of enzymes, complex protein derivatives, on a number of reactions. The latter type of catalysis is of the first interest, because it appears that most of the chemical reactions that occur in living organisms are brought about through the catalytic effect of enzymes, so that the understanding of enzyme action would be the greatest possible contribution to the understanding of the life-process. It does not follow that all cases of catalysis are to be explained in the same way: a catalyst by definition is something that alters the velocity of a reaction without being used up in the process, and this effect might be brought about in many different ways.

In 1833 Faraday put forward a theory of the catalytic action of metals which afforded at least a partial explanation. Metals can absorb considerable quantities of gases as a surface film, and he supposed that the result was to increase the concentration of the gases and in effect to conduct the reaction at very high pressure. This theory, in its original form, was not adequate because it did not explain the fact that only certain gas-reactions are catalysed, and only by certain metals. Moreover, the concentration of gas so attained is not enough to account for the result. Yet this theory, as modified by Langmuir and others, has proved effective.

When enzymes were discovered, also in 1833, a second theory of catalysis was put forward. Liebig proposed the theory that enzymes underwent ' molecular vibrations ' which by contact threw other molecules into such a state that reaction resulted. This theory was useless because there was no means of discovering this hypothetical vibration or of conjecturing the manner in which it might cause reaction; it was therefore insusceptible of proof or disproof.

A third theory, put forward in 1854 by A. W. Williamson, was that the catalyst acted by forming an ' intermediate compound '. Thus alcohol, when heated alone, does not break up into ether and water, but in presence of sulphuric acid it does so, the sulphuric acid being unaltered in quantity.[1] Williamson showed that the alcohol reacted with sulphuric acid to form ' sulphovinic acid ' (ethyl hydrogen sulphate), which reacted with alcohol to form ether and sulphuric acid, which was thereby restored. Thus, apart from the effect of side-reactions, dilution with water, etc., a given quantity of sulphuric acid might transform an unlimited quantity of alcohol into ether and water:

$$C_2H_5OH \quad + H_2SO_4 \quad = C_2H_5.HSO_4 \quad + H_2O$$
$$2C_2H_5.HSO_4 + C_2H_5OH = C_2H_5{-}O{-}C_2H_5 + H_2SO_4.$$

This intermediate-compound theory of catalysis was applied to many other cases of catalysis and gives a true account of some of them.

Interest in catalysis has always been keen, because a number of the most important industrial processes (Chapter Twenty-four) have always been carried out by catalytic processes; and all through the century new catalysts for new reactions were being discovered by chance or rule-of-thumb.

A system by which it could be predicted theoretically that a certain substance would act as a catalyst for a certain reaction was obviously desirable, but it cannot be said to have been attained even to-day. However, one shining example of prediction is to be found in the now obsolete Deacon process for making chlorine (1870). The problem was to find a way by which hydrogen chloride, a waste product from the chemical industry, should be caused to react with the oxygen of the air to form water and chlorine, to be used in making bleaching powder:

$$4HCl + O_2 \rightarrow 2H_2O + Cl_2.$$

Deacon, adopting the intermediate-compound theory, sought

[1] Except as the result of other reactions, inseparable from but taking no part in the etherification.

for some compound (A) which might combine with hydrochloric acid and oxygen, forming a second compound (B) that
might break down, giving chlorine and restoring A. He hit
upon copper-salts as the answer, and his prediction was
justified by the result, for the reactions

$$2Cu_2Cl_2 + 4HCl + O_2 = 4CuCl_2 + 2H_2O$$
$$4CuCl_2 = 2Cu_2Cl_2 + 2Cl_2$$

proved to be the foundation of a successful process.

When the principles of thermodynamics were taken into
account by chemists it was evident that the catalyst, being
unchanged, did not supply any energy, and therefore the final
state of the reaction, which was determined by energy considerations, would be the same whether the catalyst were there
or not. Wilhelm Ostwald in 1886 laid down the principle
that a catalyst could accelerate or decelerate a reaction but
could not affect the final equilibrium, nor yet start a
reaction which was not (albeit very slowly) in progress.
He defined (1896) a catalyst as a substance which changes
the velocity of a given chemical reaction. His attitude was
perhaps too theoretical, laying as he did all the emphasis
on energy relationships and totally neglecting molecular
mechanisms.

Catalysis long remained one of the most inexplicable of phenomena. The position was made even more puzzling by the
extraordinary results, obtained in 1894 and after, by H. B.
Baker, indicating that a great variety of well-known reactions
would not take place in the complete absence of water, which
therefore seemed to be a universal catalyst. It cannot be said
that these results have yet been explained and their validity is
doubted.

The work of recent years has thrown a good deal of light
upon the mechanism of catalysis. The intermediate-compound
theory is certainly a true explanation of certain cases and need
not be further discussed. Great progress has, however, been
made towards an understanding of the catalysis of reactions
by means of metal surfaces—an example of which was given
in the reaction of hydrogen and oxygen in presence of platinum.
The fundamental work of Langmuir (1912–16) showed that a
tungsten surface heated in hydrogen could attach to itself a
layer of hydrogen atoms (not molecules) and that these were

chemically combined—held by valency linkage and not by the sort of physical attraction that, for example, holds together the molecules of a liquid. The existence of this chemically-retained atomic layer of gas was confirmed for iron, copper, nickel and platinum round about 1924–26. This afforded an explanation of catalysis by metal surfaces. Thus if a mixture of hydrogen and some reducible gas is passed over heated platinum or nickel, the hydrogen is attached to the surface of the metal in the form of single atoms, which combine far more readily with any possible reactant than do the ordinary hydrogen molecules. Other types of catalysts were explained by the attachment to the metal of two different kinds of molecules, which were liberated therefrom in an active state and in close proximity. It has been shown that all this activity is concentrated in certain areas of the metal surface, probably the edges of the small metallic crystals, where there are atoms having free valency electrons. The reason why metals are the effective catalysts seems to be that they possess loosely-bound electrons which can form linkages with an atom or molecule and can be easily released to it.

The catalysts which are so intensely effective in causing the combination of hydrogen are all of this metallic type, but many apparently inert surfaces, such as glass, affect the rate of gas-reactions. It may be the local attraction of ions in their crystal structure that is effective.

The effect of acid, *i.e.* of hydrogen ions, in catalysing so many reactions (of which the conversion of starch to sugar was given as an example) remained completely obscure till recent years. From 1906 onwards attempts were made by W. C. M. Lewis to explain the phenomenon by supposing that the hydrogen ions took up infra-red radiation and passed this energy on to the reacting molecules, but this has now been discredited. We do not yet understand why hydrogen ion is so effective a catalyst, but the present view is that the ion brings energy to just that part of the molecule which is to take part in the reaction, whereas the ordinary collisions transfer energy to any part of the molecule. Hydrogen ion, then, causes energy to be used in activating the molecule rather than in increasing its energy in ways that do not tend to chemical reaction, *i.e.* in increasing its velocity or rate of rotation.

Industrial Catalysis

The industrial chemist of the nineteenth century knew very little about the mechanism of catalysis but it was a phenomenon quite familiar to him. The chamber and contact processes for sulphuric acid, the Deacon process for chlorine, the oxidation of ammonia to nitric acid in presence of platinum and many others were employed in practice.

Nevertheless the spectacular development of catalytic processes belongs to the twentieth century. To-day, in fact, some eighty great chemical manufacturers depend on catalytic processes, some of them, like the petroleum industry, of vast economic importance. It is realized that all gas-reactions are subject to the influence of catalysts and that the nature of these may entirely alter the character of the product. A great deal of empirical research has been concentrated upon catalysts; the main practical principle that has emerged is the use of a ' promoter ', a small quantity of a second substance mixed with the principal catalyst and enhancing its action: the use of such promoters dates from about 1910. The extreme importance of catalytic processes to-day will be abundantly demonstrated by the examples given in Chapter Twenty-five.

Photo-chemistry

That light is a factor influencing certain chemical reactions has been recognized since the eighteenth century. In the first quarter of the nineteenth century a beginning was made with photography, and by 1850 this was a process of great interest to which a great deal of practical research was directed. Thus we find between 1840 and 1914 great developments in practical photography but comparatively little understanding of the principles underlying the action of light on chemical compounds. The action of light on silver salts was investigated by J. H. Schulze as early as 1727, and in 1802 Wedgwood and Davy printed images on leather and paper sensitized with silver nitrate. In 1822 J. Nicéphore Niepce succeeded in producing the first permanent photograph by the use of asphaltum, but this was a printing process and lay outside the main line of development. In 1837 the Rev. J. B. Reade made use of gallic acid to hasten printing of the silver image. The significance of this was grasped by W. H. F. Talbot and led him to his development of the Calotype process, described below. Reade

PLATE XXI

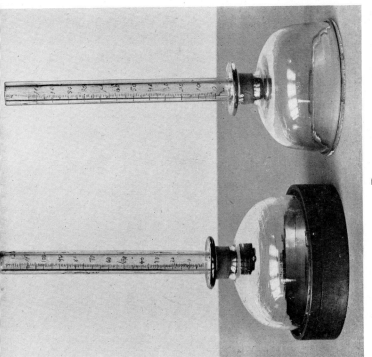

B

A

A.—Machine Made, to design by Woolrich, by Primes of Birmingham, 1844. This is the earliest electrical machine of any magnitude and is interesting as having been used to supply two electro-plating baths (see pp. 383 ff.).

B.—Osmometers Used by Thomas Graham, 1854 (see p. 367).

PLATE XXII

A.—Tank Car being Filled with Liquid Oxygen (see p. 423).

B.—Paper Photograph: 'A Window in Lacock Abbey' taken by Fox Talbot, August, 1835 (see p. 416).

almost certainly discovered fixation by sodium thiosulphate in 1837, but did not develop the idea.

The use of silver salts to produce a permanent image was made practicable by Sir John Herschel's discovery of fixation by means of sodium thiosulphate in 1839. This discovery was utilized by Daguerre, who produced the first useful photographs on plates of silvered copper, and also by Talbot, who in 1841 introduced the Calotype, in which the negative was of paper impregnated with silver iodide and washed over before use with a mixture of acetic acid, gallic acid and silver nitrate. The image was developed by more silver nitrate and gallic acid. Paper negatives were inconvenient, even when rendered transparent by waxing, and a method of coating glass with a mixture of silver compounds and organic matter was sought. In 1847 Niepce de St. Victor accomplished this by the albumen process, and in 1851 Scott Archer published an account of the wet-collodion process, so called because the plates were exposed while wet. In this, the first really practicable system of photography for the amateur, collodion (nitrocellulose dissolved in ether and alcohol) containing ammonium (or cadmium) iodide and bromide was used to coat a glass plate and, when partially dried, was immersed in a slightly acid solution of silver nitrate. It was then exposed in the camera, developed with ferrous sulphate or pyrogallol and fixed. The disadvantages of the process were, first, the need to do all this when the photograph was to be taken and, secondly, the comparative length of the exposure. The collodion process was supreme till 1871, when Dr. R. L. Maddox found the means of emulsifying silver bromide in gelatine and developing the latent image with pyrogallol. This was the foundation of the modern dry plates, which were first marketed in 1874. Bromide paper was also brought out in that year. The dry plates were much faster than the wet-collodion plates.

All these plates suffered from lack of sensitiveness to green, yellow and red light, and from 1873 the addition of various colouring matters was practised in order to obtain true rendering of gradations of tone. Orthochromatic plates date from the late '80's and were very greatly improved by the use of the cyanin dyes from 1903 onward.

The main contribution of industrial chemistry to photography was in the provision of pure materials, the synthesis and manufacture of numerous developers, mostly amino-phenols, in the years 1880–91, and also of dye-stuffs for colour sensitization.   We must pass over the enormous amount of research which has led to the increase of sensitiveness and decrease of exposure, but the work of F. Hurter and C. V. Driffield on measurement of the speed of plates and quality of negatives (1890), and of Sheppard and Mees on the action of sulphur compounds in gelatin, have been particularly important.

The importance of photography might have been expected to lead to corresponding activity in photo-chemistry, the theory of the action of light upon chemical compounds.   In fact, however, this subject proved to be obdurate to the efforts of the nineteenth-century workers.   The most important re-searches of this period were those of Bunsen and Roscoe (1854–59) on the reaction of hydrogen and chlorine.   These gases do not react in the dark at room-temperature, but do so in light at a rate depending on the intensity of the light. T. Grotthus (1818) and J. W. Draper (1839) had established that it was only the light that was absorbed that brought about reaction: and Bunsen and Roscoe established that the amount of chemical action depended on the product of the intensity of the light and the time of exposure.   The sensitization to light of certain reactions by the addition of a substance taking no part therein was much studied from the 1870's onward, but until the quantum theory was applied to photo-chemistry it remained a collection of empirical generalizations.   The introduction of the quantum theory into photo-chemical theory by A. Einstein in 1912 was the real beginning of theor-etical photo-chemistry.   The quantum theory of radiation was originated by Max Planck in 1900, but the new and fruitful period of photo-chemical research began with the paper of Einstein, in 1912, announcing the Photo-chemical Equivalent Law—that the photo-chemical decomposition of a single mole-cule results from the absorption of a single quantum by this molecule.   In fact this rule predicted quantitative results in some cases with great accuracy, but it is now clear that the results of absorbing a quantum may not be a reaction but only an activation (p. 406); furthermore, that a chain-reaction may also be initiated, so causing the quantity of material changed to be much greater than the theory predicted.   In fact, the law must be considered as indicating only the first step that may initiate reactions, which are then to be considered in the light of chemical kinetics. The study of spectra, which has so greatly developed in recent years, has shown the relationships between the wavelenghts of light absorbed and the chemical constitution of bodies and has shown that photo-chemical action is not confined to a few reactions but is a very general phenomenon. The majority of organic compounds are decomposed by light of appropriate wavelength under suitable conditions of temperature. The subject is to-day in a state of great activity.

CHAPTER TWENTY-FIVE

Industrial Gas-reactions

Gas-reactions before 1880

A NUMBER of important recent developments in industrial chemistry may be classified under the heading of Industrial Gases. What is the reason for the great development in this field? In the first place, the gases are for the most part very simple and easily available materials. Air costs nothing, and water little more; coal and coke are the cheapest forms of carbon; and so carbon monoxide, carbon dioxide and hydrogen, obtained by the reaction of coke with air or water, are likewise among the least costly of materials. Natural gas from oil-fields, almost a waste product at the beginning of the century, is produced in enormous quantity, as are also the gases evolved in the cracking of petroleum. To obtain useful products from these materials was therefore an obvious goal of chemical industry, and it has been accomplished by discovering and realizing conditions under which reactions that do not take place or give little yield under the conditions of the normal chemical laboratory will give adequate yields in reasonable time.

Why was the field of industrial gas-reactions but little explored before the twentieth century? First, because the theory of gases, physical and chemical, was only then being properly worked out. The development of the kinetic theory of gases that led to the liquefaction of what were formerly called ' permanent gases ' dates from the closing years of the nineteenth century, and the more detailed theory of gas-reactions only from the early twentieth. The majority of useful gas-reactions are those that form more complex molecules from less complex; they therefore operate most efficiently at high pressures. This principle was not known till *c.* 1885, and was not properly understood by industrialists until the turn of the century. Even after this was appreciated, the handling of gases at the high pressures required, both for their liquefaction and for these gas-reactions, demanded a far more advanced engineering technique, using stronger and more resistant materials, than could have been contemplated in the age of iron machinery and plant.

In practice the only gas-reactions of high industrial importance that were extensively practised in the nineteenth century were the lead-chamber process for making sulphuric acid (p. 190) and the Deacon process for chlorine. Both processes require the aid of catalysts, as do almost all gas-reactions.

The theory of catalysts has already been discussed in Chapter Twenty-four. Deacon's process (p. 192) for making chlorine from hydrogen chloride was a catalysed gas-reaction, in which hydrogen chloride, a by-product of the Le Blanc process, was mixed with air and passed over heated copper salts; these acted as a catalyst, bringing about the reaction of hydrogen chloride and oxygen, yielding chlorine and water. This was simpler in principle than in practice. The process was difficult to maintain at full efficiency; moreover, the chlorine obtained was much diluted with atmospheric nitrogen. It is, however, of much interest as a process for which the catalyst was discovered by chemical reasoning (p. 413) and not by trial and error.

Little light was thrown on the catalytic action of metals and other surfaces which did not appear to react chemically with the materials whose reaction they catalysed, until the attention of physical chemists was forcibly directed to it by the huge industrial importance of the contact process for sulphuric acid, of hydrogenation and ammonia synthesis, in all of which surface-catalysts played the principal part. In the years after 1920 the theories of Langmuir and others (p. 414) went far to clear up our understanding of heterogeneous catalysis and to aid the industrialist in making use of it (p. 424).

The influence of pressure on the rate and extent of the reaction of gases could have been deduced from the law of mass action enunciated in 1864 by Guldberg and Waage. Physical chemistry was, however, still in its infancy and it was the epoch-making *Études de dynamique chimique* of van't Hoff, published in 1884, that showed its importance to the theoretical chemist. We have seen that the studies of catalysis published by Ostwald in 1888 laid down certain principles (p. 414) which attracted the interest of the inorganic chemist. We may think, then, of van't Hoff as the fertilizing influence, Nernst and Ostwald as the teachers, and such men as R. Knietsch and Fritz Haber as the outstanding links between the higher ranges of chemical theory on one side and the construction of economic engineering plant on the other.

Indeed, the ability to construct plant to withstand heat, corrosion and pressures reckoned in tons per square inch was scarcely to be contemplated before the present century. It required special steels of great strength and resistance to heat and corrosion. These special steels were coming to the fore at this period as a development of Goldschmidt's aluminothermic method, already described.

The Liquefaction of Gases

The liquefaction of gases is a physical rather than a chemical process, but its results have been extremely important for industrial chemistry, since they afford the most economical means of separating the constituents of many gas-mixtures, and notably of air.

Little attempt had been made in the nineteenth century to prepare nitrogen on the large scale, because it was not then known to undergo any useful reactions. Oxygen, on the other hand, was in some demand, limited, however, by its cost. Up till the 1890's it was still very commonly made by heating potassium chlorate and cost £8–£10 per 1,000 cubic feet. Brin's ingenious cyclic process of exposing heated barium monoxide to compressed air, whereupon it absorbed oxygen, forming barium peroxide, and then releasing the pressure, whereupon the peroxide decomposed to the monoxide and oxygen, was patented in 1879 and was developed about 1886; the result was a reduction of the cost of oxygen to a twentieth of the former figure. In 1895 oxygen began to be produced in the U.S.A. by the electrolysis of water, and this remained the standard method until the period round 1910. The liquefaction process, which began with Linde's patent of 1902 and became common practice in the period of World War I, brought its cost to a third of the Brin figure, at which price it became a cheap industrial material. Furthermore, this latter process was capable of separating, not only pure oxygen, but also the pure nitrogen which was required for ammonia synthesis.

We have already dealt with the development of the liquefaction of gases on the laboratory scale (p. 326). A mixture of two liquids of different boiling-points can usually be separated by distillation, and, since the boiling-points of liquid oxygen and nitrogen were known to be $-182°$ C. and $-193°$ C. respectively, the possibility was realized even before the technical production of liquid air became possible. In 1895 three different types of air-liquefaction plant were patented by Hampson in England, Tripler in America and Linde in Germany. Linde, unlike the others, had specially directed his attention to the separation of the constituents of air, and all the essential features of the modern process appear in his patents of 1902 and 1903. The principle is that of the fractionating column. Air is liquefied and evaporates: the vapour is richer in nitrogen, the liquid in oxygen. Part of the nitrogen-rich vapour is again liquefied, and this liquid is run down a column up which the remainder of the nitrogen-rich vapour is passing. The result is to liquefy and wash down the column most of the oxygen in the vapour and to evaporate most of the nitrogen in the liquid. Ultimately nearly pure gaseous nitrogen and liquid oxygen are obtained. The process has, of course, been greatly improved in the fifty years of its employment and other processes, similar in principle, have been evolved. The result has been to make available for industrial chemistry the pure constituents of the air.

The first industrial developments arising from the liquefaction of air resulted from the availability of cheap oxygen. Before 1905 almost the only uses of oxygen were medical and for the oxy-coal-gas flame of the limelight. The medical use of oxygen was so expensive, moreover, that it was but little applied: to-day its use is a routine procedure in the administration of anæsthetics as well as in the relief of pulmonary insufficiency. The first development of oxygen as an industrial material was in the field of metallurgy. In 1899 Fletcher showed that an oxygen-fed blow-pipe could fuse holes in iron, and in 1901 Menne in Germany used it for clearing the blocked tuyeres (air-jets) of blast-furnaces. Acetylene cannot be safely stored under high pressure in cylinders, but in 1899 it was found to be very soluble in acetone under pressure, and

shortly after it was sold in this form.   In 1903 the oxy-acetylene
blow-pipe came into use for welding, and in the following year
it was found to be possible to cut iron by first heating with the
oxy-acetylene flame and then allowing the iron to burn in a
jet of oxygen.   This method has revolutionized the handling
of heavy masses of steel and is now capable of cutting metal
with much accuracy and speed.   Among other uses of the
oxygen blow-pipe is the working of hard glass and silica ware.

The separation of reasonably pure nitrogen by the air-
liquefaction processes greatly facilitated some of the processes
for nitrogen fixation, which are treated in a separate section
(pp. 426 *et seq.*).

We may also mention the separation in a pure condition
of the several inert gases, helium, neon, argon, krypton and
xenon (p. 331).   The use of argon for filling the bulbs of
filament lamps was developed by Langmuir about 1914.   The
neon tube and some other forms of discharge lamp were also
made possible by the air-liquefaction process.   The great
development of these dates from the 1920's.

The liquefaction process has also been applied since 1912 to
water-gas, the mixture of carbon monoxide and hydrogen
obtained by passing steam through red-hot coke, or passing
a mixture of steam and methane over a nickel catalyst at
$800°–900°$ C.   The carbon monoxide can be liquefied, leaving
the hydrogen, which is used for ammonia synthesis, hydrogenation of oils, etc.   Liquefaction and fractionation are also used to
separate the constituents of hydrocarbon gases derived from
the cracking of petroleum (p. 270).

The Contact Process for Sulphuric Acid

The lead-chamber process, described on p. 190, was
evolved from an empirical prescientific process, and its theory
was but slowly elucidated.   The contact process, on the other
hand, was from the beginning derived from theoretical
considerations.

In the early years of the nineteenth century much attention
was given to catalysis (p. 411); the activity of platinum
in causing the combination of hydrogen and oxygen, as in
Döbereiner's lamp, was, for example, a familiar phenomenon.
In 1831 Peregrine Phillips, a British vinegar manufacturer,
took out a patent for making sulphuric acid by passing

' sulphurous-acid gas ' (*i.e.* sulphur dioxide) and air in proper proportions through a porcelain tube maintained at a yellow heat and containing finely-divided platinum; the resulting ' sulphuric-acid gas ' (sulphur trioxide) was to be absorbed in water in a tower packed with pebbles. We know nothing more about this discovery save that it was found difficult to realize it in practice, and little or no progress was made with it during the succeeding thirty years. At this time the lead-chamber process was producing sulphuric acid of reasonably high concentration, and this was suitable for nearly all industrial purposes. Nordhausen, or fuming sulphuric acid, the ' oleum ' of modern times, was manufactured, in such small quantities as were required, by the old method of distilling ferrous sulphate. But as the dye industry developed fuming sulphuric acid became a necessity, and the demand raised the price of the Nordhausen acid, whereupon men began to search for a cheaper way of making it.

The first step towards cheapening oleum was taken by Squire and Messel, who in 1875 took out a patent for turning the ordinary sulphuric acid from the chamber-process into oleum; this they did by decomposing it at a red-heat into sulphur dioxide, oxygen and steam, condensing the latter and passing the sulphur dioxide and oxygen over platinized pumice, so forming sulphur trioxide, which was absorbed in water or sulphuric acid. This process was a success, as were similar methods originated by Winkler in Germany about the same time. But the purpose of the modern contact process is not to make oleum from ordinary sulphuric acid, but to make oleum or ordinary acid directly from sulphur dioxide, oxygen and water. In the years following 1880 numerous patents were taken out and fuming acid was made in some quantity from sulphur dioxide, made by burning sulphur. Sulphur was still rather expensive and so it was desirable to use the gas from the combustion of pyrites. The chief difficulties were, first, to know the correct proportions of sulphur dioxide and air; secondly, to appreciate and avoid the possibility of the ' poisoning ' of the catalyst by the arsenic and dust present in the impure sulphur dioxide from pyrites; and thirdly, to absorb the sulphur trioxide completely.

The early development of the process was empirical and made no use of the theory of gas-reactions. Theoretical chemistry had found its home in Germany, and it was the researches carried out by the German manufacturers of organic chemicals, especially the Badische Anilin and Soda Fabrik, that solved these problems and made the process a success. In 1898 the above-mentioned firm took out a patent for the making of sulphuric acid from pyrites gas, carefully washed free from impurity. In 1901 Dr. R. Knietsch [1] gave a remarkable lecture to the German Chemical Society, in which the whole theory and practice of the process was explained. The theory of the process was now understood, but contact acid remained a German product until World War I. Contact acid was very much better than chamber acid, however purified, for the nitration of toluene to T.N.T. Consequently, both in England and the U.S.A. contact plants were set up, and after the war continued to supply contact acid to the organic chemical industries developing in those countries. The supply of platinum for catalyst remained a difficulty. Vanadium pentoxide was used in Germany as a substitute from 1914; it came into use in the U.S.A. only about 1926, but is now common practice.

At the present time more than half of the world's sulphuric acid is made by the contact process.

The newest extension of sulphuric acid manufacture is to obtain it from calcium sulphate in the form of the mineral anhydrite. It has been operated only on a modest scale but may well prove to have an important future.

The Fixation of Nitrogen: (i) by the Electric Arc

The plant physiologists and agricultural chemists of the nineteenth century established the rôle of nitrogen in the physiology of plants, whereupon it became clear that the nitrogen of the atmosphere could not be utilized by them except through the agency of nitrogen-fixing bacteria. It became clear also that the fertility of soil from which large crops were continually being removed could only be maintained by supplies of nitrogen compounds in a form in which they could be utilized by plants, either directly or through the agency of soil bacteria. The only nitrogenous substances, other than plant or animal products, which could then be applied to the soil were ammonium salts and nitrates.

[1] Knietsch. *Berichte d. deutschen chemischen Gesellschaft*, **34,** 4069 (1901).

Ammonium salts, derived from the purification of coal-gas (p. 209), had long been in use as fertilizers, as had also the sodium nitrate extracted from the caliche deposits of Chile (p. 295). These sources were insufficient; moreover, it appeared that the supplies of sodium nitrate would be exhausted within a century. It seemed, indeed, that unless new sources of nitrogenous fertilizers could be found, the world could not produce enough food to supply its rapidly rising population. The threat was emphasized by Sir William Crookes in his British Association address of 1898. By that time the chemical industry was just becoming capable of tackling the nitrogen problem, and to-day it no longer exists.

It was, however, another and sinister aspect of nitrogen-fixation that was actually effective in bringing the process into world-wide use. Modern explosives are nitro-compounds or nitrates and require nitric acid for their making. It is therefore a matter of policy for every country to be able to make its own nitric acid. It is said, with great probability, that Germany was not prepared to go to war until 1914, when she was able to produce nitric acid from the air; and England was seriously threatened in 1917, when submarine warfare almost cut off the supply of nitrates from Chile.

The first process by which the nitrogen of the air was converted into useful compounds on the large scale was the direct combination of nitrogen and oxygen in the electric arc. The reaction had been demonstrated by Henry Cavendish as long ago as 1784, but none could have seemed less promising as a foundation for an industry. In 1895, however, Lord Rayleigh (p. 325) used this reaction to remove the oxygen and nitrogen from air in order to isolate and investigate the residue, in which he and Sir William Ramsay later discovered argon and the other inert gases. Rayleigh used an arc in place of Cavendish's spark and incidentally found that oxygen and nitrogen could be made to combine with no very great expenditure of electricity. This work of Rayleigh's, intended for a wholly different purpose, showed the way to the fixation of nitrogen. Attempts to utilize it on the technical scale were made from 1899, and in 1902 an arc process was operated on the large scale by the Atmospheric Products Co. at Niagara Falls. It did not prove to be financially successful, and the first commercially sound method was that of the Norwegians,

Birkeland and Eyde, who set up their first furnace in 1903 and whose process, although somewhat overshadowed by the Haber process, is still used in Norway, where electricity can be generated from water-power at a very low cost. In the Birkeland-Eyde process the arc is spread by means of an electromagnet into a thin disc or ' sun ', some 6 feet in diameter, through which the air passes. The issuing gases, when cool, consist of unchanged air and nitrogen dioxide, and when passed through water they form nitric acid. This may be concentrated or converted into calcium nitrate, which is sold as a fertilizer. Sodium nitrite is also made and is sold to the makers of azo-dyes.

Other types of arc-furnaces—for example, the Schönherr and the Pauling—were soon invented, but the Birkeland-Eyde has proved to be the most enduring. The production of calcium nitrate rose from 1,600 tons in 1907 to 100,000 tons in 1919.

The arc-process produces nitric acid or nitrate, while the other nitrogen-fixing processes produce ammonia. Nitric acid and nitrates cannot readily be converted into ammonia: on the other hand, ammonia is readily oxidized to nitric acid.

The Fixation of Nitrogen: (ii) by the Cyanamide Process

The history of the calcium carbide industry has already been discussed (p. 392). The process of converting it into calcium cyanamide was discovered by the German chemist F. Rothe, and was first brought into industrial use at Odda, in Norway, in 1907. Calcium cyanamide can be used as a fertilizer (*nitrolim*), for in contact with moist earth it is hydrolysed and forms ammonia, which bacteria oxidize to the nitrates utilized by plants. Alternatively, it may be treated with water in the factory and so converted into ammonia, which can then be oxidized to nitric acid. The process rapidly became popular and factories were quickly set up in the U.S.A., in Canada and in Germany, where it was the main source of synthetic nitric acid before 1917. Experiments on the production of ammonia and nitric acid from cyanamide were made in America from 1914, and were so successful that later a very large plant was set up at Muscle Shoals, Alabama, but at the end of the war it was considered uneconomic and was shut down in 1919.

The making of calcium carbide, has already been described. To make cyanamide, calcium carbide is finely crushed or powdered and heated in an atmosphere of nitrogen, which slowly converts it into calcium cyanamide. The process demanded a supply of reasonably pure nitrogen, which had not previously been required for any industrial process. This was provided at Odda, at Muscle Shoals and at most of the other works by the fractionation of liquid air by the Linde process. The cyanamide was converted into ammonia by heating with dilute caustic-soda solution.

The conversion of this ammonia into nitric acid was required in order to fulfil the requirements of the organic-chemical industry, and especially of that part of it which provides modern explosives.

The process is in principle very simple, being the oxidation of ammonia by means of air in presence of a catalyst, normally platinum. Nitric oxide is formed and reacts with air and water (as in the Birkeland-Eyde process), forming nitric acid. This reaction was investigated as early as 1839 by Kuhlmann, but the conditions which led to a high yield of nitric acid were by no means easy to discover, and it was not until 1900 that Ostwald and Brauer investigated it scientifically. Patents were taken out in 1902 and the first technical plant was erected in Germany in 1909. The process was in full operation there in 1914, turning out some 250 tons of nitric acid daily. The platinum catalyst was in some German works replaced by mixtures of iron oxide with various ' promoters '. Other industrial countries followed suit during or after World War I.

The Fixation of Nitrogen: (iii) by the Haber Process

The Haber process, for making synthetic ammonia by the reaction of highly-compressed nitrogen and hydrogen in contact with a catalyst, is a landmark in the history of industrial chemistry. It was the first process that was worked out on pure thermodynamical principles; again, it was the first example of the use of really high pressures in chemical industry. The great physical chemist, W. Nernst, worked out the theoretical conditions, while F. Haber, physical chemist and industrialist, together with C. Bosch brought it into practical use. A working process was established by about 1905, and in 1910 it was taken up by the Badische Anilin-und-Soda Fabrik and rapidly perfected. In 1917 the huge Leuna works was opened: by 1918 over 200,000 tons of ammonia per year were being synthesized in Germany alone.

For this process a mixture of nitrogen and hydrogen was required. It was made from air, water and coke. By blowing steam over heated coke, water-gas was obtained, containing approximately equal volumes of carbon monoxide and hydrogen,

$$H_2O + C \rightarrow CO + H_2.$$

The addition of steam to the mixture, which is passed over a heated metal catalyst, leads to the reaction

$$H_2O + CO \rightarrow H_2 + CO_2.$$

The carbon dioxide is dissolved in water under pressure and hydrogen remains. By mixing air with the steam blown over the heated coke as much nitrogen as was required could be introduced. The resulting mixture of nitrogen and hydrogen was subjected to the hitherto unheard-of pressure of 200 atmospheres at a temperature of 555° C. and was continually circulated over a catalyst (metallic osmium), under which conditions it combined to form ammonia,

$$N_2 + 3H_2 \rightleftharpoons 2NH_3.$$

This was extracted by solution in water and could be converted into ammonium sulphate or any other form required.

Ammonia for use as a fertilizer must be converted into a solid neutral substance. Sulphuric acid, the traditional medium, is comparatively expensive and in most soils provides no useful food. The Haber and Ostwald process together made ammonium nitrate the easiest of fertilizers to produce on the large scale. It is therefore widely used despite the many serious explosions to which it has given rise. Recently carbon dioxide and ammonia have been directly combined to form water and urea, $CO(NH_2)_2$, which is an excellent fertilizer.

The Haber process has, in fact, proved to be the successful method of fixing the nitrogen of the air. Great Britain and America both mastered the technique towards the end of World War I, and have since set up very large plants for the production of fertilizers and nitric acid.

Hydrogenation

Hydrogen had only minor uses before the twentieth century.

The great industry of hydrogenation, which to-day provides us with edible fats, solvents, motor spirit and the like, started from the researches of P. Sabatier about 1897. The method which he developed was the passing of a mixture of hydrogen and the vapour of an organic compound over a metallic catalyst, normally finely-divided nickel. This process brought about a large variety of reactions, notably the reduction of double linkages,

$$\diagdown C = C \diagdown \quad \text{to single linkages} \quad \begin{matrix} H & H \\ | & | \\ C - C \\ \diagup \quad \diagdown \end{matrix}$$

Sabatier's work attracted no little attention and in 1902 a German patent was taken out for the conversion, by means of hydrogen and a nickel catalyst, of certain oils, the molecules of which contained these double linkages, into hard fats the molecules of which had single linkages. Normann in 1903 patented the simple process of bubbling hydrogen through the heated oil in which the finely-divided nickel was suspended. This process converted vegetable oils, such as cotton-seed oil, which was very abundant in the U.S.A., and also whale-oil and fish-oils in Europe, into hard white fats that could be used as lard-substitutes or for making margarine, which had been invented by Mège Mouriés in the late '60's. There was naturally some prejudice against their use as food-stuffs, but the blockade of 1914–18 forced their use upon the Germans. They were, in fact, found to be excellent foods and the industry has continued to be an important one ever since. The fats so made have also numerous other applications.

The demand for hydrogen was greatly increased, and the first sources were the electrolytic manufacture of caustic soda and the electrolysis of water. When further supplies were needed it was made from water-gas, the mixture of hydrogen and carbon monoxide made by blowing steam over heated coke. From this the hydrogen could be separated by liquefaction of the carbon monoxide (Linde-Frank-Caro process), or by admixture with steam and catalytic conversion into hydrogen and carbon dioxide, subsequently removed by solution in water.

The hydrogenation of oils was carried out at atmospheric pressure or but little higher. It appeared, however, from the theory of gas-reactions that the reaction of hydrogen with organic compounds should be much accelerated by pressure. The Haber process for ammonia synthesis (pp. 429–30) had already given an example of what could be done by such high pressure. Moreover, Ipatiev, about 1911, worked out a modification of Sabatier's methods in which hydrogen at pressures of 100 atmospheres and more was used. This process proved to be more effective than the reductions at lower pressures formerly employed. Frederick Bergius from about 1913 worked out methods of hydrogenating substances simply by reaction with hydrogen under great pressure and without a metallic catalyst. His efforts and those of many others, especially in Germany, were directed to making motor spirit, for which that country was dependent on outside sources. He and others worked out processes for hydrogenating coal and tars which proved invaluable as war-time resorts, though unable to compete on level terms with natural petroleum. In Great Britain, Imperial Chemical Industries acquired the Empire rights of the Bergius process and after further experiment started up in 1935 a large-scale plant for conversion of coal into motor spirit. Coal consists largely of hydrocarbons of high molecular weight, and when very finely-divided coal dispersed in oil is heated with a catalyst in an atmosphere of hydrogen at 250 atmospheres pressure it gives a heavy oil, which can be further hydrogenated so as to give petrol equal to about 60% of the weight of the coal. Coal-tar and creosote can also be hydrogenated to motor spirit.

A number of industrially important processes depend on the hydrogenation of carbon monoxide. Water-gas is a mixture of carbon monoxide and hydrogen and, either alone or enriched with hydrogen, it can be passed over various catalysts and yield products of industrial use.

A very important process based on this reaction is the Fischer-Tropsch process for synthetic motor fuel. This consists of the passing of purified water-gas over certain catalysts (containing, *e.g.* iron oxide or cobalt oxide, with a small proportion of thoria, deposited on kiesselguhr). At 180°–200° C. and, surprisingly enough, at atmospheric pressure about 80 % of the carbon monoxide forms hydrocarbons of a type very useful as Diesel fuels. The experiments of Fischer and Tropsch began about 1923, and the process was greatly developed in Germany from about 1935, producing enormous quantities of motor fuel from the inferior brown coal which is abundant in that country.

In the period between the wars hydrogenation was further extended. Some solid by-products of industry which were then produced in excess of demand were converted into useful solvents or fuels. Thus naphthalene was hydrogenated to the solvents tetralin (c. 1918) and decalin, and phenol to cyclohexanol, to-day the principal source of nylon. Phenol to-day is no longer, however, a drug on the market, for the demand for plastics (p. 261) has put it in short supply.

The oil companies about 1929 took up the process as a means of removing sulphur and nitrogen from oils and of splitting and reducing the heavy hydrocarbons to lighter ones, which could be used as constituents of motor spirit.

Another very important product of the hydrogenation of carbon monoxide is methyl alcohol (methanol), a useful solvent, motor fuel and source of formaldehyde for the plastics industry.

The synthesis of methanol from carbon monoxide and hydrogen does not occur except under special conditions. Thus carbon monoxide and hydrogen do not apparently react, but consideration of their volume-energy relationships shows (p. 403) that at high pressures and fairly low temperatures there should be a good yield with the aid of a suitable catalyst. The process normally starts with water-gas enriched with hydrogen by various means. It is compressed to 200 atmospheres or more and passed over a catalyst usually containing zinc and chromium, but sometimes copper. The Badische Anilin-und-Soda Fabrik started work on the reaction in 1913, but only after 1922, when the French chemist Patart patented a process, did they prepare for production on a large scale. Since 1924 it has been produced in most manufacturing countries largely for conversion into formaldehyde required for the plastics industry (p. 261), and the hydrogenation process has now completely superseded the distillation of wood.

The account here given of the development of industrial gas-reactions does not altogether convey the flexibility and convenience of these processes. They are adapted to continuous operation and therefore to central control, with its economy of man-power. Alterations of conditions and catalyst enable almost every conceivable reaction of the simpler molecules to be economically carried out. It is here that the future of the chemical industry seems to lie.

CONCLUSION

THERE is no end to a history of any department of human progress save at the frontier of the present. All the tendencies chronicled in the later chapters of this book are still in operation, and, indeed, industrial chemistry is now in a more rapid state of development than at any previous time. That knowledge will continue to be increased is certain, but the future of technology depends not only upon knowledge but upon economics. The production of the various kinds of matter that man needs continually tends to be simplified, to be done with an ever smaller expenditure of human effort; but the distribution of the total human effort, as between the accomplishment of various ends, differs from decade to decade, from century to century. Yet, over all, we shall see successive discoveries bringing new ends within our limited powers. The central industrial problems of mankind are the provision of energy and raw materials and food-stuffs. The latent energy of the hydrogen nucleus, the store of material in air and water and the earth's crust, the food-stuffs that could be synthesized therefrom—all are potentially within the gift of the physico-chemical industries of the future. No one can predict the rate of our advance towards the solution of man's impotence and want; who lives shall see.

SUGGESTIONS FOR FURTHER READING

THE following list of books is not intended to be a bibliography of industrial chemistry nor to give full bibliographical information, but merely to direct the reader's attention to some books which will be found useful for further study of the matters treated in the foregoing chapters.

Wherever possible, English translations have been cited rather than the original editions, if in other languages. Many of the works have appeared in numerous editions: the date of the first edition has been given in most cases, but which edition will be most useful may depend on the period which the reader wishes to study.

PART I

CHAPTER TWO

1. Agricola.	*De Re Metallica.* Translated from the first Latin edition of 1556 by H. C. Hoover. London. 1912.
2. Albertus.	*B. Alberti Magni . . . Opera Omnia.* Ed. Augustus Borgnet. Paris. 1890–99.
3. Bailey, K. C.	*The Elder Pliny's Chapters on Chemical Subjects.* London. 1929.
4. Berthelot, P. E. M.	*Archéologie et histoire des sciences* (contains the metallurgical papyrus of Leiden). Paris. 1906.
5. —	*La Chimie au moyen âge.* 3 vols. Paris. 1893.
6. —	*Collection des anciens alchimistes grecs.* Paris. 3 pt. 1887–88.
7. Biringuccio, Vanoccio.	*De la Pirotechnia,* libri X. Venice. 1540.
8. —	*The Pirotechnia of Vanoccio Biringuccio.* Translated by C. S. Smith and M. T. Grundi. New York. 1942.
9. Diodorus Siculus.	*Bibliothecæ Historicæ,* libri XV. Many editions.
10. Dioscorides, Pedacius.	*De materia medica.* Many editions.
11. Ercker, Lazarus.	*Beschreibung Allefürnemsten Mineralischen Ertzt und Bergwercksarten.* Prag. 1574.

12. Ercker, Lazarus. *Treatise on Ores and Assaying.* Translated from the German edition of 1580. Chicago. 1951.

13. Forbes, R. J. *Metallurgy in Antiquity.* Leiden. 1950.

14. Liger, F. *La ferronnerie ancienne et moderne.* Paris. 1873, 1875.

15. Lucas, A. *Ancient Egyptian Materials and Industries.* 3rd edn. London. 1948.

16. Neuburger, A. *Die Technik des Altertums.* Leipzig. 1919.

17. — Translated by H. L. Brose as *The Technical Arts and Sciences of the Ancients.* London. 1930.

18. Nash, W. G. *The Rio Tinto Mine: its History and Romance.* London. 1904.

19. Partington, J. R. *Origins and Development of Applied Chemistry.* London. 1935.

20. — *A Short History of Chemistry.* London. 1937.

21. Pauly-Wissowa. *Real-Encyclopädie der Klassischen Alterthumswissenschaft.* (Many metallurgical articles.)

22. Percy, John. *Metallurgy.* 1861–64.

23. — *Metallurgy of Lead.* 1870.

24. Powle, Henry. *Philosophical Transactions of the Royal Society,* No. 11, 1676, p. 931.

25. (Anon.) *Probirbüchlein auff golt silver kupffer und Bley auch allerley metall wie man die zunutz arbeyten und probieren soll.* N.d.

26. — *Probirbuechlein. Bergwerck und Probirbuechlein.* A translation of the *Bergbuechlein* . . . and of the *Probierbuechlein,* a sixteenth-century work on assaying. New York. 1949.

27. Ramazzini, Bernardino. *De morbis artificum diatriba.* Mutinae. 1700.

28. — Translated as " *Health Preserved* in two treatises. (1) On the diseases of artificers." Translated by R. James. 2nd edn. London. 1750.

29. Rosen, George. *The History of Miners' Diseases.* New York. 1943.

30. Swedenborg, Emanuel. *Regnum subterraneum sive minerale de ferro . . . de cupro et orichalco.* 3 vols. Dresden and Leipzig. 1734.

31. — Translated by A. H. Searle as Swedenborg's *Treatise on Copper.* London. 1938.

32. Theophilus. *Theophilus qui et Regerus . . . libri III de diversis artibus seu diversarum artium schedula.* An essay upon various arts. Translated by R. Hendrie. 1847.

33. Winston, Charles.   A more satisfactory English translation of Theophilus is given in Appendix A of *An Inquiry into the difference of style observable in Ancient Glass Paintings.* Oxford and London. 1867.

Chapter Three

34. Higgins, B.   *Experiments and observations made with the view of improving the art of composing and applying calcareous cements. . . .* London. 1780.

35. Hope, W. H. St. J.   *Windsor Castle.* London. 1913.

36. Knoop, D., and Jones, G. F.   *The Mediæval Mason.* Manchester. 1933.

37. Loriot, A. J.   *A practical Essay on Cement and Artificial Stone.* (Translation.) London. 1774.

38. Parker, James.   *Copy of a letter from Mr. T. Telford containing a course of experiments made by him on Mr. J. Parker's cement.*

39. Pasley, C. A.   *Observations upon the natural water cements of England, also artificial cements.* London. 1830.

40. Smeaton, J.   *Reports of the late John Smeaton.* 4 vols. London. 1812–14.

41. Vicat, L. J.   *A practical and scientific treatise on calcareous mortars and cements, artificial and natural.* Translated with notes by J. T. Smith. London. 1837.

42. Vitruvius.   *De Architectura Libri Decem.* Many editions and translations.

See also (19) Partington, (17) Neuburger, (21) Pauly-Wissowa.

Chapter Four

43. Burton, W.   *A General History of Porcelain.* London. 1921.

44. Creel, H. G.   *The Birth of China.* London. 1936.

45. d'Entrecolles, Pére.   *Lettres édifiantes et curieuses écrites des missions étrangères.* Tom. XVIII, p. 234. Paris. 1781.

46. Hetherington, A. L.   *Chinese Ceramic Glazes.* South Pasadena. 1948.

47. Honey, W. B.   *Ceramic Art of China.* London. 1945.

48. —   *European Ceramic Art from the End of the Middle Ages to about* 1815. London. 1949.

49. Li, Ch'iao-p'ing.   *Chemical Arts of Old China.* 1948.

50. Piccolpasso, Cipriano.   *I tre libri dell'arte del vasajo.* Rome. 1857.

51. —   *Les troys libres de l'art du potier.* Translated by C. Popelyn. Paris. 1860.

See also (17) Neuburger, (19) Partington.

CHAPTER FIVE

52. Honey, W. B.   *Glass, A Handbook*, etc. London. 1946.
53. Neri, A.   *L'Arte Vetraria distinta in libri sette.* Firenze
                          1612.
54. —   Translated by Christopher Merret as *The
                          Art of Glass.* London. 1662.
55. Thompson, R. Campbell. *Dictionary of Assyrian Chemistry and Geology*
                          Appendix II. Oxford. 1936.

See also (1) Agricola, (5) Berthelot, (19) Partington, (32) Theophilus.

CHAPTER SIX

56. Cennini, Cennino.   *Il Libre d'Arte.* Text and English transla-
                          tion by D. V. Thompson, jr. New Haven
                          and London. 1932–33.
57. Thompson, D. V.   *The Materials of Medieval Painting.* London.
                          1936.

See also (15) Lucas, (19) Partington, (16) Neuburger.

CHAPTER SEVEN

58. Brunschwig,[1] Hieronymus. Numerous works between 1500 and 1532
                          and especially: *Liber de arte Distillandi de
                          Compositis.* 1512.
59. Clow, A. and N. L.   *The Chemical Revolution—a Contribution to
                          Social Technology.* London. 1952.
60. Cordus, Valerius.   *De artificiosis extractionibus liber. n.d.*
61. Gesner, Conrad.   *Thesaurus Euonymi Philiatri . . .* Tiguri.
                          1552. There are many later editions.
62. Glauber, J. R.   *Opera chymica.* Frankfurt am Main. 1658–
                          59.
63. —   Translated as *The Works of the Highly Ex-
                          perienced and Famous Chymist John Rudolph
                          Glauber.* London. 1689.
64. Helmont, J. B. van.   *Ortus Medicinæ.* Amsterdam. 1648.
65. —   Translated as *Oriatrike or Physick Refined.*
                          London. 1662.
66. Lonicer, Adam.   *Naturalis Historiæ opus novum.* Frankfurt
                          1551.
67. Mattioli, P. A.   *Opera omnia.* Frankfurt. 1598.
68. Monardes, Nicolas.   *De Simplicibus medicamentis.* Antwerp.
                          1574. Numerous earlier editions.
69. Parkes, S.   *Chemical Essays.* 2nd edn. 2 vols.
                          London. 1823.

See also (1) Agricola, (11) Ercker, (26) Probierbüchlein.

CHAPTER EIGHT

70. Bacon, Roger.   *Opera quædam hactenus inedita* (Appendix I),
                          Ed. J. S. Brewer. London. 1859.

[1] Numerous variant spellings are found, *e.g.* Braunschweig.

71. Bacon, Roger.   *Essays contributed by various Writers.* Ed.
                              A. G. Little. Oxford. 1914.
72. Bryant and May.   *The History of Matches.* London. 1928.
73. Brock, A. St. H.   *Pyrotechnics, the History and Art of Firework-
                              making.* London. 1928.
74.   —   *A History of Fireworks.* London. 1949.
75. Anon.   *Feuerwerkpulverbuch von 1420.* Ed. Hassen-
                              stein. Munich. 1941.
76. Ellis, O. C. de C.   *A History of Fire and Flame.* London. 1932.
77. Galloway, R. L.   *History of Coal-mining in Great Britain.*
                              London. 1882.
78. Marcus Græcus.   *Book of Fires.* (Translation in Berthelot,
                              No. 5 above.)
79. Nef, J. U.   *The Rise of the British Coal Industry.* London.
                              1932.
80. O'Dea, W. T.   *Darkness into Daylight.* London. 1948.
      See also (1) Agricola, (15) Lucas), (16) Neuburger, (19) Partington,
                              (24) Powle.

CHAPTER NINE

81. Bancroft, E.   *Experimental researches concerning the philo-
                              sophy of permanent colours.* London. 1794.
82. Singer, C.   *The Earliest Chemical Industry.* London.
                              1948. (Contains a very complete list of
                              references.)
      See also (15) Lucas, (17) Neuburger, (19) Partington, (57) Cennini.

CHAPTER TEN

83. Allessio, Piemontese.   *De secreti* . . . Venice. 1557.
84.   —   Translated as *The Secretes of Alexis of
                              Piemont.* London. 1558. There are
                              numerous English editions.
85. Chevreul, M. E.   *Recherches chimiques sur les corps gras d'origine
                              animale.* Paris. 1823.
86. Art. " Savonnerie.'   *Encyclopédie. Dictionnaire raisonné des
                              Sciences.* (Diderot and d'Alembert.) Tom.
                              XIV.
      See also (15) Lucas, (16) Neuburger, (19) Partington.

CHAPTER ELEVEN

87. Abulcasis (Khalaf ibn   *Liber Servitoris,* libri XXVII. Bulchasin
    'Abbas-al-Zahrawi).   Benaberazerin. Numerous editions. 1479–
                              1623.
88. Basilius, Valentinus.   *Triumph-Wagen Antimonii.* Leipzig. 1604.
89.   —   Translated as *The Triumphal Chariot of
                              Antimony.* London. 1661, and 1678.
90. Kremers, E., and Urdang, *History of Pharmacy.* Philadelphia. 1951.
    G.

91. Libavius, Andreas.   *Alchymia*. 2nd edn. **Frankfurt.** 1606.
92. Motherby, G.   *Medical Dictionary*. London. 1775.
93. Paracelsus.   The best collected edition is that of Sudhoff; A. E. Waite's English translation is useful, but not fully reliable.
94. Pomet, P.   *Histoire Générale des Drogues*. Paris. 1694.
95. —   Translated as *A General History of Drugs*. London. 1712.
96. Tachenius, O.   *Hippocrates Chymicus*. Brunswick. 1668.
97. —   Translated as *O. Tachenius, his Hippocrates Chymicus*. London. 1690.

See also (10) Discorides, (15) Lucas), (19) Partington.

CHAPTER TWELVE

98. Deerr, N. F.   *The History of Sugar*. London. 1949–50.
99. Diels, H.   " Die Entdeckung des Alkohols." *Abhandl. der kgl. preuss. Akad. der Wiss.*, 1913, p. 27.
100. Cadet de Vaux, A. E.   *Instruction sur l'art de faire le vin*. Paris. 1799–1800.
101. Erman, A., and Ranke, H.   *Aegypten und aegyptisches Leben in Altertum*. Tübingen. 1923.
102. Forbes, R. J.   *Short History of the Art of Distillation*. Leiden. 1948.
103. Henderson, A.   *History of Ancient and Modern Wines*. London. 1934.
104. Lippmann, E. O. von.   *Geschichte des Zuckers*. Leipzig. 1890.
105. Pauly-Wissowa (21).   Article " Zythos."
105a. Sanders, G. P.   *Cheese Varieties and Descriptions*. Washington, D.C. 1953.
106. Taylor, F. Sherwood.   *The Alchemists*. New York. 1949. London. 1952.

See also (19) Partington.

PART II

GENERAL WORKS BEARING ON PART II

107. Beilstein, F. C.   *Die Chemische Gross-Industrie auf der Weltausstellung zu Wien in Jahre* 1873. Leipzig. 1873.
108. Findlay, A.   *Chemistry in the Service of Man*. 7th edn. London. 1947.
109. Groves, C. E., and Thorp, W.   *Chemical Technology*. London. 1889.
110. Hardie, D. W. F.   *History of the Chemical Industry in Widnes*. Liverpool: Imperial Chemical Industries, Ltd. 1950.
111. Haynes, Williams.   *American Chemical Industry*. 6 vols. New York. 1945–55.
112. Jacob, J.   *Traité elementaire de chimie experimentale et appliquée*. Paris. 1867.

113. Kolb, J.   *Sur l'évolution actuelle de la grande industrie chimique.* Sociéte industrielle du nord de la France. Lille. 1883.

114. Martuis, C. A.   *Verzeichnis der Chemischen Fabriken Deutschlands.* Berlin. 1880.

115. Miall, S.   *A History of the British Chemical Industry.* London. 1931.

116. Morgan, G. T.   *Achievements of British Chemical Industry in the last 25 Years.* (Cantor lecture.) London: Royal Society of Arts. 1939.

117. Morgan, G. T., and Pratt, D. D.   *British Chemical Industry, its Rise and Development.* London. 1938.

118. Pilcher, R. B., and Butler-Jones, F.   *What Industry owes to Chemical Science.* 3rd edn. 1945.

119. Read, W. T.   *Industrial Chemistry.* 3rd edn. London. 1943.

120. Riegel, E. F.   *Industrial Chemistry.* New York. 1942.

121. Rogers, A.   *Industrial Chemistry.* 6th edn. 2 vols. New York. 1943.

122. Shreve, R. N.   *The Chemical Process Industries.* London. 1945.

123. Thorpe, T. E.   *Dictionary of Applied Chemistry.* Present and older editions.

124. Ungewitter, Claus.   *Chemie in Deutschland, Rückblick und Ausblick.* Berlin. 1938.

125. Warrington, C. J. S., and Nicholls, R. V. V.   *A History of Chemistry in Canada.* Toronto. 1949.

CHAPTER THIRTEEN

126. Chaptal, J. A.   *Chimie appliquée aux arts.* Paris. 1807.

127. Bergman, T.   *Physical and Chemical Essays.* Translation by E. Cullen. London. 1784.

128. Black, J.   *Experiments upon Magnesia Alba, Quick-lime and other Alcaline Substances.* [1755.] Edinburgh: Alembic Club. 1893.

129. Boyle, R.   *Experiments, Notes, etc., about the Mechanical Origine or Production of divers particular Qualities . . . together with some Reflections upon the Hypothesis of Alcali and Acidum.* Oxford. 1675.

130. Encyclopædias.   Numerous eighteenth- and nineteenth-century encyclopædias, notably John Harris's *Lexicon Technicum*, the *Grande Encyclopédie* of Diderot and D'Alembert, Rees's *Cyclopedia*, etc., are valuable sources for eighteenth-century chemical industry.

131. Robison, J.   *Lectures on the elements of chemistry, delivered in the University of Edinburgh, by the late Joseph Black.* Edinburgh. 1803.

See also (59) Clow, (96) Tachenius.

CHAPTER FOURTEEN

132. Berzelius, J. J.   *Traité de Chimie.* 8 vols. Paris. 1829–33.
                                 (Translation of *Larbok i kemien.* Stock-
                                 holm. 1817–30.)

133. Dumas, J.   *Traité du chimie appliquée.* Paris. 1828.

134. Muspratt, S.   *Chemistry as applied to Arts and Manufactures.*
                                 London. 1860.

135. Remusat, P. de.   *Les Science Naturelles. Etudes sur leur
                                 histoire et sur leurs plus récents progrès.* Paris.
                                 1857.

136. Ure, Andrew.   *Dictionary of Arts, Manufactures and Mines.*
                                 London. 1839.

CHAPTER FIFTEEN

137. Berthelot, M.   *Chimie Organique fondée sur la synthèse.*
                                 Paris. 1860.

138. Cannizzaro, S.   *Sketch of a Course of Chemical Philosophy.*
                                 [1858]. Alembic Club reprint. Edinburgh.
                                 1910.

139. Dumas, J.   *Chimie physiologique et médicale.*   Paris.
                                 1846.

140. Gerhardt, C.   *Traité de chimie organique.* 4 vols. Paris.
                                 1853–56.

141. Kekulé, A.   " Uber die Konstitution und die meta-
                                 morphosen der Chemische Verbindungen,
                                 etc." Ostwald's *Klassiker,* No. 145.
                                 Leipzig. 1904.

142. —   *Lehrbuch der Organische Chemie.* Erlangen.
                                 1861–67.

143. Schorlemmer, C.   *The Rise and Development of Organic
                                 Chemistry.* London. 1879.

144. van't Hoff, J. H.   *Chemistry in Space.* (Translation.) Oxford.
                                 1900.

CHAPTER SIXTEEN

145. Brunk, H.   " History of the Commercial Manufacture
                                 of Artificial Indigo." *Chemical News,*
                                 Vol. 86, p. 211. London. 1902.

146. Cain, J. C., and   *The Synthetic Dyestuffs.* (Introductory
     Thorpe, J. F.   historical chapter.) 7th edn. London.
                                 1933.

147. Caro, H.   *Uber die Entwicklung der Theer-Farben-
                                 Industrie.* Berlin. 1893.

148. —   Obituary. *Berichte der Chemischen Gesells-
                                 chaft,* 45. 1912.

149.   Hofmann Memorial Lecture. *Proceedings
                                 of the Chemical Society,* 132. 1893.

150. Ladenburg, H.   *Lectures on the History of the Development of Chemistry since the time of Lavoisier.* (Translation.) London. 1900.

151. Lightfoot, J.   *The Chemical History and Progress of Aniline Black.* Burnley. 1871.

152. Morton, James.   " History of the Development of Fast Dyeing and Dyes." *Journal of the Royal Society of Arts,* Vol. 74, p. 544.

153. Naudin, L.   *Aperçu historique de l'industrie de l'alcool: progrès depuis la fin du XVIIIᵉ siècle.* Paris. 1881.

154. Perkin, W. H.   *History of Alizarin and its production from Coal-Tar.* London. 1879.

155. —   " The Origin of the Coal-Tar Industry and the Contributions of Hofmann and his Pupils." *Journal of the Chemical Society,* Vol. 70, p. 596. 1896.

156. Piesse, G. W. S.   *Art of Perfumery.* London. 1855–91.

157. Thorpe, T. E.   " On the Rise and Development of Synthetical Chemistry." *Fortnightly Review,* May 1893.

CHAPTER SEVENTEEN

158. Bauer, A. A. E. and Hunterberger, F.   *Lehrbuch der chemischen Technik.* Vienna. 1859.

159. Berthelot, M.   " L'evolution générale des méthodes dans les industries chimiques." *Revue générale des Science,* July 30th, 1900.

160. Buchner, M.   *Die chemische Industrie und Metallurgie in der zweiter Hälfte unsers Jahrhunderts.* Graz. 1893.

161. Bunsen, R. W.   *Gasometry.* London. 1857.

162. Clarke, F. W.   " Chemistry in the United States." *Science,* Vol. 5, p. 117.

163. Garcon, J.   *Histoire de la chimie en France.* Paris. 1900.

164. Lunge, G. S.   *A Theoretical and Practical Treatise on the Manufacture of Sulphuric Acid and Alkali.* London. 1879–80.

165. Mallet, J. W.   " Reviews of Industrial Chemistry." *American Chemical Journal,* 1879.

166. Moissan, H.   *Le Fluor et ses Composés.* Paris. 1900.

167. —   *Recherches sur l'isoliment du fluor.* Paris. 1887.

168. Newbury, S. B.   " Reviews and Reports." *American Chemical Journal,* XI, 1884, pp. 124, 199.

169. Orfila, M. J. B.   *Traité des poisons.* Paris. 1818.

170. Ostwald, W.   *Scientific Foundations of Analytical Chemistry.* London. 1900.

171.   *Progress and Conditions of several Departments of Industrial Chemistry.* U.S. Commissions for the Paris Exhibition, 1867. Reports I and II.

172. Sidgwick, N. V.   *Electronic Theory of Valency.* Oxford. 1927.

173. Smith, J. L.   "The Century's Progress in Industrial Chemistry." *American Chemist*, Vol. V, pp. 61–70. New York. 1875.

174. Tatlock, R. R.   *The Past, Present and Prospective Conditions of some of the leading Chemical Industries of Glasgow and the West of England.* Glasgow. 1883.

175. Werner, A.   *New Ideas on Inorganic Chemistry.* London. 1911.

176. Wirtz, A.   *Dictionnaire de Chimie Pure et Appliquée.* (1867–70.)

CHAPTER EIGHTEEN

177. Chittenden, R. H.   *The Development of Physiological Chemistry in the United States.* New York. 1930.

178. Davy, H.   *Elements of Agricultural Chemistry.* London. 1813.

179. Foster, M.   *History of Physiology.* Cambridge. 1901.

180. Harrow, B.   *Textbook of Biochemistry.* Philadelphia and London. 1950. (Gives a wide selection of references.)

181. Lawes, J. B., and   *The Rothamsted Memoirs of Agricultural*
     Gilbert, J. B.   *Chemistry and Physiology.* (1860–90.)

182.   —   *The Rothamsted Experiments.* London. 1895.

183. Lieben, F.   *Geschichte der physiologischen Chemie.* 1935.

184. Liebig, J. von.   *Organic Chemistry in its application to Agriculture and Physiology.* 1840.

185. Osler, W.   *The Evolution of Modern Medicine.* New Haven. 1921.

186. Taylor, F. Sherwood.   *The Conquest of Bacteria.* London. 1942.

CHAPTER NINETEEN

187. Friend, J. N.   *Man and the Chemical Elements.* London. 1951.

188.   —   "The Historical and Industrial Discovery of the Elements." *Chemistry and Industry*, 1940.

189. Ramsay, W.   *The Gases of the Atmosphere. The History of their Discovery.* London. 1896. (Several later editions.)

190. Travers, M. W.   *The Discovery of the Rare Gases.* London. 1930.

CHAPTER TWENTY-ONE

191. Aston, F. W.   *Isotopes.* London. 1922.
192. Bohr, N.   *The Theory of Spectra and Atomic Constitution.* Cambridge. 1922.
193. Mendelejef, D. I.   *The Principles of Chemistry.* London. 1905.
194. Rutherford, E.   *Radioactivity.* Cambridge. 1905.
195. Rutherford, E., Chad-   *Radiations from Radioactive Substances.* Cam-
     wick, J., and Ellis, A. D.   bridge. 1930.
196. Soddy, F.   *The Chemistry of the Radio-elements.* London. 1911, 1914.
197. Thomson, J. J.   *The Corpuscular Theory of Matter.* Cambridge. 1907.

CHAPTER TWENTY-TWO

198. Astbury, W. T.   *Fundamentals of Fibre Structure.* London. 1933.
199.   —   *Textile Fibres under the X-rays.* London. 1943.
200. Bragg, W. L.   *The Crystalline State.* London. 1933.
201.   —   *The History of X-ray Analysis.* London. 1943.
202. Green, H.   *Industrial Rheology and Rheological Structures.* New York and London. 1949.
203. Hume-Rothery, W.   *The Metallic State. Electrical Properties and Theories.* Oxford. 1931.
204. Ostwald, W. F.   *Electrochemie. Ihre Geschichte und Lehre.* Leipzig. 1894–95.
205.   —   *Solutions.* (Translation.) London. 1891.
206. Perrin, J.   *Atoms.* London. 1916.
207. Millikan, R. A.   *The Electron, its Isolation and Measurement and the Determination of some of its Properties.* Chicago. 1917.
208. Robertson, J. M.   *Organic Crystals and Molecules.* Ithaca, N.Y. 1953.
209. van der Waals, J. D.   " The Continuity of the Liquid and Gaseous States." London. Physical Society. *Physical Memoirs,* 1890, 1.

CHAPTER TWENTY-THREE

210. Allmand, A. J.   *Principles of Applied Electrochemistry.* London. 1912.
211. Creighton, H. J. M., and *Principles and Applications of Electrochemistry.*
     Koehler, W. A.   New York and London. 1934, 1935.
212. Faraday, M.   *Experimental Researches in Electricity.* London. 1839.
213. Hale, A. J.   *Applications of Electrolysis in Chemical Industry.* London. 1918.

214. Löb, W.   *Electrochemistry of Organic Compounds.* New York. 1906.
215. Richards, J. W.   *Aluminium, its History.* Philadelphia. 1887.

CHAPTER TWENTY-FOUR

216. Berthelot, M.   *Essai de méchanique chimique fondée sur la thermochemie.* Paris. 1879.
217. —   *Explosives and their Power.* (Translation.) London. 1892.
218. Gibbs, J. W.   *Collected Works.* New York. 1928.
219. Nernst, W.   *The New Heat Theorem: its Foundations in Theory and Experiment.* London. 1926.
220. Hinshelwood, C. N.   *The Kinetics of Chemical Change in Gaseous Systems.* Oxford. 1926 and subsequent editions.
221. Roozeboom, H. W. B.   *Die heterogenen Gleichgewichte vom Standpunkts der Phasenlehre.* Braunschweig. 1901–18.
222. van't Hoff, H. J.   *Studies in Chemical Dynamics.* Amsterdam. 1896.

CHAPTER TWENTY-FIVE

223. Brenemann, A. A.   " Historical Summary of the Fixation of Atmospheric Nitrogen." *Journal of the American Chemical Society,* Vol. 11, p. 1889.
224. Green, S. J.   *Industrial Catalysis.* London. 1928.
225. Partington, J. R., and Parker, L. H.   *The Nitrogen Industry.* London. 1922.
226. Wells, A. E., and Fogg, D. E.   *The Manufacture of Sulphuric Acid in the United States.* Washington. 1920.
227. Fairlie, A. M.   *Sulphuric Acid Manufacture.* New York. 1936.

Consult also modern general works as listed above, *e.g.* (111) Haynes, (121) Rogers.

INDEX

Q